Written, photographed, compiled
and edited by Keith Langston
Editorial Assistant: Ronald W Mills
Picture Editor: Sue Mills
Design: Libby Ward
Additional Material: Roger Murray and David Hall
Project Editor: Colin Tyson
Production Editors: Richard Gibson and Tony Hoyland
Publishing Director: Malcolm Wheeler
Finance Director: Brian V Hill
Managing Director: Terry Clark

Additional contributions and photographs
supplied with grateful thanks by:
The Dibnah Family, Diane Carney, Neil Carney, Jimmy
Crooks, David Devine, Bill Greenhalgh, Alf Molyneux,
Bill Richards, Jim Stevenson,
The View From The North,
Peter Underwood LRPS,
Simon Warner,
Michael Webber.

Produced for
Mortons Media Group Ltd
by Perceptive Images,
Winsford, Cheshire.

Published by
Mortons Media Group Ltd,
Media Centre, Morton Way, Horncastle,
Lincolnshire LN9 6JR.
Tel. 01507 523456.

Printed by
William Gibbons & Son, Wolverhampton.

Published May 2005
© Perceptive Images/Mortons Media Group Ltd.

ISBN 9 7480954 244262

MORTONS
Media Group Ltd
Independent publishers since 1885

Pictured here is ▶ proud grandfather Fred with Isobel – the latest addition to the Dibnah family, a cute young lady born to Lorna and Alistair. She arrived in this world on the very day that Fred was in London collecting his MBE (7 July 2004). This photograph was taken two days after he returned from the capital.

A very young Jack ▶ on the living van steps.

Lorna, Jack, Jayne, ▶▶ Caroline and Roger.

Fred Dibnah
the family man

Dr Fred Dibnah, MBE, steeplejack and television presenter, was born on 28 April 1938. He died after a long illness on 6 November 2004, aged 66.

Following his career in television, Fred became a high-profile media personality and the fame that accompanied that status never affected him, or in any way changed his down-to-earth demeanour. He will be remembered not only for his many practical achievements, but also for encouraging thousands of others to care about our industrial heritage. That people from all walks of life have appreciated his efforts is without doubt. He enriched many lives through his work that he always looked on, not as a chore, but as a pleasure.

Proof of his many successes is fortunately preserved in tangible artefacts, on film and in the written word. His official recognition was highlighted by the award of the MBE which deservedly came. He had earlier been accorded the tribute of receiving not one, but two honorary degrees. But, moving away from the public side of his life, let us not forget that, first and foremost, Fred was very much a family man.

Born, like a great many of his admirers, in humble circumstances, he was brought up to appreciate the values of companionship, honesty and the satisfaction to be gained from a job well done. As eaders digest the comments of his friends and colleagues in this all-too-brief compliment to him, they will see that the one word which constantly comes to mind is love. He was a greatly loved human being, and he left his mark on the world he lived in and accordingly it is a better place for his having been there.

Thanks are due to the many people who have unselfishly passed on accounts of their involvement with Fred so that others can enjoy the retelling of them.

Fred is survived by his brother, Graham, and his three wives, Alison, Sue and Sheila.

He was the proud father of five children: to Alison there are daughters Jane, Lorna and Caroline, and to Sue there are sons Jack and Roger. With his last wife, Sheila, Fred took on the mantle of stepfather to her son, Nathan. He was a loving grandfather to Jane's sons, Christopher and Daniel, and also to the newest addition to the family, Isobel, who was born to Lorna the day he received his MBE.

Fred's family have been kind enough to allow us an insight into their private world by agreeing to a collection of their personal photographic memories being included in this tribute. Heartfelt thanks are due to them, so let us remember that we are in a privileged position and, as such, we should enjoy the images and thereafter respect the family's privacy. ▶

◀ Jack and Fred share a moment on location.

◀◀ Lorna, Fred and Jayne.

Relaxing with Jack ▶
and Roger after
filming in London.

Fred and Sheila at ▶▶
Buckingham Palace
after receiving his
MBE.

Always referred to ▶
by the family as
'Uncle', here is Jake
Tomlinson seen
during the
restoration of the
convertible.

1991. Fred holding ▶▶
Jack, while Sue
holds 'baby' Roger.

Roger pulling the ▶
chains that work the
bosun's chair.

Steeplejack! ▶▶

Caroline, Alison, Lorna and Jayne.

Roger in the snow at Radcliffe Road.

Never one to be afraid of heights, Fred plays Father Christmas on the chimney of his mother's house in 1997.

1993. Roger helps with cleaning the roller wheels.

Jack with a home-made engine (buggy) at the family home in Radcliffe Road, Bolton.

Lorna.

COMING-OF-AGE

DIBNAH—Mr. and Mrs. F. DIBNAH, 8, Alfred-st., Bolton, wish to announce the coming-of-age of their eldest son, FREDERICK, on April 29th, 1959.

Your health and happiness always. —Mam, Dad and Graham.

Fred's coming-of-age announcement in 1959, placed in the local paper by his parents.

Master of art. Fred's artistic talents on a letter addressed to his mother, whilst serving in Germany.

Christmas Day 1995. Fred playing with a set of terracotta bricks.

Lorna and Roger at a chimney topple.

Fred proudly shows off a home-made hydraulic riveter at his home workshop in Bolton in the summer of 2004.

At home with Fred Dibnah

In the early spring of 2004, *Old Glory* magazine decided to talk to Fred about his then-forthcoming TV series *Made In Britain* as many of that journal's readers had been approached with a view to being included in the filming sequences. In order to set the scene, Fred was interviewed during a series of visits to his Bolton home.

'At home with Fred Dibnah' proved to be one of the most popular items ever carried by the magazine and was something Fred himself said he enjoyed reading.

Fred's enthusiasm for the publication had grown over the years and therefore it was no surprise when he asked one of its writers and photographers, Keith Langston, to cover the story of the filming. But first, the story of those visits to Bolton.

History gave us some great British engineers who fascinated the whole of the developing world with their ingenuity. Modern generations have been able to 'revisit' those engineering workshops of the past through the magic of television and so can appreciate the achievements of those great artisans and entrepreneurs. This good fortune is enhanced by the unique descriptive skills and oratory style of a man who, if born in a previous age, would have striven to have been a contemporary of Brunel, Stephenson, Arkwright and the like. Fred Dibnah is that man.

With Fred, what you saw was very definitely what you got. Some say, and not without a little humour, that you would never catch him with clean hands. That does sum up this proud son of Bolton who would never ask anyone to do anything he wouldn't tackle himself. The great beauty of Fred's love of engineering and, in particular, all matters steam, was that he was not content merely to explain how something works - he needed to be sure that you understood the 'nuts and bolts' as well.

The wonderful gift he had was embodied in that God-given skill which all great teachers possess. He would read the understanding, or lack of it, in the recipient's eyes, and thereafter tailored his discourse to a level of complication his senses told him the listener was able to comprehend. He so refined this knack that he was even able to communicate in this manner through a TV camera, as those devotees of his many programmes will be happy to confirm.

You got the feeling, listening to Fred, that your understanding of the subject was what really mattered to him, and all his descriptive powers were focused on achieving that end. It was a sharing thing. He knew how, and that knowledge had given him satisfaction. He wanted you to share that understanding and therefore he was offering you something he saw as pleasure.

The word 'raconteur' can confidently be used to describe the story-telling eloquence and expertise of Mr Fred Dibnah. Storytellers since Adam was a lad have been our greatest link with the past and it is through them that so much of our history has been passed down. Scoff not at the art of slight exaggeration or verbal embellishment but consider whether, without their employment, you would have taken in the details of that all-important, but perhaps otherwise boring, story.

A piece of chalk, a pencil and a length of stick against the soft earth have all been the tools of the natural orator over the years. Add to these an adjustable spanner and a home-made hydraulic riveter and you have Fred Dibnah.

What, you might ask, started him on this strange but wonderful life of danger and discovery? How could a joiner from post-war Lancashire become a media icon, with the advent of satellite TV on a global basis, and yet still be 'Na then, Fred' to so many on a daily basis?

A writer colleague told me: "Leave plenty of time when you call on Fred. It's a kind of manic open house where engineering problems are related and solved on a relentless basis; and they take precedence over all else. Except, that is, when midday approaches and everything really does stop for the pies."

He was absolutely right and, furthermore, at noon, without ceremony, the 'boss', having been told that it was his turn, wandered off to make the tea.

In the moments that followed, victuals enjoyed and a mug in hand, the storyteller qualities in Fred seemed to reach new levels and he needed no encouragement to relate the details of his current crusade - 'the matter of the mine shaft in the back yard' and what he considered to be the metropolitan borough council's 'strange ►

Fred working on the mineshaft.

Fred uses his superb drawing skills to illustrate the details of the mineshaft.

Building the winding house roof.

attitude' towards it. But more of that later.

The steam bug infected Fred at a very early age following illicit visits to his father's place of work, a bleach factory. Everyone in those days, he recalled, took their main holidays during the traditional Wakes period and that meant factory shutdowns and time off work for most, but not for his father. Mr Dibnah Snr was a labourer and, as such, was often engaged in that all-important part of factory life – 'shut-down maintenance'.

He would leave a fencing plank pulled loose so that young Fred could gain entry to the works and join him among all the steam contraptions, pulleys and belts. To a young man with the enquiring mind of Fred, the bleach factory was an absolute Aladdin's cave and viewing it sowed the seeds in that youthful mind that were to flourish in adulthood and bring forth the love he held for steam power.

One of Fred's greatest regrets was that his native Bolton is no longer rich in engineering firms producing and repairing machinery, but instead he proffered: "Bolton is now the world leader in the production of disposable bedpans and paper products closely associated with the disposal system of the human anatomy.

Times do, of course, have to change, but will we, as a nation, live to regret the loss of all those great engineering skills? We are still breeding fertile minds but what are we filling these young heads with now, compared to the skills of the past our forefathers were able to offer us? It may have been said before, but the discontinuation of the indentured apprentice schemes has a lot to answer for. Don't believe me? Then try getting hold of a time-served plumber when you need one."

Talking of matters educational, it is worthy of note at this point to recall that Fred was the recipient of two honorary doctorates – one from Birmingham University and the other bestowed by the Robert Gordon University of Aberdeen. In both instances, the recognitions were accorded by the relevant engineering faculties but, in typical manner, Fred preferred to recount that they were, in his opinion, given for what he called 'back street mechanic-ing'.

Fred's schooling at St Michael's, Great Lever, saw an early indication of his interest in engineering, when he won a prize, aged 11, for building a model steamship. This was followed by a secondary education that included a session at Bolton College of Art – hence the honing of his self-evident and natural draughtsman skills.

Among his contemporaries at that seat of learning was a young man named Donald Jackson, who is now Queen Elizabeth II's official 'scribe'.

Fred was set to the tools and thus the finer points of 'wood butchery' were taught to him, a trade his father was sure would see his son earn good money and gain security. While pursuing that craft, Fred became fascinated with high buildings and, in particular, the

◄◄ Fred checking the quality of the paint finish on the Aveling's side tank.

◄ An early penchant for tall towers? Fred the Army cook building a stack of beer cans in the Naafi.

techniques of steeplejacking began to interest him.

Away from workaday joinery, he began to earn extra cash performing 'foreigners' at the weekends. Those extra tasks included the maintenance of weathervanes and the repairing of lightning conductors on chimneys. Fred was not yet scaling the real monsters that were to become his eventual trademarks, but structures of a more modest nature which, he recalled, were 'only' around 100ft high!

This extra income included the then-huge sum of £60, earned for pointing a local mill owner's house. That imbursement led to the burgeoning Dibnah business empire purchasing its first mode of transport – a 1927 AJS motorcycle which, after a degree of restoration, became Fred's pride and joy.

Standing in the way of his business expansion plans were his youthful looks, as he put it. "No one would, on seeing this young fellow at their door, think of him as being capable of climbing the chimney, let alone repairing it."

Friendship was to be the architect of his salvation and his old art school master, Lonsdale Bonner, was to come to his aid.

He 'happened upon' Fred cleaning his ladders one day. "What's all this, Dibnah?" the teacher asked.

"It's a steeplejack business I'm starting up," Fred told him. Fred went on to explain the problems of his youth getting in the way of obtaining work.

The teacher said: "Tell you what, I will go and see some people for you."

So it was he who initially knocked on the doors and got the work. For that invaluable service Fred paid him a tenner a job. By the time the customer saw the young steeplejack it was too late to turn back. He was up the ladder with the work well under way. "It was a great scheme," Fred added with a wry grin, "Lonsdale could

get where castor o l couldn't; we had a lot more work in no time at all."

While his TV programmes have latterly focused on the industrial heritage side of Fred's life, it should, of course, be remembered that, for a long time, he earned his living climbing things – usually very tall things. It was that work which first brought him to the attention of the BBC but first he was summoned, as a great many were in those times, to lend a hand elsewhere.

Fred was called on to serve Crown and country for a couple of years. Another institution of the past which some believe would be the panacea for all ills if reinstated, National Service was to request the pleasure of his company. Fred was, as far as he said he could remember, not responsible for poisoning anyone but his spell as an Army cook, coming as it did after the statutory spell of 'square-bashing', thankfully did not last very long.

Germany, or to be precise the then Army of Occupation in West Germany, was to be the extent of this 'Join the Army, see the world' young man's travels but, in a phrase much used today by those of a certain political leaning, 'things could only get better'. "Soldiers," said Fred, "did then, as now, the soldiering, the officers shouted a lot and, in general (nc pun intended), seemed to live better."

Part of living better, at least on the camp Fred was posted to, involved riding horses and even, as it turned out, 'riding to hounds' That, he recalled, proved to be an excellent thing for furthering his Army career. There was an old farmhouse with an outbuilding on the outskirts of the camp and it looked as though the 'heavy mob' had used it for grenade practice on a regular basis. It needed rebuilding, and Fred was to be one of the conscripted workers.

A high ranker said: "You're a joiner in civvy ►

Almost ready for the road, Fred stands proudly with the Aveling & Porter convertible engine – 27 years in the restoration.

street, Dibnah. Get the place fixed up, man, and keep it that way."

This looked a good plan, said Fred: "Wonderful, no square-bashing or early morning guard duty, just work on the tools. I was given a couple of mates to help me and we then spent most of the next year or so putting the roof back on the farm and fixing up the barns."

When it was all done the officers moved in a dozen or so hounds, for the purpose of hunting wild boar. "Know anything about doggies, Dibnah?" asked the CO. "I couldn't say 'yes, Sir' quick enough," he recalled. "Even though I hadn't come across many hunting dogs back home in Bolton, this looked like being a great skive and meal ticket, to boot. I had, up to then, never tasted wild boar.

"What made the whole Army period half-tolerable were the letters from my mam, God bless her, with news of local happenings but, more importantly, the odd postal order, the proceeds of which I squandered on luxuries like decent shaving soap and beer that didn't fight back as you swallowed it.

"But what her letters did tell me was how the steeplejacking was going on back home and who was doing what. Mind you, I didn't think Bolton would run out of chimneys while I was playing at being Master of the Black Forest Hunt. Two years' National Service did me no harm at all and I have loved dogs ever since!"

After the Army, Fred was faced with the choice of returning to joinery or trying to establish himself as a steeplejack. He chose the latter and, building on his pre-National Service achievements, again went looking for work. The motorcycle came in very handy for it allowed Fred to get around the region. Armed with binoculars, he could examine chimneys for damage to the steel bands and, with that knowledge, hopefully persuade the owners to give him the job of repairing them.

But he recalls that things were slow and, at first, he spent only three days of the week working and the rest of the time in a suit, watch chain and all, looking for more work. He did, he confided, come very close to returning to joinery and then, as happens so many times in life, fate takes a hand, in this case from an unexpected quarter.

One thing Fred does say about the Army is that it legally brought him close to things that he'd always had a fascination with – guns. This brings us nicely to the matter of a certain canon. One of the jobs Fred had hankered after was the repair of the weather vanes on the parish church in Bolton. Best suit again donned and astride his highly polished AJS, he arrived with due trepidation at the door of the good Canon Norburn, the Vicar of Bolton.

In he went to see this very important man, in his words, "full of apprehension and a fear of rejection". Little did he know but he had nothing to fear; in fact, as things turned out, he needed only to have a healthy regard for the 130ft height of the church tower.

The venerable gentleman took a real shine to Fred's AJS and, what's more, the vicar had parked in his drive an immaculate 1929 Humber car complete with 'railway carriage door handles' and a Weymann fabric body. It was, said Fred "like love at first sight – him with the motor bike and me with the car".

So off they went, chatting 10 to the dozen about the way he would fix the weathercock. How it came about Fred didn't recall but the pair got round to talking about the gangster Al Capone. Maybe it was because of the style of the vicar's car?

Then, much to Fred's delight, he started talking about guns.

"Well, vicar," said Fred, after listening intently to his enthusiastic description of his gun collection, "I have a 9mm Luger pistol."

▶

◀ Fred the teacher, explaining how the throatplate for the Aveling & Porter traction engine was made.

◀◀ Fred examining the mineshaft in his back garden.

Fred working on his Aveling steam road roller.

This statement, he said "grabbed the gentleman's attention quicker than a gold sovereign on the collecting plate of a Sunday".

The vicar then told Fred that he had a fascination for firearms and went on to confess that he had a small stock of 9mm ammunition stored in the manse, a startling revelation which came as something of a mild shock to Fred, who said: "Well, vicar, I am afraid that my Luger is locked away in my mother's writing desk as she doesn't like me having it, let alone it being loose around the house."

He recalls that there was no putting off the clerical gent once he knew of the classic gun's existence. "Can you get at it, son?" the vicar asked with a strange look in his eyes. All Fred could do was to tell it the way it was, and be damned. "Well, I do know how to pick the lock –

in case of an emergency," the young steeplejack told him.

"Could this be classed as an emergency?" the excited vicar queried.

"It could be," Fred replied, "as it's Friday and my mother will be out cleaning the Gas Works offices all afternoon."

Fred recalled that they set off there and then, the vicar in the car, together with an official-looking briefcase which, later Fred learned, contained the ammo and his pistols, and Fred on the AJS. Fred's words describing what happened next can only be described as pure theatre, and, as such, priceless.

"Picture the scene: this huge black box on wheels outside our little terraced house, curtains twitching across the street and me and vicar in the front parlour. Not a speck of dust anywhere, which would be the only plus

Fred was an expert at making weather vanes and he often used recycled materials.

point if my mother ever got to know that Canon Norburn had been there. So there I was, picking the lock on the dresser with a practised ease, which was not unnoticed by the cleric, while he looked on approvingly. Well, we got the gun and off we went, in that brilliant car, 'up country' to Belmont, where he knew a friendly farmer.

"The next thing it's as if the Wild West has come to Bolton, tin-can shooting of the highest order. But, until you have seen a clerical gentleman with a gun in each fist like Billy the Kid, and his cassock pulled up on one side and tucked into his trouser pocket, you have never lived. He was a crackshot and a really nice guy.

"I did, of course, get the job and, as a matter of fact, I reckon it set me up locally and I have never been short of work from that day to this. That climb, as it turned out, attracted the interest of the local papers and a half

page in the *Bolton Evening News* followed with pictures, and it did our business no harm at all.

"Canon Norburn finished up being transferred to Birmingham and he passed away in that neck of the woods. As for my dear mum, she never knew that he'd been in her front parlour although, on many occasions afterwards, I was to say to her, after she had finished a particularly thorough cleaning session, "you could bring anyone here mother, even the Vicar of Bolton!"'

With regard to his TV career, Fred has no qualms in 'naming the guilty party'. It was just over 30 years ago that BBC North West reporter Alistair McDonald got wind of a repair that Fred was going to effect to the clock tower at Bolton Town Hall. Fred's account of that episode in his life has been reported many times, but these are his own words describing what he always said ▶

Building the pillars to support the steam winding engine platform.

◀◀ Roger in the mineshaft.

was the start of his 'telly career'.

"Down he comes to view the job in a very natty little sports car. I'd been told that the young 'telly' man was a bit of a rock climber. Good, I thought, a 200ft climb up the side of a town hall will be just up his street. Perhaps we could do the interview up on the clock face? I had a plank going from the tower and across the face, so he arrives and climbs up the inside of the tower and suddenly there he is looking out at the work site. I am standing out on the aforementioned plank 200ft up showing off the new stone pillars we had made for the job.

"Are you coming out, then?" I asked, pointing to the plank. His reply is unprintable, as they say, but we did the interview anyway and it went out at the end of the evening news bulletin.

"A few weeks later he rang to ask if he could come and see me with a TV producer. I said why not, and told him where we'd be at the time and that was that. Well, the telly folk arrived and this guy with Alistair looked like Stewart Granger, about seven foot tall, all dressed in denim, baseball cap and huge cowboy boots.

"We chatted, or rather he talked and the rest of us listened, and it was mainly in a 'media' language, which I couldn't make head nor tale of. At the end of the evening I said: 'What do you want me to do, give you a ring when we are going to do something dangerous or

exciting?' 'No,' he said, 'we'll ring you.' Well, that was the end of my TV career, I thought.

"Now normality had almost returned to my life when Alistair McDonald, who could never be called a quitter, had a hand in things again. He had been harassing people in BBC Oxford Road, Manchester, as a consequence of which I received a call from a very nice lady called Jean Thompson. Subsequently she arrives – and with her another Stewart Granger, only this time a smaller version and much older but nevertheless the same kind of boots, long-peaked cap and nicely tailored denim outfit.

"If anything I got on with the first would-be Adonis better than I did with this one. I attempted to show him, with the help of a pencil and sheet of paper, how steeplejacks get a ladder fixed up a chimney. We had about one-and-a-half imaginary ladders up this imaginary chimney when he waves his arms. Stop! Stop! We'll have the viewers turning off in droves; it's far too boring. Quick chat with his lady colleague and there he was, gone.

"Blown it again, I thought. But the more I pondered, the more I was sure that the first part of any programme about 'our job' would need to contain the method of putting the ladders in place. Phone rings again – it was Jean from the BBC. 'Can we come over on Wednesday?' They did and we had another argument about the ladders. All of a sudden, Stewart Granger MkII shows

◀
Ready to go, the
Aveling & Porter
convertible ready
for the road.

signs of capitulation. 'Where are you working?' he asks.
'On a big chimney at Shaw, near Oldham,' I tell him.
'Jean, we will call there tomorrow and have a look for
ourselves,' he says, and off they go again."

Fred recalls that he had just got to the top of the
245ft chimney when the BBC pair turned up in their
Mini at 8.30am.

"That was it. 'Cowboy boots' instantly got the bug.
They came that first time in a Mini and, as time went by,
moved on to a Porsche. I'd still got my clapped-out Land-
Rover. We were up and running and, to add to things, I
had just won the cup at Burtonwood Vintage Show with
my road roller *Betsy*, so that brought the steam element
into the plot."

There were at that time (April 2004) three main
projects occupying Fred's fertile mind. The first was very
much normal by his standards: the continued restoration
of an Aveling & Porter convertible steam tractor, maker's
number 7838. The second task was something with
which he was well-experienced: the making of another
series of TV programmes for the BBC - filmed by David
Hall and his team from *The View from the North* in Leeds.

However the third one, even for Fred Dibnah, was a little
unusual: the design and sinking of a five-foot diameter
70ft deep mine shaft leading to a 5ft 6in-bore tunnel, the
associated head gear and engine house for which he had
long since had permission to build. Unusual? Well, you must
suppose so when you are told it is in his back yard and
possibly in a place where lesser mortals would have
preferred a barbecue. The strange thing is that, when you
got to know Fred, the execution of this task, which had
most of the Bolton city fathers excited, seemed like a
perfectly natural thing to do.

This frenzied pack of civic officials and councillors
called on just about every authority they could think of
to have the project permanently stopped. But all they
succeeded in doing up to that moment was having a halt
called to work while a review took place. It may be that,
in Bolton, an Englishman's home is still his castle but it
cannot, by their reasoning, be his simulated coalmine.

Fred, according to much local opinion, had a point
when he claimed that, to some of the council's officials,
any reminder of the area's past 'cloth cap' image was an
anathema and could not be tolerated. Oh yes, they were ▶

pleased as punch that Fred's work had been recognised by the awarding of an MBE.

'Isn't that good for the local image?' you can imagine them saying. But can we attempt to remind the up-and-coming generation of Boltonians of their heritage in those far-off days when little children were sent down into the ground to dig coal? Dear me, no, that would never do.

Fred surmised at the time: "It could be that they are afraid of me becoming a tourist attraction. If so, that's rubbish. Already parties of youngsters have attended our workshop to learn something about the ways of the past. There is hardly going to be more of them; it's just another bit of history for them to be reminded of."

Thankfully millions of people are now aware of the saga following the penultimate TV series; it has even (already) been repeated because of the interest it generated.

Who, having seen it, will forget the bow and arrow incident. It may have looked pure fantasy but it was based on sound engineering practice.

The skill of creating a working size bore using an iron 'sinking ring' was fully explained in the series. That age-old technique was something many people had either never heard of or else had forgotten about. A good team could, by Fred's reckoning, advance the shaft's depth by as much as two feet in a working day.

The plan called for the shaft to join with the slightly inclined tunnel and could, with the addition of railway lines and the utilisation of four trucks (coal tubs coupled in two pairs), be able to demonstrate the way in which coal was raised to the surface. The work had progressed steadily over several months, as time permitted between steeplejacking, filming for TV, public appearances and working on the 'convertible', and then came the order to stop work.

Some well-meaning soul, who must have stood on tip-toes on the top of Fred's adequate boundary fence to even see the work, reported the matter to the council. The publicity created a growing pile of correspondence from local people in support of the venture, some of them very eminent persons and, as Fred was taken ill, the so-called Darcy Lever Mining Company was preparing to go to appeal to have the work cessation order lifted.

One of the parties called to inspect Fred's pit shaft were the Mines Safety & Rescue people from Selby in Yorkshire. They found nothing wrong; on the contrary, they thought it was a very good idea and looked forward to seeing it finished. The council also called in geological experts and that inspection had an amusing outcome. Their claim inferred that the hillside on which Fred had started sinking the shaft would become unstable because of the work. In fact, they reported that, since Fred had started sinking the shaft and brick-lining it, he had made the hillside much more stable than it previously was!

The Aveling & Porter convertible compound steam tractor, which Fred had been in the process of restoring, or perhaps more accurately, totally rebuilding, was a real labour of love that had been ongoing for the last 27 years. In the spring of 2004 it was, in Mr Dibnah's words, "just about ready to embark on a grand tour of the UK". It was

▶ Fred the schoolboy.

▶▶ Dr Fred Dibnah. Fred after receiving his honorary doctorate from the University of Birmingham.

to be coupled to a fine, newly reconstructed living van that was rescued as severely fire-damaged from a field in Burnley. The superbly finished engine would go on to share top billing in the new TV series and, as a part of this, it would be proudly driven around the streets of the nation's capital.

The compound was originally built for Somerset County Council in 1912 and configured as a tractor. However, by 1914 it had been commandeered by the War Department and sent off to France in the form of a road roller. It came back war surplus and was used for all of its working life as a roller by Devon County Council. It was, towards the end of that life, parked in a layby where someone stole all the brass fittings from it. It was then advertised for sale by tender.

It was subsequently bought, those 40 years ago, by a friend of Fred's for only £200. He said that, at the time, he was green with envy, having just paid £175 for his roller. The machine (registered TA 2436), looked to be in very good order but, on closer inspection, that was found not to be entirely the case.

Several years later, in 1977, Fred bought the convertible and moved it to his Bolton workshop. At that time he said it looked very good, lagging on the boiler etc, belly tanks all lined out and a smart paint job. But there were tell-tale signs for all to see including a big L-shaped weld on the side of the boiler right underneath the point where the high-pressure valve spindle is.

The standard of the riveting on the boiler also left a lot to be desired. It quickly became obvious to Fred that this boiler barrel would never pass muster and so the 27-year slog began. The front axle was found not to be original and was, in fact, from a Garret No 4 tractor, while the front wheels were also the wrong ones and were even of different diameters. They obviously needed to be replaced by a suitable Aveling pair, and new bearings fitted, before the restoration could be deemed complete.

The tender, belly tanks, boiler barrel and ash pan were all replaced by newly manufactured substitute parts but the biggest job by far was the fabrication of a new throatplate. X-ray examination had revealed no less than 27 cracks in the old one. In helping with the manufacture of a new one, Fred picked out the Hyde-based firm of Bowns for special praise. They are, he said at the time, "the kind of outfit that steam men should support".

Having been privileged to study up close this remarkable Lancastrian and witness first-hand his grasp of so many diverse engineering techniques, there is only one conclusion to draw: Fred Dibnah would have made a success of whatever business he'd chosen. Come to think of it, what should he have put on his passport – joiner, steeplejack, engineer, mechanic (back street or otherwise), storyteller, mining contractor, television presenter or just plain Great Briton?

Following Fred's untimely death, one of his admirers wrote in answer to that question: "None of the above; try national treasure." I am sure we would all like to be associated with the remarks of that gentleman. ■

◄ Fred the soldier.

◄◄ Fred on the top of Bolton Parish Church.

Fred at Buckingham Palace having just received the Medal of the British Empire from the Queen on 7 July 2004.

Roger has a practice drive at Wellington Barracks.

The Irish Guards were host to the engine and film crew at Wellington Barracks in Birdcage Walk. Fred thanks the officer in charge.

A capital affair
Fred collects his MBE

To stand on the corner of Birdcage Walk and Parliament Square in the rush hour and witness the passing of an Aveling & Porter convertible steam tractor and living van is one thing; to hear the cry: "Rook, it's Fled Dribner" exclaimed in unison by an excited group of tourists from the Orient is entirely something else.

Both these happenings will rot be quickly forgotten by those fortunate enough to have been on hand to witness them.

To cap it all, diametrically-opposed technological happenings became almost commonplace as the day unfolded. More specifically, it was the capture of images of a 1914 steam engine on the microchips of state-of-the-art 'picture' phones, their excited owners despatching those once-in-a-lifetime pictures to contacts worldwide.

It would, we had mused on the journey south, be interesting to know if the populace of this overcrowded and manic city would be familiar with the highly polished art of our Fred. There was no better place to start than with a member of that special breed of capital-dwellers, the London cabbie, our pilot on a journey from Euston to the appointed meeting-place. Not quite the perfect answer, but not bad for a start: "Lov 'im, straight I do, gov! Especially the bit abart the mine in his street. They live a different life up there in Yorkshire, straight they do."

We paid the fare and tactfully corrected his geography, but it was not bad for a start.

Our next 'pilot of the bus lanes' was a gentleman definitely not born within the sound of Bow bells. In fact he told us, though unnecessarily on account of his rich nasal accent, that he was a Scouser. Apart from trying to claim Fred's birthright for Maggie May's city, he declared that he was an avid watcher of the TV programmes and even confessed to having his lacy tape them when he was on late shift.

A Transport For London bus inspector was next. "Leave off, mate! Who ain't seen the trick wiv the bow and arra. What was that all abart?" We put him wise and made a sharp exit. During a break in filming, the crew swapped stories and it seemed that they had all had similar experiences when asking about our boy, save for one gentleman who thought Fred was in a boy band. Come to think of it, if called to he could well play that role successfully!

So now the only worry was whether 'Her indoors up the b g house' would recognise him when the time came. After all, the keeper of her parks had forbidden a perambulation up The Mall with the little compound. The plan for Fred to arrive at 'Buck House' via The Mall on the engine was unfortunately scuppered by officials who declared that the weight of the engine and living van would be too great for their road system.

However, help was at hand and the Adjutant to the Irish Guards, Alex Turner, was thankfully able to offer the crew the facilities of Wellington Barracks, a location within easy walking distance of the palace. Even better was the fact that the Aveling and Alan Atkinson's low-loader would, as a consequence, have a really secure resting-place while in town.

The route chosen for the 'victory parade' (and that term is justified if the constant cheers, waves and hooting of car horns was anything to go by) started with a trip up Birdcage Walk followed by a circuit of Parliament Square and Westminster Green. Thereafter the Houses of Parliament were circled in an anti-clockwise manner via Millbank and then a crossing of Lambeth Bridge being followed by a smart run up Lambeth Palace Road and a left on and over Westminster Bridge.

The next circuit, necessitating a sharp right turn off the bridge and in sight of the London Eye, saw the 'Bolton Wanderers' travel in a northerly direction along Victoria Embankment. A left just before the Hungerford railway bridge brought our travellers into Northumberland Avenue and then, by hanging a left at Nelson's Column to Whitehall and up past the Cenotaph. Whitehall brought the boys back to Parliament Square, at which point the watching public were treated to the sight of the Aveling & Porter making a further circumnavigation of the whole route including another 'pass' of the Palace of Westminster.

By this time those oriental tourists were quite ecstatic and seemed to have doubled in number. A brief glimpse of 'Red Ken' on the Green as he talked to a party of placard-waving demonstrators seemed to be cut short by a sharp shower of rain. Some wag on our crew asked if that nice Mr Livingstone had really come to see if Fred had paid the London Congestion Charge. And, if you're wondering, yes, he had. Or at least Alan had paid it for him.

Northumberland Avenue, out of all the roads on the route, had seemed to stick in Fred's memory and the reason was to become obvious. It was approaching ▶

Fred, Jack and Roger – 'The Bolton Wanderers' – have arrived in town.

Jack and Alan have a well-earned breakfast sandwich after lighting up the engine prior to the run around the capital.

The clothes, they do say, maketh the man. Either way, it's still our Fred, as he emerges from the living van to applause all round from the crew and the watching soldiers on the parade ground at Wellington Barracks.

Before and after the formalities, a celebratory run around the capital was undertaken with a rush-hour trip up Birdcage Walk, direction Parliament Square. The tourists get a sight of the Aveling & Porter in the morning sunshine and the TVFTN film crew are in the living van.

lunchtime, when a voice on the 'ship-to-shore' communication system, to wit Big Alf and David Hall the producer's mobile phone link, announced that a very nice hostelry with great windows and a black and white timbered façade had been spotted on a previous circuit.

This fine watering-hole turned out to be the Sherlock Holmes public house at the northern end of Northumberland Avenue. "Can we park up OK?" was the logical question from the crew chief. "Watch me," was the affirmative reply from 'the man' on the lean, mean, green steam machine.

Now coincidences, some would have you believe, are more common than enough while others would swear that the opposite is true. As all settled down to a quiet sojourn at the pavement tables outside the pub (our summer had abated and sunshine had fleetingly returned), one such occurrence was to take place.

A very strong military-type voice with a 'clipped' delivery momentarily broke the tranquillity of the scene: "You have got no taller, Mr Dibnah!"

"And you no smaller, Major," replied Fred as quick as a flash. A watching member of the crew was quickly despatched inside the bar to procure a vessel for the officer and he joined the lunch party. Now here is the coincidence bit. Given that London is a fair big town, even by Bolton's standard, what was the chance of Fred meeting up again with the man who, in his words, "had queued behind him at the Palace"?

Major Richard Courteney-Harris, a serving officer with the Queen's Lancashire Regiment, had received an MBE at the same ceremony as Fred. He was out walking the town with his delightful wife, Karen, and their children when he just happened upon the Sherlock Holmes. A nice reunion? Well, of course. Elementary, my dear reader.

◀ Whitehall.

◀◀ The Great British icon – and a Great Briton.

◀ Returning to the barracks after the parade around London.

While this impromptu MBE celebration party was in full cry, the attention of the group was drawn to the parked-up engine and van. "Something is occurring," said Big Alf and the situation could, he said, "require the tact, diplomacy and charm of Fred". Now traffic wardens anywhere are a breed unto themselves, but the London contingent of that calling are something special.

A lot of head-scratching and muttering was taking place on the footpath at which the steamer was parked. These actions were followed by a guy with a shuffling walk circling around the ensemble while casting steely glares at the double yellow lines. This activity culminated in a question or two. "What is it and what's it doing parked here?" Remarks such as "bet his clamp won't fit that" and "throw your booking pad in the fire, mate" were emanating from onlookers who had assembled.

Fred arrived on the scene. He told the custodian of the yellow lines that 'the driver of a steam conveyance is entitled to park anywhere in order to attend to his fire or take water'. He further explained that a failure to do so would result in a huge bang as a result of which the local glazier might need to pay a visit to Northumberland Avenue. The dear man was charmed and hastened down the street declaring "leave it wiv ya, mate!"

Accordingly it could be said that the Dibnahs and their steam tractor had charmed the capital. Fred thoroughly enjoyed his well-deserved visit to the palace and *The View From the North* got the whole thing on film. Summing up that great day, the only thing that remained to be said, pinching a quote from Julius Caesar, was: Veni, Vidi, Vici". ∎

◀ Fred and the Major.

▶

Weighing up the
shot before
filming, from left:
Jack, Fred,
producer David
Hall and Alf.

The TV producer's story

David Hall is the head of Leeds-based TV production
company 'The View From The North' and not only
did he work closely with Fred on the making of
many television programmes, the two men became, and
remained, close friends. Filming for what was to be the
last series of programmes for BBC2 entitled *Made In
Britain* was completed only the month before Fred died.

My friend and colleague
Fred Dibnah: by David Hall

Fred Dibnah was first seen on our screens in 1979 and
has been there ever since, thanks initially to a series of
television documentaries about his career as a steeplejack
and then further programmes highlighting his hobby as a
restorer of steam engines. Having served his screen
apprenticeship fully, he effortlessly made the transition
from being the documentary subject to being a superb
documentary presenter.

Fred was a man born out of his own time. He always said
he should have lived in the Victorian age and his heroes
were the great engineers of that time. Growing up as a
youth in the 1940s in Bolton, Lancashire, he fell in love

with the decaying industrial landscape around him and
developed the interests that were to stay with him for the
rest of his life – steeplejacking and steam engines.

Fred served a full apprenticeship as a joiner, but all the
time, despite parental disapproval, he pursued his goal of
becoming a steeplejack. Over many years he studied the
way that steeplejacks erected their ladders and scaffold
and, in doing so, he saw what he considered to be their
faults and so developed his own methods.

Fred is best known for 'felling' chimneys but that is the
job he liked least; his preference was that of restoration
and he would always point proudly to chimneys and
church steeples that he had restored. Some people
mistakenly think that Fred 'blows up chimneys', but that
was never the way he worked; he had his own way.

Steeplejacking was his profession; steam engines were
his passion. From his early childhood he remembered the
engine sheds at the end of his road, the great mill
engines endlessly turning, producing Lancashire's thread
and the last of the steam road vehicles still conveying
goods around Bolton's highways.

It was those memories that fostered the idea of steam
preservation. Fred started by purchasing a steam roller
and then undertaking to fully restore it. Uneasy with

◀

The start of it all, Fred with ex-BBC reporter Alistair Macdonald.

modern methods and new fangled tools, Fred decided to equip himself with a workshop powered by steam, renovating a small portable engine to provide the driving power for his machine tools.

Until 25 years ago, Fred was only a steeplejack who had an interest in steam engines. Then, while he was working on the town hall in Bolton, gilding the topmost finial, the local BBC TV news programme filmed a short item about him. As a result of this, Fred was approached by a TV producer with a view to making a half-hour film as part of a series about people with unusual occupations. After several months of filming, the finished article was an hour-long documentary, *Fred Dibnah – Steeplejack,* which was first aired in 1979.

From that time on he has rarely been away from our

screens. He became for millions of viewers the embodiment of old-fashioned commonsense, straight talking and frank speaking. With Fred you always got what it said on the tin and his forthright views on anything and everything turned him into something of a folk hero.

When he turned to presenting his own programmes his blunt, no-nonsense style made a welcome change from the so-called television professionals. His genius lay in being able to communicate with the audience in simple, direct, colloquial English.

The audience not only enjoyed watching Fred, they trusted him because he was one of them. Fame and personality never spoiled him. Wherever he went he always found time to chat to anybody who cared to ▶

◀

Jon Doyle checks out a couple of radio microphones prior to filming.

◀◀

Fred is fascinated by the modern technology used by sound engineer Nigel Chatters.

The film crew are concentrating on something out of shot behind the traction engine. In fact they were filming Alf tapping a barrel of real ale!

Roger Dibnah with TVFTN production assistant Kate Siney. The smiling faces were typical of the location filming days.

listen to one of his stories, to sign an autograph or pose for a photo that will now forever have pride of place in many a family album.

Few people on television have been better at talking to ordinary working people and putting them at their ease. But what we loved more than anything with Fred was his passion and enthusiasm. Fred had a passion for anything to do with our industrial past and an infectious enthusiasm for the engineering, mechanical and craft skills of the past. But there was always a sense of sadness; a great sense of loss for the sights and sounds of industries that have long disappeared.

In all of his programmes Fred's approach was very hands-on. He lived every schoolboy's dream, travelling on the footplates and driving the engines. Fred always said he should have been born in the Victorian age and his heroes were the great engineers of that time, none more than the great Isambard Kingdom Brunel.

But steam and engineering weren't his only loves. Having worked with wood for around seven years, Fred could talk with authority about the work of the carpenters and woodcarvers and he was able to give a knowledgeable account of their skills and a true appreciation of their achievements.

In everything he did Fred was a perfectionist and he had great admiration for the craft and skills of builders, carpenters, stonemasons and engineers. While admiring the finished products, he was just as interested in the way the job was done and in the working conditions surrounding it. He was always able to put himself in the place of those workers.

Because he had been there and done it himself he could speak with an authority that few academics have and he could really appreciate the scale of the achievements of a medieval builder. Fred's approach was always hands-on so, whatever the job, he'd have a go at it. Wherever he went, if there was a job being demonstrated that involved skilled work with his hands, Fred could and would successfully try it.

As a young man Fred went to art school, and the

drawings that he did to illustrate how things were built were so good that he could have earned a living as an illustrator. His practical demonstrations illustrated perfectly how things were built or how things worked, even if some of them did end in disaster.

Wherever he went and whatever he saw, he'd always 'got one like it at home' or 'in my back garden'. Although he loved travelling around the country to tell us about Britain's great industrial and architectural heritage, he was always glad to get back to his first love, his own back garden and his beloved workshops. There is nothing that better sums up what Fred Dibnah was all about than his back garden, which he'd transformed into a one-man industrial heritage centre dominated by a 25ft high chimney and pit head gear.

Fred's cancer was diagnosed in 2001, but he never let it stop him doing the things he loved doing, including starting to dig a 100ft deep mine shaft to go with the pit head gear in his garden. Right up to the end, Fred was determined to achieve one last great ambition, something he had started many years before.

He wanted to complete the restoration of the traction engine he'd been working on for the last 27 years and then set off with it on a grand tour of Britain. On that journey he would go in search of the skills and technology that had made it possible to build an engine like his in the first place. With the help of his mates he got the engine finished and it was a great day in Fred's life when it steamed up the drive and on the public highway for the first time.

Getting a traction engine and living van around the country on today's roads with a television crew in tow wasn't going to be easy, but he made it. The highlight of the tour was a trip to London. Fred was awarded an MBE for his services to industrial heritage and broadcasting in the 2004 New Year's Honours List. And he went to the palace to collect it on his beloved engine. Fred completed the journey and the filming for his last series in September 2004, just a few weeks before he went into hospital for the last time.

People have often asked me what made Fred a special

broadcaster and, in answering, I have to return to those two words 'passion' and 'enthusiasm', and observe that he coupled them with a great knowledge of how things were built and how they worked. Whether it was a flying buttress or a beam engine, Fred knew how and why.

As I've mentioned, he could draw things with great accuracy. My own particular favourite was the drawing he did to illustrate how Wren built his dome at St Paul's Cathedral.

Fred would have a go at anything. Stone carving, ornamental plasterwork, trimming and splitting slate were just some of the many skills he mastered. However, in Fred's case the real bonus lay in the fact that he could then engage directly with an audience and help them understand how the job was done.

In a way Fred was the spokesman for many people. Straight talking and frank speaking, he expressed the views of a vast silent majority and, in a time when everybody in the public eye had to observe the doctrine of political correctness, Fred was refreshingly politically incorrect and people appreciated that he always called a spade a spade.

The viewing public recognised that Fred wasn't really part of the world of television. He was a working man who said and did things in his own way, and in a manner they could identify with. He was totally unaffected by the fame that came to him and he had a frank, open and honest no-frills approach to programme making.

Fred was a producer's dream and he was always a joy to work with; importantly, he got on with all the crew. There were never any tantrums or awkwardness. He would always go along with what we were doing. No 'look at me I'm a star'. There were, however, some drawbacks to working with him, especially on a tight, time-sensitive shoot!

He could never ignore members of the public who approached him when we were filming and he treated everyone like a friend, usually within two minutes of striking up a conversation with them. Even if the cameras were about to roll, he would disappear if he saw something he wanted to look at, or someone he decided to talk to. He found sticking to scripts a bit too restrictive and, though he would follow the gist of them, he more often than not told the story in his own way. Right to the end, Fred never understood the mechanics of filming but the resultant programmes were nevertheless entertaining and universally loved.

I consider it a great privilege to have worked with Fred. He was one of British television's greatest characters. He was a lovely man to work with and also a great pal to go for a pint with. Fred enriched our lives because he made them more interesting; he brought more fun into them because there were always a lot of laughs when Fred was around and he spiced things up by adding a bit of danger.

With Fred's death we've lost a great character, and all our lives are going to be the poorer for it. But he will be remembered through his programmes, his engines and his workshop, which hopefully will be able to be preserved.

TVFTN produced an hour-long tribute special which was aired on BBC2 and it was rated as one of the most liked and appreciated programmes in the UK Audience Appreciation Ratings for the whole of 2004. It's a mark of how much Fred and the programmes were enjoyed. The film company have now released a DVD containing a fuller version of that programme and the superb and unique footage they shot in Oldham on the occasion of Fred's last 'chimney downing' in May 2004 as part of the *Made In Britain* series (see advertisement, page 91). ■

◄

A local guide shows the boys the 'Big Hole' while the film crew get to work at a copper mine for the final series. David Hall, cameraman Rob Taylor and sound man Nigel Chatters.

A cheeky grin as Fred prepares to ride off into the night, something he greatly enjoyed doing.

Fred remembered: Michael Webber

Many people are impressed by the dangerous work steeplejacks carry out on a daily, almost routine, basis but the majority of them have no desire to join such an artisan at his labours. However, one young gentleman was so impressed and overawed by the skills he'd observed Fred Dibnah practising that, come what may, he was determined to copy the skills of his mentor. Not only was he fascinated by of the art of climbing chimneys, he was also enthralled by the allure of steam.

Michael Webber, who lived in Bolton for many years, now lives and works in Lancing, West Sussex and he runs his own company of engineers and boilermakers. They are involved with the building and restoration of vintage machinery and, in particular, steam engines. Perhaps no surprises there, then!

Back in 1970, the city fathers of Bolton decided to create what is now the pedestrianised Town Hall Square and, having decided to banish motor vehicles for good from the area, they arranged a celebration by way of a charity event where five steam vehicles were invited to parade in the newly designated pedestrian area. That is where his involvement with Fred started, as he now relates:

I was taken to the Town Hall Square event by my father, as he knew I was, to say the least, keen on steam vehicles. While growing up I had occasion to visit a well-known Bolton steam man named Tom Albert on several occasions and, seeing his Burrell showman's engine 'His Lordship' at work was always a great thrill. I was to learn later that the same gentleman had been a great inspiration to Fred and was probably responsible for him looking for, and eventually buying, his own engine.

On the occasion of the steam event I was only 12 years old and Fred about 32, but I remember it as if it were yesterday. Why? Because I got to ride on a steam vehicle for the very first time and that was entirely down to Fred. A photographer had asked him to put a kid on the engine footplate to create a more newsworthy picture.

Fred reacted by bending over the side of the engine and calling me to climb up on the footplate. I was chuffed. The cameraman then asked him if it was possible to dirty my face in order to add to the effect. This Fred did by rubbing his oil- and coal-stained palms on both sides of my face. Magic! I then looked like an engineman and, furthermore, I was not only being photographed with the famous Fred, I had been promised a ride on the steam roller.

When I think back, it was obvious then that Fred reacted more favourably to people who he detected had an interest in the things he liked and, fortunately for me, I had shown that interest. It was one happy schoolboy who went home at the end of that day with a grubby face he didn't want his mother to wash, ever.

By the time I was 15 I was, like most kids, heavily involved in schoolwork and studying for my examinations, not an easy thing to do at any time but particularly difficult when all that I could think about was steam engines and hopefully learning the art of climbing chimneys. I had started to visit Fred's work yard when my schoolwork allowed – most weekends and holidays.

By this time, I had persuaded my father that the family image would be enhanced greatly by us owning a steam roller, and we had purchased an Aveling & Porter example in 1975, which was the same model as Fred's. The roller came from Ravensthorpe in Yorkshire and, in fact, was from the same place as the replacement forks needed for Fred's machine following 'The Last Drop disaster', a tale well told on Page 68 by my good friend and fellow-conspirator, Bill Greenhalgh.

Even to my young eyes, it became obvious that Fred's standard of work was higher than any other I have ever encountered within the restoration world. He was a perfection st, and only the best would suffice for him. His restored roller was an absolute dream and, as the saying goes, really did tick over like a well-oiled sewing machine. I was to learn under sadder circumstances, many years later, that the master had never lost his touch. On the day of his funeral and in the company of his son, Jack I got to drive the superbly restored Aveling & Porter convertible

I was, of course, still keen to climb on chimneys and liked nothing more than being able to visit a site with Fred and his team, which inevitably included Donald Payton, who worked as a very reliable and steadfast 'grounder'. Climbing is, without doubt, the thrill and high-profile part of the job but, as Fred would tell me on many occasions, a good grounder was worth his weight in gold, and there were not many, if any, better than Donald. But he was the man who wouldn't let me climb. ▶

I could unload the ropes and fill and empty the buckets, and even on odd occasion drive the Land-Rover, but he wouldn't let me near the ladders. If I sneakily started to climb, Donald would let me get about 20 feet up and then thwack me with the ropes until he'd made me come down.

As I was getting tired of this veto on my climbing, I decided that a course of drastic action was necessary. Fred was at the time working on a super traditional 200-footer at Gilner Mill in Bolton, a job I'd visited on several occasions during that September. There were three decks of staging around the top of the chimney – the top deck at approximately 180ft – and all the ladders were in place.

I worked away on my maths homework but the warm late summer evening and my thoughts of climbing a chimney got the better of me. So, unnoticed by anyone, I slipped quietly out of the house at about 9pm and headed for the site. Having worked there I knew the night watchman and where he was likely to be at this time on a Sunday night – in his cabin watching a portable TV.

I knew that the mill had floodlights that illuminated the chimney up to a height of about 40ft, and that after that it was total darkness. Without a care in the world and bursting with confidence, I started to climb and was

quickly above the illuminated section. I then carried on upwards and, with a little effort and a lot of care, I reached the first of the three levels of decking. Over the edge I went and sat transfixed, staring down at the ball of yellow light directly below and the town of Bolton spread out before me, with the lights of Lancashire twinkling in the distance.

The next move, I thought, was to leave some sort of message for Fred. He would then know I'd been there and, hopefully, in turn tell Donald I was OK, and maybe, just maybe, they would then let me climb with them. Then, in a flash, I remembered that Fred always laid his tools out in a particular order, and he had left them at the close of work on the very top staging, right where I could then see them. That's it, I thought, I'll climb up to the top and arrange the tools in a different way so that no one can say I haven't been there.

I stayed a little longer enjoying the view, and then climbed down, dodging the night watchman as I went. I started walking home, and then thought: "What will Fred think when he sees the tools have been moved? He'll blame the students." I could almost hear him shouting down to Donald: "The bloody kids have been up here at the weekend!" No way was I going to let that possible

thought steal my moment of g ory.

In a quick about-turn I decided to walk to Fred's house instead of my own. I knocked cn the door and stood there, as proud as punch, no doubt bolstered up by the sheer adrenaline of my first big solo climb. It was now 10pm on a Sunday night but I didn't care, least not until Fred opened the door.

"What's to do, lad? What are you doing out at this time of night? Shouldn't you be at home, young man?" enquired a very puzzled Fred. "I've been up Gilner Mill chimney, right up to the stagir g, and so you w ll know, I've moved your tools around," I blurted out. "Have you now? Well, you'd better get hcme to bed before you are missed, and don't be late next Saturday." That was it! Accepted into the fold! Donalc then changed completely and, together with Fred, started teaching me the correct ways of steeplejack working.

The boys were very, very careful and, under Fred's watchful eye and guidance, very little ever went wrong, and absolutely nothing was lef: to chance. But we did have our moments. One guy happily tying his newly purchased Christmas tree to the top of his car never knew how close he came. We were working on a chimney, the bottom 12ft of which was screened from the footpath and roadway by a brick wall.

It was cold and icy, and we were being especially careful. Fred was constructing a work platform around the top of the chimney, to facilitate which Donald had fixed new scaffolding planks to the rope so that they could be hauled up to the work area. Just as they got to the top, one of the new boards slipped from the rope and headed rapidly down the side of the chimney.

Fortunately for all concerned, it stayed close to the structure and landed out of sight of the guy with the Chr stmas tree, lodging between the chimney and the perimeter wall. Fred recalled that, from the top of the chimney, he viewed the chap noticeably jump at the noise of the crash but, after looking round, he saw nothing wrong and continued loading the tree.

Several days later, on the same job, I remembered remarking to Fred that the decking boards would be unsafe as the ground was covered in frozen snow and that they would be worse being, as they were, 184ft higher up. However, we were behind with this job, and in steeplejacking winter days can be short with as little as two hours actually spent in productive effort.

Not wishing to waste more time, Fred simply stated: "Yeah! Yeah! We'll be all right, lad, just follow me up and take care."

When we reached the work

platform, Fred carefully climbed over, on to the fla:, and then proceeded to turn the planks over one by one. That way we were working on perfectly dry timber; I believe the word is ingenuity.

Like so many people, I have a thousand tales to tell and, because of the memory of them, a little part of him will always be alive within those of us who knew him well. Many of the tales concerned the ro ler, which was not just Fred's pride and joy. It was very definitely something to be enjoyed. Many a summer's evenir g, for no other reason than 'just because', he would steam her up and off we would trundle, maybe only as far as Aunty Leana's Off-Licence, to get the money back on the empty Guinness bottles and then go for chips.

Fred and I were quite keen on roading off well into the night and, as I didn't drink, he was able to partake as we parked at various hostelries, and then we would meander ▶

◀ The five stages of decking on this chimney in Swan Lane, Bolton give a good impression of the height that young daredevil Michael Webber climbed in the dark.

Michael Webber (nearest camera) aboard the Aveling in the company of Jack Dibnah and undertaker John Howarth, braving the elements as they take Fred on his last journey.

on home or wherever. One such 'wherever' involved us firing up again after a comfort stop at a pub. Looking inside the living van, Fred noticed that his young family were all soundly asleep. Eventually we had got steam up again, at which point Fred latched the living van door securely, and we manoeuvred carefully off the pavement and on the roadway.

Unbeknown to us on the engine, and after a few more hours of happy steaming, all hell was breaking loose inside the van. Fred eventually heard noises! We stopped and he jumped down to the door of the van, unbolting it, and cautiously looked inside.

His wife and daughters were sitting on the floor in the middle of the van. They had been woken up and then completely engulfed in paraphernalia of all kinds. Pans, tools, coal, spanners of all shapes, tins of beans, Brasso, clothes, shoes, wellington boots and the kettle had all shaken themselves from their storage spaces and rained down. They had, it transpired, been trying to attract our attention for more than an hour. Oops!

Fred was a man whom, once you'd met, you would never forget. To those of us who knew him before his popularity as a TV entertainer, it came as no surprise at all. He was a man you just wanted to know. We lost regular contact with each other when I went to live and work in the 'soft south', as he called it, but thankfully we did get together again before he left us. I am very grateful for having known him and it was his encouragement that helped me follow my chosen career as a steam engineer.

I hope to be able to return the compliment by passing on my skills to the next generation. ∎

Michael's last tribute:

I WAS given the task of preparing and decorating our trailer as I saw fit for Fred's funeral. I wanted to get the coffin high up, so that it would stand out and be seen in a crowd. Fred's red ladders, so often seen snaking up a chimney, were perfect for carrying the coffin.

Three ladders were cleaned and relettered with a new stencil 'F Dibnah & Sons', varnished, then mounted and secured to a Clayton & Shuttleworth living van steering forecarriage. A narrow set of ball bearing rollers was manufactured to fit inside the sides of the top ladder between the rungs. This made rolling the coffin on and off easier.

The elephant was borrowed from The Bolton Museum, part of Bolton Borough coat-of-arms. This Indian elephant's connection with Bolton was cotton. It was the Indian cotton spun in the Lancashire mills that coined the phrase 'King Cotton'.

Velvet drapes, conifer and laurel leaves finished the trailer off.

Michael Webber's handiwork on the hearse.

◄

The end of Asia Mill chimney in November 1998. Most of the props are in place.

'Up & Under'
Simon Warner remembers

Expertise, strength of character and ingenuity are qualities that seem to be found in abundance among Fred's friends and colleagues. Add flair, imagination, loyalty and a good sense of humour and you have an all-round description of the unique band of people who were Fred's real pals. Simon Warner was proud to be counted in that select number.

When you are made aware that Simon's business logo slogan is 'Up & Under', you may justifiably wonder why. However, it's easy to understand when you know that he is both a steeplejack and a gravedigger. The later calling came when his dad (now retired) was a vicar so, as a young man, Simon saw a lot of graves, and as for the former, he was taught by, and worked with, Fred.

Simon takes up the story:

After leaving school in 1932 I went to Bury Technical College to continue with further education and that was by doing an engineering course. Living in the Bolton area, I was aware of this guy called Fred Dibnah who 'did steeplejacking work' and his involvement with that activity caught and held my attention, as the subject had always interested me greatly – so much so, that I plucked up the courage and went to see Fred one evening to discuss the possibility of me working with him in some capacity.

He was very nice to me but tried to dissuade me, by pointing out that most of the mills had been demolished ►

Fred relies on the old-fashioned hammer while the 'sponsored' nail gun can be seen swinging on the rope below him. He couldn't master its double safety catch mechanism. Simon Warner (left) and Fred on Badger Homes' chimney at Chorley.

◄ Simon and Fred pose on the top of a chimney. Note the lightning conductor tied to the ladder and about to be fixed to the structure.

◄◄ Fred swings in a bosun's chair high above the housing estate.

and saying that 'there will soon be no chimneys left to repair'. He was probably right, I thought, but surely there were still many churches where his services were required?

At the time I was disappointed that nothing positive came from our conversation. His advice was to stick to the engineering and gravedigging. (I was gravedigger at Stand Church, Whitefield where my father was Rector). Even though I was disappointed at the outcome of my visit, I still had the eager longing to work with him in his most unusual occupation. This thought never left me.

Some 10 years later, while at Bolton Institute and then working for an engineering degree, I saw Fred's TV programme. It spurred me on to contact him again. On this visit I arrived on my 1971 Triumph 650cc Tiger motorcycle, knowing that Fred also had an old cherished machine, an AJS motorcycle. Fred was doing something, which I later became aware was a regular thing: he was showing a group around the workshop and sheds which housed his steam engines and other equipment.

I tagged on to this group; and, when they left, I stayed behind. I reminded him of my previous visit and said that I still had hopes of being able to work with him. It turned out that Fred was due to fell a chimney in Warrington the next week and he encouragingly

suggested that it might be possible for me to assist in some small way. I gave him my name, address and phone number in the hope that I would hear from him.

I was already climbing at this time and worked in the film industry as a rigger, fixing lights and sound gear etc, and that was something I really enjoyed. I had passed my Heavy Goods Vehicle licence but still dug graves when called on to do so.

However, more then anything else I still wanted to do some steeplejacking with Fred.

This time the phone did ring and Fred invited me to be at his house early on the following Monday morning and so join him on a job. I was there in good time and turned up at Fred's ready and eager to help. We worked hard all week getting the chimney ready for dropping and, come the following Sunday, all was ready. Fred gave me the honour of sounding the horn that indicated the chimney was ready to fall.

My parents were among the big crowd who had turned out to see this event and later told me that the experience of being so close to this very high chimney as it was about to collapse left me as white as a sheet! It was, as anyone who has been close to one will confirm, an unforgettable experience. That week was the start of a seven-year working association with Fred and the experiences are ►

► Some of the typical damage that Fred and his team were called upon to repair.

►► Repair underway,. Note the newly-seated band.

counted as being among the best in my life so far.

I worked for him on and off, on a part-time basis, until I finished my studies at Bolton Institute, after which I then worked with him almost full-time until 1999.

This period was a steep learning curve for me, as Fred taught me to become a competent steeplejack. He cultivated the laid-back, devil-may-care persona, but let me assure you: when he was climbing no risks were ever taken. All the gear was checked out and nothing was left to chance. On any job we all knew what we were each to do and when we were to do it.

Interestingly, Fred would not climb on ladders I had fixed to a chimney for about two years; it took him that long to be sure I knew exactly what I was doing.

Our very interesting work took us all over the UK, up church towers and spires and repairing and demolishing chimneys. There are a great many stories to be told and the TV coverage of Fred, even as comprehensive as it is, shows only a small part of his challenging and fascinating working life.

The story of the Canvey Island chimney is told elsewhere in this tribute and I am sure you will find it both interesting and amusing, but there is one tale I must also tell as the picture to accompany it is priceless – but then, most pictures of him are!

We will describe this company as a famous firm who produce power tools specifically designed for shooting fixings and nails into all kinds of material, including brick. The equipment replaces the need for conventional

hammers, and therefore eliminates the difficulty in using them with one hand holding the nail and the other the hammer, ie while climbing. At least that was the theory, but it didn't apply in Fred's case.

We were booked to drop a chimney for the construction company Badger Homes in Chorley and, in order to publicise their operation, the company asked for a banner to be nailed on to the condemned chimney, a feature which is quite normal and often requested by the client. In this case it was sort of 'double bubble' as the nail gun manufacturers had asked Fred if we could use their latest product to fix the banner. They had a photographer on hand, telephoto lens and all, with which to get stunning publicity shots. Good plan!

So up we go, one of us swinging on each side of the stack and both of us gunning the fabric to the bricks as we slowly worked around the edge of the banner. Or at least, I thought that was what was happening. I became aware that Fred was going a bit slower than me and then realised why. He was using a traditional hammer and nails; the state-of-the-art gun was hanging out of use on a rope below him.

So much for the promotional work. He had apparently failed to master the double safety catch mechanism on the tool and had given up and gone over to the tried-and-trusted old way – a perfect example of how he hated modern technology and confirmation that he only really trusted traditional methods.

Fred's other work involved making weather vanes, and

◄ Barrow Bridge Mill, Bolton. Fred with the lightning conductor.

◄◄ A job well done. Fred sits back to admire his work.

◄ Eddie Chatwood, a regular member of Fred's team.

◄◄ Brew time at altitude. Simon Warner with Fred.

►

repairing and making components for static and steam engines. All Fred's workshop machinery was steam driven and I was impressed with the accuracy that was achievable with such basic engineering instruments, again when compared with so-called modern engineering technology.

A notable experience of a static engine rebuild, which I worked on with Fred, can be seen at Wetheriggs Pottery near Penrith. The pottery was restored in 1994 and the steam machinery was restored by us in 1995 and was featured in one of the earlier Dibnah programmes. This fine visitor attraction is a pure 19th century industrial monument steeped in a history of incredible creative spirit and endeavour, and the fact that it is today the UK's only steam-powered pottery is testimony to that.

When I finished working with Fred, I returned to the entertainment industry as a 'rigger' in arenas and conference centres. This is very interesting work. You get to set up the gear for all the so-called stars of today and we climb using the latest materials and techniques. I even worked on the Manchester Commonwealth Games. But nothing comes even close to my vivid and lasting memories of working with Fred in general and on the chimneys in particular.

I heard the sad news of his death at a time when I was working on a mill chimney in Yorkshire and so had the opportunity to leave my own commemorative mark. Anyone climbing the chimney of that preserved structure, the Lister Mill at Bradford, in the future, will find that I have left a marker in Fred's memory. Like a great many people, I will miss him but I'll never forget him. ■

The first blow is struck: Fred and Mick Barry start drilling another condemned chimney.

The props are in place and Fred checks his calculations.

A nonchalant Fred in 1990 – note the moustache!

Chimney demolition

Born in pre-war Britain during 1938 Fred Dibnah was, according to his mother, always interested in his surroundings and, in particular, anything to do with climbing or that involved steam. As a boy he loved to watch steeplejacks at work on the chimneys and tall buildings of his Lancashire home town of Bolton. From his bedroom window he could see steam locomotives at work, and he would sit and watch them for hours.

While watching those artisans, he studied the way that they erected their ladders and built scaffolding, no doubt formulating in his mind the way he would do the job when his time came. The time did, of course, arrive when, like most people, he needed to choose how to earn a living and support a family. It was to his love of climbing tall structures that he turned in order to be able to put bread on the family table.

When Fred celebrated his 21st birthday on 29 April 1959, post-war Britain was preparing to enter the so-called Swinging 60s. Conservative Prime Minister Harold MacMillan had a year earlier made the statement he will always be remembered for: "Let us be frank about it: most of our people have never had it so good."

But work for Fred and, indeed, for many more in the north of England, was not that easy to come by. Life was hard and work challenging, but Fred Dibnah was always up to the task.

The traditional industries were starting to show signs of age and irreversibly the industrial Britain that Fred loved was undergoing changes which, for better or ill, would irrevocably and completely reshape the nation. The demise of those traditional factories and, indeed, the redundancy of their very fabric was at first a good thing for Fred's growing enterprise. Factory chimneys, which for many years had been carefully built and then lovingly maintained, would now need to be demolished.

The well-built traditional boiler house chimneys were represented in Fred eyes as structures of great beauty, and he often referred to them as each being the greatest compliment anyone could ever pay to the people who built them, those people being workers he justifiably referred to as 'hard men'. To simply destroy them with dynamite at the end of their useful lives did not appeal to Fred Dibnah and anyway, he reasoned, because of their location, many would need to be more carefully dismantled.

This kind of demolition Fred and his colleagues often achieved by what he once termed 'back'ards construction'. Having climbed the condemned chimney, Fred then removed the bricks course by course and either dropped or lowered them safely to the ground. But there was another way that got the job done: no explosive charge was employed but plenty of drama was created. The use of this method Fred made all his own.

From the 1970s onwards Fred's fame as a toppler of chimneys (and tower-type structures) became legendary. Whether it was assisting in the creation of a retail park by removing the control tower from a WWII airfield or the removal of a Victorian chimney for a modern-day housing developer, the system was firstly, dramatically successful and secondly, bound to draw the crowds. Using his tried and trusted method, Fred safely reduced many a once-proud structure to rubble.

Fred's last chimney

The following account is from the occasion of what was destined to become Fred's last chimney. He dropped the structure exactly as planned on Sunday 9 May 2004.

The way in which Fred dramatically enforced the 'No Smoking' rule for old factory chimneys was without doubt something any observer would remember for ever. Neither big bangs nor a display of aerial pyrotechnics figured in Fred's methodology but the outcome was just as effective and equally dramatic.

Travelling along Manchester's Oldham Road on a quiet ▶

▶ Fred explains to camera what is going to happen.

▶▶ The Manchester police helicopter circles the doomed chimney.

Sunday morning can be a leisurely affair, especially if none of the area's senior football teams is at home, so you could be excused for wondering why, on a non-matchday, the crowds were heading towards the old cotton town. Signs announcing street closures were being placed at junctions and the peace and quiet was shattered by the drone of an attendant police helicopter.

What is more, its loudspeaker was warning of the aforementioned road closures. Why? Yes, you guessed it, Fred was in town and he was going to 'knock one down' (chimney that is, not a pint – that came later!) in order to erect even more dwellings to satisfy the appetite of this property-hungry generation. Messrs George Wimpey needed to clear yet another ex-industrial site.

The older buildings, at Lion Mill in Royton, had been conventionally demolished but the 100-year-old, 300ft stack remained intact. What is more, being within 50ft of the still-in-use portions of the mill, its demise could obviously only be achieved by employing skills of a very special kind. The builders had already started redeveloping the site, on which there are existing residential properties, so no explosives was very obviously the order of the day.

County Demolition Ltd, a Manchester company, knew just what was needed or, more accurately, just who was needed. The developer had decided, quite rightly, to turn this occasion into a very different Sunday lunchtime treat for their guests and added to the big occasion atmosphere by inviting TV film and outside broadcast crews. In fact, the company responsible for Fred's TV programmes had three crews recording the event and Sky News took it live.

The surrounding streets were jam-packed with members of the public keen to see the 'downing' and no vacant local vantage point could be found even as much as two hours before the climax of the event. The representatives of Greater Manchester Police had a prime view with their flying machine circling the fated structure and several other officers mingled with the expectant, excited and good-natured crowds.

The invited guests and VIPs, in the secure compound at the base of the chimney, had been well and truly fed and watered by the courtesy catering unit and, having been allowed to mingle with the demolition crew and even meet the 'top man', they were slowly moved back behind the safety barriers by 'hi-vis'-jacketed staff, as the clock

▶ It'll go in a minute.

▶▶ Any minute now, don't miss it.

▶▶▶ 'Did you like that?'

◀
Roger and Mick Barry each collect a trophy.

◀◀
Roger Dibnah sports his dad's top hat.

approached the appointed time of 1pm.

Fred's tried-and-tested method is, on the face of it, simplicity itself, although, of course, the danger is very real, and only by applying the skills born of many years' experience did Bolton's most popular son make it look so easy.

Having decided in which direction they want the redundant structure to fall, the demolition gang first clear a site a good bit larger than what would be its estimated 'lying down' size.

It is then the turn of Fred and his helpers to take over.

Slots are chiselled in the side of the chimney and the bricks are removed from the opening, making it roughly 3ft high by 1ft wide or, if you prefer, two-bricks wide by 12 bricks high (apologies to those of a metric leaning, but the dimensions were measured with a 30-year-old 'yardstick'). Two sections of scaffolding plank (approximately 8in wide) are then cut so that their length just exceeds the thickness of the brick layers in the chimney wall. In this particular instance that dimension was just over 27 inches.

The next step is to insert the 'filling' in the scaffolding plank sandwich, a piece of wooden telegraph pole or similar, which takes on the roll of a 'pit prop' and holds up the bricks above it, taking the place of those removed.

After leaving a section of three bricks in width the exercise is repeated at a position farther round the base of the chimney until (as in this case) 10 such props are in place.

The bricks between the props are then carefully removed so that the chimney, on the side of the chosen direction of the drop, is entirely supported by the newly inserted wooden supports. Now, with the aid of an electric drill – though Fred recalls that, in the past, a good old chest brace was used – a couple of holes are drilled through, the width of each pit prop. The holes are, says Fred, put there as the result of an observation during an earlier chimney drop and their purpose, he says, 'will become obvious'.

The next essential ingredient is the timber debris from the surrounding demolished buildings, and selected sections of this are packed between the props from the bottom to the top of the letterbox-shaped slot. That done, a huge bonfire of the remaining scrap wood is built against the side of the chimney, covering the props and the inserted wood. The next ingredient is gallons and gallons of diesel fuel until all the wood is well and truly soaked.

All that is now required to topple the chimney is a piece of wood approximately two inches in length and one-eighth of an inch in cross-section. Provided the brimstone covering on one end of that piece of wood is nice and dry, the quick application of the laws governing friction will do the rest. Hence the holes in the props. Fred's earlier observation involved a split prop where he saw that the combustion was aided by the flames being able to get inside the wood quicker. As the resultant fire gets hold, the supports will burn away and Isaac Newton's law will do the rest!

With the appointed time approaching, and the VIP watchers all moved to a safe distance, Fred pronounced that this burn would last for no less than 20 minutes and no more than 25. The match was struck and, within minutes, the blaze took a good hold, aided by the diesel oil and, as if in an act of defiance of its eventual fate, the chimney began to smoke profusely as the timber packed inside the structure ignited.

The sky was black with smoke and the watching public downwind were showered with soot carried in what would be the great chimney's last-gasp breath. The huge crowd of spectators were enthralled and almost completely silent, as the fire roared onward and upward with the black cloud turning to a hotter, lighter colour and the heat created causing the nearby watchers to take a step or two backwards.

Fred had confided that, when the end of the chimney's stand was almost nigh, he expected a brick or two to split and that would, he prophesied, be the signal heralding the collapse of the stack. He had also told the Press and TV cameramen to listen and look very attentively as he would not be able to repeat the show should they fail to capture it on film!

As 20 minutes into the burn approached, the crowd were, it seemed, even quieter, and several began squinting nervously into video and still camera eyepieces. ▶

▶ Bill Greenhalgh helps Fred to drill holes in the telegraph pole props at Burtonwood.

▶▶ Preparing the fire at Burtonwood, Fred throws on the diesel while Roger Murray looks on.

At 22 minutes 'in', there was heard a single sharp crack, resembling that of a hunting rifle being discharged, following which the growing excitement among the onlookers became almost palpable.

Within seconds of that tell-tale retort, a huge split opened in the back of the chimney and a section of brickwork fell from the front, in the direction of the intended fall, and in the twinkling of an eye, in fact during the duration of just 10 frames of electronically exposed film, it was all over.

The Lion Mill chimney was no more, and it lay in a smoking dusty pile, exactly where Fred had said it would. All that remained was for the demolition man's 'brick-cruncher' machines, which had been parked nearby in anticipation, to grind up the remains of this once-proud structure.

Within days the bricklayers, joiners and other artisans would be starting to put up the new houses, removing forever these particular traces of our industrial past.

As for the crowds, they went on their way happily, having been well-entertained with many of them, including this correspondent, proudly carrying a soot-covered brick as a memento of what would be, for most, a once-in-a-lifetime occasion.

▶ Fred and the Burtonwood tower.

▶▶ The fire is lit.

◀

Burtonwood gone.

◀◀

Burtoonwood going.
Note Fred running
bottom left of
picture!

General Patton's revenge

Let us return, for a moment, to the demolition of the aforementioned control tower, which was situated on Burtonwood Airfield, an ex-RAF (and USAF) operational base on the outskirts of Warrington. The flattening of the tower was to make way for the inevitible retail park.

The airbase opened in 1940, just in time to supply Spitfires for the Battle of Britain, and was probably the largest military base in Europe during WWII. With 18 miles of surface roadway and a peak of 18,063 personnel, this huge site had a massive impact on the Warrington area and its population.

Many thousands of American service personnel were based at Burtonwood as it was the maintenance and supply base for the USAF in Europe. It repaired and modified equipment, especially aircraft, for use by 70 US bases, reputedly bringing production line methods to Britain for the first time. The very famous General George S Patton was also associated with the area during WWII and especially in the run-up to D-Day. This job was to have a sting in the tail, or perhaps sting is the wrong word!

Fred was contracted to demolish a very sturdy concrete control tower, it being one of the last vestiges remaining from those far-off days, but it was now standing in the way of the developers. Nothing at all went wrong with the 'burn down' as that superb set of black and white photographs, taken at the time and reproduced here, clearly show. In fact it was a textbook operation, except that flying from the famous base had not, it seemed, been completely discontinued.

Unbeknown to Fred, his crew, the watching dignitaries and the public who turned out in great numbers, a family, or should we say a flight, of ducks was happily living in the top of the old tower. The rumble caused as one of the tower's legs collapsed, preceding its total disintegration, seemed to act as a wake-up call – or should I say 'order to scramble' – and the startled ducks took flight. They embarked upon a bombing run, on a flightpath that took them directly over the watching crowd, the incident proving without doubt that sudden fright can be a stimulus to ducks' bodily functions.

5am knock-up

Dropping chimneys is, of course, dangerous work, and therefore the unwarranted interference of other people is highly undesirable. Neil Carney recalls an occasion in Cockermouth, Cumbria, which could have had a disastrous outcome following one such unauthorised act of interference:

In 1993 we were contracted to demolish a chimney just outside Cockermouth and, after several days on the usual preparation work, we had returned late to our lodgings on the night prior to the event and retired, only to be woken at 5am by our landlady.

She informed us rather abruptly, that the police were at the door and wanted to speak to Fred, as there was a fire at the site, near to the base of the chimney. We dressed hurriedly and raced off to the job without even having time to grab a brew. On arrival we saw a huge fire blazing at the bottom of the chimney and some way off to the side of the chimney, the flashing blue light of a Cumbrian Fire Service appliance.

The fire brigade, not being able to ascertain in the pitch darkness the direction in which we intended to drop the chimney, were quite rightly having none of it and had, in the interest of safety, decided not to move in to extinguish the fire until they had the chance to talk to Fred. The emergency services were of the opinion that some enterprising individuals, probably well-fuelled with alcohol on the Saturday night, had decided to do the job for us.

We had not built the necessary bonfire to turn the props, but the timber to do so was on site and these DIY demolitionists had dragged some of that material to the side of the chimney and lit it. By the time the police and fire brigade got there the perpetrators of the stupid act were nowhere to be seen. They had done a runner, probably not realising that they had put the lives of the firemen and police at risk, not to mention us guys who now had to sort out the problem.

Fortunately, the fire they started was nowhere near big enough, but it had removed and considerably weakened a lot of the supporting props. Now one very important thing ▶

about this method is that you don't remove the last few bricks on each side of the opening until the 'drop' day. In this case that golden rule saved a disaster.

The chimney remained standing, and a few extra props were hurriedly, but very carefully, fitted into place. The interference of those idiots had caused a big delay, as further firewood had to be procured and brought to the site. In fact, we struggled to find enough and really should have had a lot more.

The drop was delayed and the VIP guests stood around chatting while we prepared a new fire. They were getting more and more fed up and had started to drift away. The new fire was eventually laid and it burned completely away, roaring well up the stack but without causing the chimney even to seriously crack, never mind drop. The fire just wasn't big enough.

There was nothing else to do but to cut out a little more brickwork and, as we did so, we finally got some well-deserved good luck. This chimney was standing on a square plinth, and that portion was cement-rendered so, as we carried out the dodgy manoeuvre of removing bricks on either side of the opening, to what was now an unpropped chimney, tell-tale cracks started appearing in the cement coating.

As the cracks got bigger and more frequent it was obvious that our chimney was finally on the move. About two minutes later, we had moved away to a safe distance, and a huge tell-tale crack appeared in the chimney proper. Then down it went, falling exactly where we wanted it to. Unfortunately, it was almost dark by this time, as a consequence of which, most of the spectators had gone home!

'Concrete Bob' has the last laugh

The great civil engineer Robert McAlpine was a pioneer in the use of concrete in building. The beautiful Glenfinnan Viaduct in Scotland was the first such structure to be

built in the UK using the material. This is an impressive curved creation, 100ft high and 416 yards long, consisting of 21 arched spans of 50ft each and carrying a section of the picturesque railway route from Fort William to Mallaig. It is a line that in the summer months is still used by steam trains.

The gentleman was more often referred to, not by his full title of Sir Robert McAlpine, but by his nickname. This fact was for years celebrated by the nameplates carried on a Class 37 diesel locomotive that displayed 'Concrete Bob' on one side and his full title on the other. His techniques became widely used in the construction industry and helped to establish reinforced concrete as a universally-accepted building medium.

The material had been used in the late 1960s to construct a 300ft chimney on Canvey Island in Essex, which utilised a massive 2500 tons of the stuff. This smokestack had become redundant, so Fred was called to see if his method would be suitable for downing the monster. The prognosis was good and, apart from taking special care of the reinforcing bars within the concrete, Fred thought that the job would be nothing out of the ordinary.

The site was to be cleared to make way for the construction of a new Safeway supermarket and the Canvey Island demolition team consisted of Fred with fellow-steeplejack Simon Warner and his long-standing assistant in such matters, Mick Berry. Great excitement and anticipation, as always on these contracts, greeted the arrival of Fred's team. The boys arrived in Essex on 2 September 1997.

Fred established just where he was intending to 'drop' the chimney and then agreed the relevant safety precautions. The construction boss then issued instructions to his team. They were, he told them, to get new crushed white stone and build a roadway and car park at a suitable distance for the use of the VIP visitors, who were all invited to view the 'drop'.

In addition, a scaffolding grandstand was built and a

tower constructed for the use of the local TV news crew. "In fact," recalled Simon Warner, "nothing was left to chance." He even remembered that the firm had booked the fire brigade to be on hand at the appointed time to damp down the dust by creating a curtain of water on two sides of the chimney, and to achieve that they had laid out hoses with stop ends and full of vertically pointing holes. It was a very rare late summer, a very hot and dry one and, as we started work, the September weather was good!

The preparation was, Fred figured, likely to take 14 days and that included estimating for him being off-site to attend an appointment with the magistrates in Bolton over the matter of him burning wood in a smoke-controlled zone. There was to be a steam traction engine rally in Essex, which coincided with the estimated finish date of the work, and Fred intended taking the roller there while Mick and Simon drove back to Bolton. It was to be the normal cut-and-prop technique except that Fred wanted to drill and cut the vertical reinforcing steel rods around the structure as well. The thought was that, having cut some, the others (around the back, away from the intended fire) could be severed as the fire got going.

They were all duly marked up and the boys got down to the task of cutting the chosen ones out and then chopping out the sections of concrete on the side of the fall. They ▶

would then put in the props, which would temporarily support the chimney. There was on site a great pile of scrap timber, which had been brought by the contractors for use in the burn. The local TV people turned up to do a little 'before' filming and the Fred dutifully explained to them the intricacies of the project.

Fred went off Bolton and duly returned on 17 September. He confirmed with the boys that the drop was still set for the next day and, while doing so, he observed that the contractor's bunting was no more than fluttering in the moderate breeze. "Good," he thought. The temporary car park was looking like it had been there for ever and the contractor guys left on site were all happily in the cabin doing what many think builders do best, having a brew.

The boys started to show Fred what was left to do and each went about his allotted task, doing a bit more jack hammering at the extremes of the cut-out section and checking the props. It was just after that, Simon recalled, that it started to rain – not water but little tiny bits of concrete!

The boys, who were all working on the same side, stopped work for a minute and nothing happened, so they decided it was just a bit of loose from the drilling. They started to drill again and then the concrete rain started in earnest, but this time they were not tiny specks but quite big lumps, and they were getting bigger by the split-second and a lot more numerous.

Fred yelled: "Run! We're not in charge of this bugger!"

The boys started by instinct to run in the direction they knew to be the opposite one from the intended fall. Mick, according to Simon, broke the four-minute mile and became the first man to do so while wearing a hard hat and steel toe-capped shoes. Panic! At about 60ft from the crumbling chimney, Fred tripped on a bit of reinforcing wire and was down on the deck and 60ft behind Simon. Mick, he says, was already in the winner's enclosure.

Simon remarked that he had often heard the expression 'frozen to the spot' and at that moment said he was. His head said 'run back and help Fred get up' but his brain didn't tell his limbs to move and, for an instant which seemed like an age, the pair just stayed where they were. Fred slowly rolled over and then struggled to his feet and still they both just stared as the chimney then dropped vertically down with a mighty whoosh, all 2500 tons of it – right before their eyes. An almost out-of-breath Fred just pointed and shouted above the noise: "Bloody hell, a day early but right on target!"

As if the shock of the premature drop was not enough, Simon then recalled that he had parked his Land-Rover, only yards from the base of the chimney. How, he thought in a flash, do you explain that to your insurance firm? If the sudden collapse was a surprise to the three demolitionists it was an absolute bolt of lightning to the boys in the site office.

As the chimney fell before his eyes the foreman was

◄ Fred chisels away in order to fix another prop on the concrete chimney while Mick Barry looks on.

on the phone to the boss assuring him that Fred was back on site and that all was well for the big event. What he is reported to have said next as he saw the crash we will leave to your imagination, as it was definitely not printable.

"What happened next," said Simon, "was like something out of *The Wacky Races*."

Four of the guys from the site office rushed outside and jumped on anything with a motor, dumpers, JCBs etc then all raced towards them through the huge dust cloud to discover if they were all still alive.

Remember the water curtain to spray down the dust was, like the demolition, booked for the next day. Simon's Land-Rover? Well that escaped, but only just, and he recalls they did get paid. Fred maintained they should have had a bonus for being a day early, adding: "You can't trust concrete. Give me good old-fashioned bricks every time".

He went off to the rally with the roller and the boys returned home with Simon still thinking about what, in different circumstances, he would have said to the insurance agent! ∎

◄ Missed it! The Land-Rover is safe and sound.

◄◄ A day early but down nonetheless! Note the wood for the fire, now surplus to requirements. From left: Mick, Fred and Simon.

The beer commercial

Not surprisingly, Fred had a flirtation with making TV commercials and, naturally, they were in the nature of beer promotions for a then well-known regional brewer. That career was to be short-lived, although it was to begin with a highly-successful campaign. In the end, Fred's inherent honesty was to prohibit him from putting his heart and soul into the ongoing promotion of the product.

Roger Murray was charged with finding a personality to advertise a brand of traditional bitter. At the time he was with an advertising agency and they handled the advertising and marketing for a Warrington brewery and distillery. In the 1970s there was a beer war going on between traditional bitter beer and lager. The breweries were getting alarmed at the popularity of lager among the young, especially as the most popular lagers were

imported from the Continent or brewed in the UK under licence. This is Roger's account of Fred's foray into the world of TV advertising:

The brewery we were handling had flagging bitter sales and their bitter constituted the main part of their production. Market research showed that bitter should be perceived as an honest, down-to-earth beer, brewed with traditional methods using natural ingredients, with an imagery of honest, down-to-earth, working man, preferably a skilled tradesman. It was important to be portrayed as very local and 'North Country', as opposed to international, standardised and mass-produced, as in the case of lager. We needed a Hovis-type image. Remember, this was in the 1970s.

Our creative department came up with various ideas but nothing really grabbed us. It was generally agreed

◄

Fred with a pint of what he called 'the real thing'.

that we needed a good strong character to lead the campaign. Various famous names came up but, for one reason or another, they didn't fit the brief. Then I thought of Fred. Wow, there he was, staring me in the face. He was exactly what we were looking for. I went round to see him and popped the question. "Do you fancy doing a beer commercial?"

Being typically Fred he asked: "Do I get free beer?" He then put his hand to his chin and mused for a bit, as Fred does. "How much do I get?" I gave him a ballpark figure. "Bloody hell," he said, "that's 10 times more than the BBC have just offered me. Yeh, yeh, yeh, go on, I'll do it." He then chuckled: "Fancy being paid for what amounts to a piss-up in a brewery."

We drew up a storyboard using the music background of Right Said Fred; the commercial was to show him with his pit props burning down a chimney, then in the pub enjoying a pint, with Fred's voice-over at the end saying: "After a hard day's work there's nothing better than a pint of Greenall's Local Bitter."

We then fine-tuned the storyboard and produced layouts for supporting Press and poster ads, plus point-of-sale etc, and presented to the client - who went for it. We finally researched the proposed commercial with target consumer groups and they identified with Fred and the campaign message. So it was all systems go – make the commercial.

Fred found a big chimney we could demolish for the filming. We selected one of the brewery's best traditional pubs and dressed it up. We got one of the best jingle

writers in London to produce the Right Said Fred music and jingle. If I can remember all those years back accurately, I think we used Anthony Newley's voice, but I'm not absolutely sure.

We then had one big setback. The ITCA the Government watchdog at the time for television commercials, insisted that Fred would have to wear a hard hat when knocking down the chimney. Definitely not his cap. Fred was adamant: "I'm not bloody prancing round on television with a poncey hard hat on," he remonstrated. So that was it. Everything was on hold.

We did a bit of research and came to the conclusion that Fred would still add a lot of value to the campaign even in a hard hat. After a lot of persuading sitting in his parlour at night with bottles of Guinness and with the wisdom of his first wife, Alisor, Fred finally agreed to wear the hard hat. We were paying him a lot of money at the time and I think he genuinely needed it.

The big day came for the shoot. Fred had prepared the chimney the night before, with all the props and tyres for burning in place. We had done some pre-scene close-ups of Fred and Donald jack-hammering the bricks out. Luckily the shoot went without a hitch. Halfway through the burning bit, which was creating a massive pall of black smoke belching out of the top of the stricken chimney and floating right over Warrington, the fire brigade turned up thinking there was a major fire.

The chimney came down right on cue with an end shot of Fred standing on top of a pile of smoking bricks like Napoleon who had just won a battle and was surveying the scene. Unfortunately, he just didn't look right in that hard hat. We were overrunning on time, so it was decided to shoot the pub interior shots on the next day, which was a Saturday.

The next day Fred turned up with a new clean cap and all smartened up, complete with his waistcoat and watch chain. He said that he liked to have his pint in pubs looking smart: it was the done thing at weekends and, anyway, his wife had already washed the clothes he wore yesterday. We explained that it was vital to have continuity – the pub scene was supposed to happen only minutes after he'd felled the chimney! He had to look as if he had just felled it with the same dirty clothes on. It wasn't Fred's fault. The continuity people had not explained properly the sequence of the shooting.

The original plan was to shoot the chimney and pub sequences on the same day but things were delayed and time got short. We were also shooting back-to-back, making a second commercial at the same time involving his steam roller and workshop, with another selected pub in the country where he would be more smartly dressed, complete with waistcoat and chain, which was very important to him. It was confusing as some scenes had to be shot out of sequence.

Everything had to be put on hold while we whisked Fred back to Bolton to grab some suitable working clothes. They were not exactly the same as the ones he ►

▶

Fred's living van lettered especially for the commercial.

wore the day earlier but we could get away with it. We would shoot close up on him showing just head and shoulders at the bar with a pint of the hallowed product.

We got it all in the can and, after managing to extract Fred from the pub, which is always a bit of a strategic exercise as everybody wants to chat to him and he becomes everyone's friend, it was off to a sound studio to record Fred's voice-over. This is where the real problem started.

For some reason Fred could not get his mouth round the script. All he had to say was 'after a hard day's work, there is nothing better than a pint of Greenall's Local Bitter'. He could say the first bit but couldn't get the ending right. I finally had to sit in the cubicle and try to prompt him. He kept on asking for another bottle of Guinness, saying it would loosen him up a bit.

By this time he had done about 20 takes, possibly more, I can't remember exactly. What I do remember was ending up legless as he was giving me a bottle of Guinness every time he had one. Finally he announced: "I'm no good at reading from bits of bloody paper. Let me say it my own way. I'll have to stand up and do it." So we let him do his own thing. By this time he was well away with the Guinness and went straight into a monologue and rambled on and wouldn't stop – and, to make things worse, he kept on describing how good Guinness was.

By the end of the session, which I think was about midnight, everybody in the studio was legless. They reckoned that they could piece some good bits together and possibly make a coherent sentence out of it. When you watch Fred presenting on television today, it is difficult to believe that he had so much trouble delivering such a short sentence all those years ago, but I think we found the reason only weeks after the campaign had run.

The television campaign started two weeks later and it turned out to be very popular. Watching on the box at home I couldn't believe what a great commercial it turned out to be, considering all the problems. Even Fred's gravelly voice-over sounded spontaneous and sincere. The overall campaign itself was a resounding success but it was short-lived. The BBC had started a series about Fred. The first one was based on his trip with the roller and living van to the Chelford steam rally.

Every time they stopped outside a pub and Fred went for a pint, it was in a Tetley's house and he drank and appeared to be relishing Tetley's bitter. Now Tetley's were the main competitor to the brewery whose bitter we were advertising. Nothing was said at first. I had a suspicion that the BBC, not wishing to be associated with any commercial advertising Fred was involved with, steered him clear of our client's pubs. Unfortunately it kept on happening and questions were beginning to be asked, especially from our clients.

It was extremely embarrassing from the advertising agency's point of view, so I went and collared Fred and asked him what was going on. "Well, I can't stand the bloody stuff," he said.

"But you made a television commercial and took the money for it," I reasoned.

"Yeh, but you didn't say that I would have to like and drink the bloody stuff for the rest of my life," – which, of course, was absolutely true. Fred insisted that he told me at the time that he preferred other beers. Which, of course, he did, but I didn't worry over much as I knew his favourite tipple was Guinness anyway.

To be fair to the brewery, we did conduct some blind beer tasting tests in various venues within their trading area. In each case three bitter beers were tasted without the tasters knowing which beers they were trying. The beers were Greenall's Local Bitter, Tetley's Bitter, and I am not sure who produced the third one. The result of the tests, which were quite extensive, showed that few tasters could identify specific brands. The conclusion was that it was perception and image rather than actual taste that popularised a particular brand.

Fred's reasoning was that he didn't realise at the time he had to be committed to liking the beer to be in a commercial. It was just a commercial. Knowing him, I had to admit that, from his point of view, he was right. There was a simple honesty about Fred, and this was why he had great difficulty with the voice-over and we had to do so many takes.

So that was dear Fred and the end of his association with that particular brewery and very nearly all the agencies. ■

Footnote

Initially based in St Helens, Greenall's Brewery was founded in 1762 and relocated to Warrington in 1787. The company took over Shipstone's Brewery, Nottingham in 1978. They ceased brewing beer in 1991 after a change of policy, designed to allow them to concentrate on running their pubs and hotels. All Greenall's-owned brands were at that time brewed by Allied at their Leeds and Burton plants. As the new millennium got underway, Greenall's brands were brewed to begin with at the then Carlsberg Tetley-owned Leeds Brewery – a company that now trades (2005) as Carlsberg UK Ltd.

Broadcast Quality Videos for Steam Enthusiasts

On top of the world, Fred in silhouette.

Roger Murray

Climbing Fred's chimney

While the image we all have of Fred is that of a superb communicator explaining to us the intricacies of Victorian engineering and building techniques as we sit in the comfort of our homes, the reality is that he, for many years, earned his living by employing his considerable skills as a steeplejack. Only a very small minority of people would even consider earning a living by climbing the kind of buildings and structures that Fred did on a regular basis.

At the time when he was involved in the production of television commercials featuring Fred, Roger Murray was asked by his friend to join him on a climb. In order to give us some idea of what it was like to work and climb on one of Britain's tallest structures, Roger tells of the day he joined Fred at work:

It is difficult to think about Fred without relating to the time when he persuaded me to climb a chimney. I think without exaggeration that it was one of the most frightening experiences of my life. It was round the time we made the television commercial and he suggested that I go and look at this chimney as it was one of the tallest in Britain and he had erected some very imposing scaffolding round the top.

We were considering at the time including some scaffolding shots in one of the commercials, so I drove out to where the chimney was. I think it was somewhere near Burnley. I remember seeing it in the distance for miles before I got to it. It was massive. When I arrived Fred was sorting some ropes out with a colleague, Donald, at the base of the structure.

"Hello Rog. What do yer think of it then? Some bloody chimney, isn't it? It's a monument to those hard men who built it. You've got to have it in the commercial."

I looked up and even standing on the ground felt a bit dizzy. He then announced: "You've arrived just in time. I'm going up now. Why don't you come up and have a look at the scaffolding?"

I instinctively took a few steps back vigorously shaking my head. "Come on, Rog, you'll love it up there. You've never seen a view like it and, if you're going to use it in the commercial, you should see what it's like on top. Martin Lightening, the cameraman with the BBC, comes up chimneys with me, so this is your chance. Come on, be a real man," he cleverly quipped, walking over to the base of the ladder and beckoning me to follow. "I shall come up right behind you."

Why, I shall never know to this day. It must have been a wandering rogue impulse. It may have been the added (be a man) bit. I just walked over to the ladder and started to climb. I remember Donald 'the grounder' giving me a quizzical look as if he was trying to tell me something – I wish he had.

"Lean back and stick your knees out sideways," Fred shouted from below me. I had only climbed one ladder length and it quickly hit me that I had made one dreadful mistake.

"Go on, keep on going. Get into a rhythm," Fred's voice bellowed behind me again. It felt as if I was a 100 feet up already and I was only treetop height. I gingerly looked up and saw the ladder going up and up and up above me, disappearing into infinity. It was a most awful sight, especially for somebody who didn't like heights. Fred's voice bellowed up again: "Go on, keep going and lean back."

By this time I was clinging so tight into the ladder that my jacket, shirt buttons and tie were scraping up the rungs. I was dressed in a pin-striped business suit, never expecting to climb a bloody chimney, especially one of the highest in Britain. When I set off at the bottom it was a warm, sunny day. I'm sure I went through a climate change.

Farther up a wind started blowing and it became quite cold and grey. Could that have been a passing low cloud, I wondered? I felt like an ant clinging to the side of a giant drinking straw. I kept climbing, not daring to look up or down. The lines of bricks went slowly past. I noticed them in detail. The ladders seemed to be very frail and wobbly, especially where one joined the other. They also went narrower at the top of each one, which was disconcerting. ▶

The thin metal pins sticking out of the brickwork holding the ladders looked as if they could just slip out from the mortar. There were little lengths of rope tying bits of ladder together. I noticed all these things in very close focus as I went further up and up. Everything to do with the ladders seemed very whimsical and 'Heath Robinson', although I kept trying to convince myself that Fred was an absolute professional and was meticulous about his equipment.

All I could think about was how I was going to get down. As I got higher the chimney got noticeably narrower, there was an odd feeling that it could topple over with my weight. "Keep going. Lean back," shouted Fred's voice from what seemed to be a long way down below now – much lower than I had anticipated.

Oo'er, I thought, he was just behind me. I nervously peered down between my legs. It was the first time I had looked down.

The sight was unreal and made me feel sick. The ladder and the chimney just went down, down and down below my feet, which seemed to be superimposed on nothingness. It was a most horrible and unnerving sight and I felt momentarily quite faint. Fred was about 50 feet below and looked like a spider hanging on a thread with his knee through a rung and leaning back having a fag.

There was a whole landscape in miniature spread out below him. I could see Donald as a tiny dot of a figure looking up. I was transfixed and couldn't move and just clung on as hard as I could for dear life. I think you can reach a point where keeping a so-called 'stiff upper lip' and being a 'real man' suddenly buggers off and leaves you, and you throw any thought of dignity and courage to the wind. I think I was near to panic as the wind whistled past my ears.

I was sure the chimney was moving. "Go on. Keep going," Fred's voice came up again from the depths. Then I think he noticed that I was having a bit of a problem as his voice came up again: "Hang on, I'm coming up."

I must say I felt a lot better. "Come on, Rog. We're near the top. Keep going and don't look down."

He was now right underneath me.

We got to where the scaffolding was at the top. With not daring to look up, the first I knew of it was the next ladder coming back at an angle to get over the planks. "Hold on tight with your arms and keep climbing. Go on. And lean back!" he shouted. At this point I really thought my end was nigh. The last thing I wanted to do was lean back.

Climbing outwards suspended under the ladder at such an angle, it felt as if all of my body weight was held only by my fingers. I remember thinking my fingers are only little and if they give way it's 'half a day out with the undertaker', as Fred often used to say.

He came up from behind and butted me over the lip on to the scaffolding planks. I scrambled on and lay spread-eagled, flat on my back not daring to move. Fred climbed on and then started walking nonchalantly round the top

with his hands in his pockets, surveying the distant landscape. "Look at that for a view, Rog. Just think, those men who built this chimney had never heard of aeroplanes, so they were the first ever to see it. Have a look, Rog!"

I half-raised my head and twisted it sideways to try to comply with his wishes. I could just make out rows of terraced houses and the odd church steeple and factory chimney poking up through the grey murk down, down below. Everything seemed to waver in front of my eyes. It

◄◄

Carefree Fred, as
easy as walking
up stairs.

was slightly reminiscent of an LS Lowry painting done from very high up. I bet Lowry never climbed a mill chimney to look at a view. "How am I going to get down, Fred?" I whimpered.

By now he was pirouetting round the edge of the inside of the chimney, kicking loose bricks down into its big black chasm. It looked frightening and made me feel even worse. I just wanted him to sit down and hold on to something. "You will acclimatise and get used to it soon," he replied. "Just sit up and look at the view."

He then went on about the delights of being at the top of a chimney and how many men were killed building this particular one. "I just want to get down again, Fred. I've seen the scaffolding now. It looks very good and I feel bloody awful."

I must have sounded pathetic but had thrown any pride to the wind, which was now whistling round the chimney at a rate of knots. I was past even the slightest

vestige of caring. "Would you like a mug of tea and a sandwich?" enquired Fred. "That' ll make you feel better, cock. I'll get Donald to send something up in the bucket."

To cut a long story short, Fred was right – I did get a bit used to it, there was something very special about being on top of such a magnificent chimney and I did look at his scaffolding. Then came the dreaded time of going down again. I couldn't help thinking of how I was going to crawl over those planks to get on the ladder underneath. Fred sat me in a bosun's chair and lowered me over on a block and tackle as I clung to the ladder for dear life, then it was a long, knee-aching climb down, feeling better all the time. I would never ever want to repeat the performance, but at least I had climbed a mill chimney, even if without the dignity.

Some learned sage once said that life was one big tapestry, but tapestries always look faded. Fred certainly added some colour to mine! ▓

His Lordship's

Another of Roger Murray's everlasting supply of Fred stories centres on an incident that he remembers followed a drive from the West Country.

While travelling back north with Fred one evening after the pair had been looking at a ploughing engine, they decided, not unreasonably, to stop at a pub on the way back. This one was on the edge of the Cotswolds and was a lovely old stone-built coaching house type of place with, as Fred commented, 'plenty of posh cars parked outside'. This is Roger's tale of that fascinating encounter:

We parked the car and entered the pub and it wasn't long before the people at the bar were lifelong friends. As the evening wore on, a rather vocal, tweedy lady invited us back to meet her husband at the hall where they lived just outside the village, as he had a big steam engine. So off we went with half the pub in attendance.

We drove through some imposing gates and along a

green locomotive

dead-straight drive lined with trees, which seemed to go on for miles up to this big stately pile at the end. It was some hall! Her husband was charming and made us very much at home with large lead-crystal glasses of his favourite malt. I explained that I was driving, but they insisted that we stay the night. Their man would prepare a couple of rooms for us.

Then it was into the library to see the engine. It was a model of a very ancient locomotive in a big glass case. I think it was a five-inch gauge and it was about five-foot long with tender. Richard, our host, explained that it had been built for his grandfather, who was a director of the railway company, and he used to have it running round the grounds of the hall. Fred closely scrutinised it and announced: "I bet it would still fire up."

Richard's eyes lit up: "Do you really think it would? It would be wonderful to see the old girl in steam again."

"Oh yes, let's do it," exclaimed his wife clapping her hands. Without further ado we gently lifted off the indignant big ginger cat, which had been sleeping on top of the glass case, and about four of the accompanying pub customers then carefully manhandled the engine and tender on to the polished wooden parquet floor.

"Have you any coal, love?" enquired Fred. Within half-an-hour the coal had been produced and reduced to little lumps, the boiler had been filled, the moving bits oiled and, with the help of some firelighters and the lady of the house's hairdryer, the library was now a haze of smoke as the little fire crackled away with its smoke being sucked up the chimney of the green locomotive.

"It won't blow up or anything?" inquired a now slightly apprehensive Richard.

"Of course it won't, darling. Dodo used to play with it and steam it up when he was a little boy," announced his wife. I took it that Dodo was their son. Fred placated him slightly by saying that we wouldn't get it up to full pressure, just enough to make it turn the wheels. We had supported the engine slightly with two bits of wood so the driving wheels were just clear of the floor.

We had all been so busy chatting and drinking our malt as Fred was explaining how he put pit props under chimneys; accordingly we had failed to notice that the locomotive's pressure had built up very quickly. Suddenly there was some very pronounced hissing as the safety valve blew off. "Bloody hell," said Fred, "it steams up well."

With that he went and sat astride the tender and blew the whistle. The ginger cat went berserk and with its tail all bristling, ran up the big brocade curtains. Fred then manipulated the little reverser forward and opened the regulator. The locomotive's driving wheels suddenly whizzed round at an alarming rate under a cloud of steam, it came off the supporting pieces of wood and charged off across the floor with Fred trying to hang on to it. "I can't stop the bloody thing," he yelled, "the regulator's come off."

The locomotive ran on to the carpet and across the imposing room amid clouds of smoke and steam and screams of "Stop it! Stop it!" from her ladyship. Fred, who had fallen off the back of the tender, was still clutching the tiny regulator lever, tried to chase the engine across the room. The frenzied ginger cat was now virtually running round the walls making an unearthly yowling noise.

The engine hit the bookcase at the far end of the library with a resounding thud, demolishing a set of polished wood library ladders. Although it was now halted and jammed against the bookcase, the pistons were still pounding away and the driving wheels still whizzing round and tearing the thick, and obviously very expensive, carpet into big lumps, which were flying everywhere.

It was like an out-of-control combine harvester. Everybody was shouting and running round, her ladyship was screaming "Oh my God! Oh my God!" The place was thick with smoke and poor Fred was doing everything he could to stop the little monster of a thing. I think he finally pulled the reversing lever back.

Fred explained that everything happened so quickly and there was so much hot water and steam everywhere with the regulator coming off, he couldn't get his hands in to control it. Needless to say, we didn't stay the night. We stayed at the pub instead as the landlord felt it was the most hilarious thing that had happened in the village for decades. ■

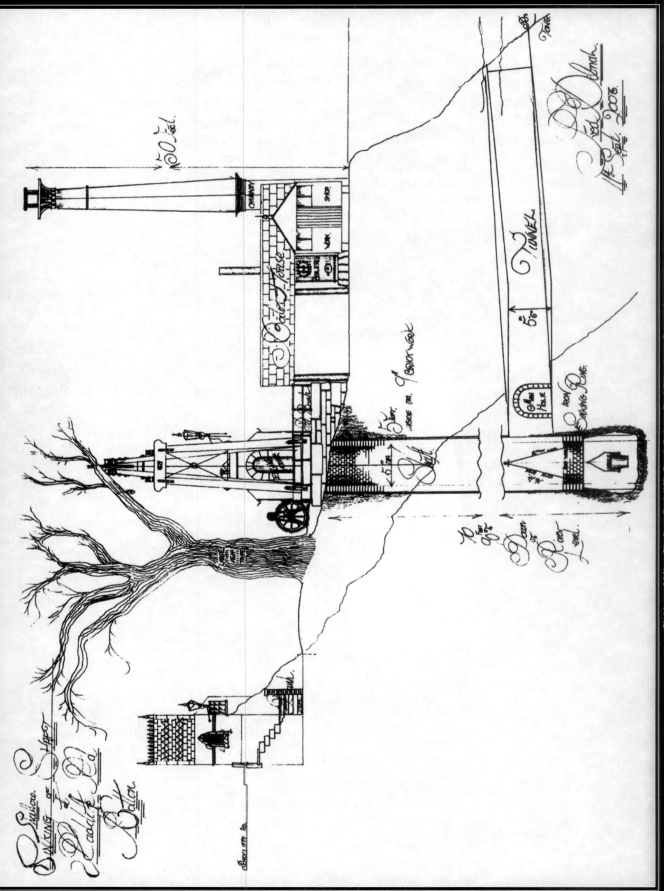

Sinking of Mine Shaft at Radcliffe Road, Bolton, Fred Dibnah 11 September 2003

6800 Grange Class

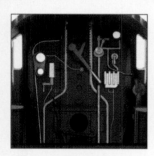

R 2402   GWR 4-6-0 'HARDWICK GRANGE' 6800 GRANGE CLASS

R 2403   BR 4-6-0 'DERWENT GRANGE' 6800 GRANGE CLASS

R 2404   BR 4-6-0 'RESOLVEN GRANGE' 6800 GRANGE CLASS WEATHERED

- 5 Pole skew wound motor
- Sprung buffers
- 3 Tender variations
- Extensive rivet detail
- Pick ups on all drive and tender wheels
- DCC Ready and NEM Couplings
- Comprehensive cab detailing

Roger Murray

Fred and the Rose Queen

It was back in the 1970s that I first met Fred. I had a traction engine and we met at rallies and suchlike. We became good friends and, over the years, I think I got to know him pretty well. As many have said of him, he was a true Victorian out of his time. He was surprisingly upright and moral in his own, eccentric kind of way and was totally dedicated to the human sweat and great engineering achievements of the Victorian age.

Most people did not know that Fred went to art school and was an accomplished artist and draughtsman. It was being a creative as well as being a wonderful engineer that made him so special. What he never realised was that he was also an absolute hoot, he really was funny. It was more to do with his own quaint way of saying things, a kind of innocent humour based on his old-fashioned perception of modern life. I shall miss Fred tremendously.

He has enriched my life with a bumper fun book of colourful tales. Nearly everything I got involved in with Fred seemed to turn into a highly memorable incident.

Fred and the Rose Queen

In the 1970s Fred had been asked if he would take his roller to a Rose Queen Festival in the town of Bollington, near Macclesfield. At the time I had a Burrell agricultural traction tngine and kept it only a few miles from Bollington. Fred felt that it would be a good idea to use my engine instead of his roller as it would save him from having to steam over from Bolton (he didn't believe in low loaders in those days!)

So it was arranged that he would drive his Land-Rover over first thing on the designated Saturday morning. We would steam up the Burrell and go to lead the Rose Queen and her entourage of floats in a procession through the merry old town.

On the day, it was one of those very still, heavy mornings without a breath of air, and the fire just wouldn't draw. Try as we did, we couldn't get a bright fire, just a lot of smoke gently curling up to the grey morning sky, and time was getting short for the trundle to Bollington. Fred reckoned it was the lousy local coal: "You don't know what good coal s down here in Cheshire," he commented, adding that he

should have brought some proper stuff from Bolton in the Land-Rover.

We had a mug of tea and some bacon butties while we patiently waited for the slightest hint of steam pressure to lift the needle off the stop. After an eternal wait, with the clock painfully ticking away, we managed to get just enough pressure up to get under way. Fred felt that the rattling of the engine along the rough road (we were on strakes) would liven the fire up a bit; it could also generate a bit of suck with the exhaust up the chimney.

I shall never know to this day what the real problem was – whether it was lousy coal, just a bad day or simply sod's law. I had cleaned the tubes and emptied the ashpan the night before. The coal had come from a good yard and I had used it on numerous occasions. After another half-hour of coaxing we managed to set off, but the engine ran out of puff about two miles from Bollington.

We just could not get any life in the fire. After a demonstration of the specialised art of lobbing selected lumps of coal on to strategic spots of the fire by Fred, we eventually got about 80psi on the clock and off we trundled again under a pall of brown smoke. By this time we were seriously late, and this was in those medieval times before we had mobiles with which to let the organisers know.

On a little country road bordered by big houses and gardens, we realised we were running short of water. A kind, unsuspecting lady agreed that we could take some water from her ornamental pond. When we put the big hose in and turned on the steam suction there was a big slurping, sucking noise and the complete pond disappeared up the pipe, leaving a gaping black hole in the lawn with fish jumping about on the bottom.

We reassured the poor lady by explaining that there was a rose on the end of the pipe so none of the fish had been sucked into the tender. She was more worried about what her husband would say when he returned home. He had only put the pond in the week before and it was his pride and joy, and there were some rare fish in there. Fred, in his inimitable way, said: "I think we'd better quickly get some water back in love or you'll be having 'em for tea." ▶

We got her hosepipe and started to fill the pond with assurances that we would call and see her husband on our way back.

Just as were about to leave an auxiliary fire engine on its way to the Rose Queen Festival stopped to see what was going on as they had seen all the steam and smoke, and they agreed to let us have some water from the fire engine. To their consternation we emptied their tank. The chief fireman mumbled that they mustn't have filled the tank properly when they left the fire station and they would have to go back to the station and fill her up quickly, as a fire engine without water is a non-starter.

And that was what it turned out to be, as they couldn't start their engine again when they tried to move off! We offered to tow them but they politely declined, explaining that it would not give much confidence to the public seeing a fire engine arriving being towed by an old traction engine. We gave our thanks and rattled off up the lane at a fast 5mph to get to the assembly point for the procession.

We got there with about five minutes to spare and were shown by an anxious, very official, official sporting a big badge, where to position the engine, which was behind the town's brass band that was to lead the procession. We were to be followed by the float with the Rose Queen and her Rose Petals all in white, followed by a float with the retiring Rose Queen and all her Petals. They all looked demure and like something out of Snow White.

I was still trying to achieve the juggling act of a bright fire with little smoke, a full glass of water and a good head of steam, praying for a little time before the start. There are some steep hills in Bollington and I wanted as full a boiler as possible to save exposing the fusible plug. Fred was on the pavement chatting to everybody, of course!

There was a balloon-seller next to the engine with a massive festoon of silver heart-shaped balloons floating about in a big cluster above him. All you could see were his little legs walking underneath. A white police car had drawn up alongside as a kind of outrider.

Everything was obviously beginning to happen as suddenly a voice shouted an order from up front somewhere; the band came to attention and then started forward with a rousing march. I gave Fred a yell to get on the engine, nudged the regulator, blew the whistle and off we went with a big chuff. The Bollington Rose Queen Festival was on the move.

The bobbing silver balloons kept pace on the pavement side and the police car kept us company on the other side. In the effort to sign his last autograph and get through the crowd of onlookers to the engine, Fred lost his cap. Whether someone whipped it off his head or he just lost it I will never know, but it seemed to transform him: he was no longer Fred. We shouted to the official with the badge to see if he could go back and try to find it, which he did, disappearing into the crowd behind us.

I have never known Fred to lose or be parted from his beloved cap, not before nor ever after that event. He even wore it in hospital. It was a real milestone event in history. Fred without his cap. He was devastated. All he could say was: "What shall I do without my bloody cap?"

He seemed quite diminutive standing beside me steering with a naked, balding head. I fell about laughing, which wasn't the most sensitive thing to do under the circumstances, as he'd already got wet through and covered in mud slipping into the empty pond, which we won't mention.

The engine behaved reasonably well until we pulled on to the main street which, I recall, goes up a hill. I gave the regulator a nudge to give it a bit of extra chuff and there was a loud 'whoomp' from up front. A black jet of water like black soup jetted up the chimney and climbed to a height of about 20ft. "She's bloody primed!" yelled Fred. "She's bloody primed."

Thank God there was no wind, but what goes up has to come down. In disbelief we both gaped in awe as the main blob of it hovered high above us like a flimsy black pancake with ragged edges. Then it began to disintegrate into smaller blobs, and in slow motion the biggest dollop came straight down on top of the man with the cluster of silver balloons. They instantly turned black.

The white police car went dull grey and all mottled and, worst of all, the white Rose Queens with their little Rose Petals all got covered in black flecks. Fred looked as if he had his cap on again, except it was shiny black blobs with streaks dripping down his ears and forehead. It was very embarrassing being in such an exposed position on top of a traction engine when this kind of thing happens. Mothers were screaming at us for getting their daughters dirty. The man with the black balloons was running round the engine whimpering that he would have to be compensated, and the men in the mottled police car just glared at us.

We were relegated to the back of the procession. Needless to say we were never invited again. Fred was relieved that few recognised him without his cap and, when anyone did have a go at him for all the mess, he just pointed towards me saying: "It's his engine, cock". ∎

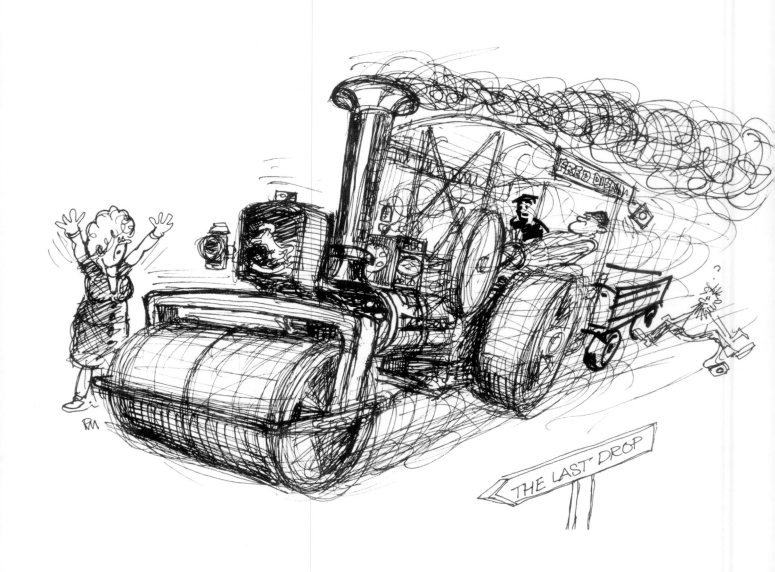

Bill Greenhalgh by the rebuilt brick pillar as he recalls that fateful day in 1974.

Bill Greenhalgh

The Last Drop disaster

Retired architect Bill Greenhalgh was associated with Fred for a length of time he describes as being 'more years than enough' and, like all of Fred's associates, has many a tale to tell. He also admits that between them they 'probably stopped a few barrels of ale going bad', a fact which, if true, would account for his unique claim. He had the distinction, he says, of being banned from the Dibnah homestead by not just one but, in turn, all three of Fred's wives!

He claims he was always the fall guy. Whenever Fred was late arriving back indoors, or was otherwise uncontactable and seemingly adrift, his name would be proffered by way of an excuse. These disqualifications led Bill on one occasion, during a particularly long banishment, to resort to drastic measures in order to contact his pal. This was long before the proliferation of mobile phones and Fred probably wouldn't have had any truck with one of those anyway.

Desperate to get in touch, he'd positioned himself across the other side of the River Tong at the rear of Fred's workshops in an attempt to make surreptitious contact, but all to no avail. Try as he might, he could not get Fred to look in his direction, and then he hit upon an idea. He hurried home and, retrieving some scrap timber from his shed, he made a placard board.

He fixed a long broom handle to the board, on which he had painted the words 'Hello Fred, How Are You' in letters six inches high. He then returned, this time to the front of the Dibnah house and paraded back and forth on Radcliffe Road, with his placard held high above the perimeter fence. This ruse did the trick: he was spotted and temporarily forgiven for leading Fred astray. He recalls that, after laughs all round, 'normal service was quickly resumed'.

The Last Drop disaster

Though others know of, and are associated with, the happenings on this quiet October Sunday in 1974, Bill wanted to be the first to recount the tale. There is good reason for that as, for more than 30 years, he has had to get used to being taunted as the man who baled out. But that is, of course, part of the end of the story; the beginning started, naturally enough, with a chimney.

The Last Drop village is situated on the edge of the Pennine Moors above Bolton and consists of a collection of 18th century farmhouses looking for all the world like a hamlet lost in time. But The Last Drop is home to one of the most prestigious hotels in the north-west of England and is owned and operated by Macdonald Hotels & Resorts. In addition to the hotel proper, there are cottages, gardens, courtyards, craft shops and a delightful village tea shop. In these modern times the village boasts extensive leisure and beauty facilities and it is also a popular venue for weddings and functions.

Back in the 1970s the owners engaged Bill Greenhalgh as a building designer, as a consequence of which he was heavily involved in the development of this complex. Rebuilding one section of the old farm, in what was to become the then North West Tourist Board's HQ but is now guest bedrooms, Bill's plans called for materials sympathetic to the surrounding buildings to be used. In line with that policy, he was looking for new chimneystacks – new, that is, in relation to that site, but old style was, of course, his preferred option.

Who else would Bill turn to in order to locate the necessary materials than his long-standing friend. Fred Dibnah was, it transpired, at that time dealing with the demolition of a Victorian mill-owner's house on the other side of town. Just maybe, thought Bill, that site could produce the goods. With enthusiasm and relishing the excuse to team up again with his steeplejack friend, he set off in search of the demolition site.

It was a very fruitful journey and Fred was easily persuaded to remove very carefully a couple of Victorian chimneystacks, after a suitable fee had been agreed. The stacks were made up of worked stone slabs octagonal in shape and about two feet across. each section being 18 inches thick. When assembled in the right order, the stones formed the shape of the chimney, and each had a nine-inch flue hole in the centre. Given that, when erected, the ▶

▶ The roller started sliding at the point where the Demdyke Suite sign is now situated.

structures were over six feet tall, the resultant pile of reclaimed Victoriana weighed over 20 tonnes.

Fred had been using his steam roller during the demolition job to pull down sections of masonry, so it was a natural conversational progression that brought the two men to agree to use the roller, and a suitable trailer, to transport the stone sections across town and up the steep hill to the village. The stone slabs had been loaded and secured on the trailer at the end of work on the previous day. Down at town level, on what started as a bright and sunny Sunday morning, Fred needed only to steam up the Aveling, hitch up the load and set off on the climb to the village.

The outward journey was uneventful, with the steam roller performing magnificently. Therefore, even at a speed of only 4mph, Fred and his crew of Bill Greenhalgh and Michael Webber reached the hotel site in good time and with the load intact, having made just one stop for water. However, on the way up they were aware that the nice early morning weather was rapidly being replaced by damper conditions, a change made more apparent by the lack of boards on the canopy roof of the roller. The uprights were in place and the side boards fixed but the roof planks were still lying in Fred's yard.

There was, in those days, a pub on site and, surprise, surprise, it was called The Drop Inn. The first priority, however, was to carefully offload the stone slabs as near as possible to the building of which they were intended to form part. The unloading was hard and therefore thirsty work, so it was not surprising that, upon its completion, the boys retired to the bar of The Drop Inn.

They do say in that area of Lancashire that, if you can't see Winter Hill clearly, it's probably going to rain, and if you can't see it at all, then it's 'appen' already raining. Consequently, the Pennine weather has a habit of getting worse before it gets better, which is precisely what

happened while the trio were taking their well-earned refreshment. In fact, Bill recalls, the light wind had turned into a moderate one and was shaking the leaves from the sodden trees. as they left the bar.

For the journey back to Bolton, Michael joined Fred on the footplate as it was his turn to steer. Bill, being relegated to hang on the back, instead opted to ride on the trailer, probably one of the best decisions he has ever made. Owing to the change in the weather and the lack of a canopy, the three were soon soaked to the skin. But otherwise, with a good fire in the roller, plenty of water in the tanks and the steam pressure adequately lifting the needle, all looked well for the downhill homeward journey.

The ensemble first travelled along the central road of the complex before making a sharp right-angled turn to the lane leading out of the village. The boys were happy and generally chatting about a job well done.

Following what happened next, Bill has always said that he has sympathy with Britain's much-maligned railway operators.

During the first 20 yards of their 300-yard journey to the main road, on a falling grade of about 1 in 80, it soon became apparent that all was not well. The newly-metalled lane was coated with wet, damp leaves and, accordingly, its surface resembled more an ice rink than a road.

All of a sudden and without warning it happened. The Aveling and trailer started to slide, there was no holding her, and the steam roller developed a mind of her own. She got into a slide that Bill says "would have done credit to Torville and Dean" and headed down the incline, gathering speed at an alarming rate.

The steamer and trailer were by this time completely out of control and, at a point about 50 yards into the descent, Bill decided that enough was enough and he jumped, diving over a stone wall and into a field, paratrooper-style. Fred frantically threw the engine into reverse and Michael manfully juggled the steering, but all to no avail. In reverse the driven rear wheels seemed only to hasten their descent and add to the slipping effect.

Having recovered from the shock and jumping quickly to his feet, Bill observed a spectacle he describes as being like something out of the great chariot race in *Ben Hur* occurring before his eyes on the damp Pennine hillside. It seemed, he said, to be happening in slow motion, with Fred and Michael hanging on for dear life in poses reminiscent of those ancient charioteers.

To the left was a very substantial stone wall, to the right and down a steep bank was the perimeter wall of a hospital and in the centre was a huge stone pillar. Whether by accident or design the roller, after first clattering over a cattle grid and demolishing a five-barred gate, then struck the solid stone pillar dead centre.

In a cloud of smoke and steam and with a sound like crashing thunder, the machine finished up elevated at 45 degrees with its front end perched on top of the rapidly crumbling mound. The actual roller was thrown to one side after the impact, on account of the forks having been smashed. The two charioteers had clung on to the end and, although very shaken, they were thankfully unhurt.

Bill scrambled back over the wall and ran towards the scene of the crash only to see the roller take another lunge forward, which that time resulted in it settling into an elevation of 45 degrees the other way around. Fred and Michael were frantically trying to 'throw out' the fire without burning themselves – not an easy task while trying to keep their balance on the precariously angled, crashed machine at the same time. On top of everything else, what they didn't want was a blown boiler.

Calmness returned to the scene and Bill recalls that, with the carnage now becoming apparent and the roller looking very much the loser in the battle with the brick pillar, the owner of the hotel (his then boss) came up the drive in his car. As the three stood rooted to the spot, he simply opened his car window, nodded at the wreck and after remarking 'silly buggers', drove off. At just about that time a resident from one of the nearby cottages, who had apparently been having his Sunday tea in his front room and had observed the spectacle first-hand, appeared with a camera.

· "Yeh! Yeh!" said Fred enthusiastically, in answer to his request to record the scene, "take as many pictures as you like but don't send 'em to the bloody *Bolton Evening News*, cock."

The boys, having made the wreck safe and cleared the debris from the roadway, covered the poor steam roller with a borrowed tarpaulin sheet and went home to contemplate their next move.

Always one to see an opportunity in every problem, Fred recalled that the forks were not the right ones for the roller anyway so this mishap would be as good a time as any to change them. He recalled that a guy in Yorkshire had once offered him some, so there ensued a journey over the hills that resulted in the acquisition of a

The chimneystack, which is effectively to blame for the disaster.

new pair of 'proper' forks.

Lifting gear was transported up to the crash site, allowing the Aveling to be repaired where it sat, still at the bottom of Last Drop Lane, a week or so later. Remarkably, it was then steamed and driven back home. But, as you may guess, that was not quite the end of the story.

As the boys prepared to set off back down the hill, a young lad came up to them waving half of the 'Invicta' plate which had broke off during the impact. "Can I have the other half, mister?" he said, pointing to the bent half-sign still screwed to the roller.

"Yes, son, you can," said Fred whipping a screwdriver out of his pocket, "but only if you tell me who was the guy who took the pictures."

"He lives in the bungalow over there, the one with the caravan in the drive," he said as he skipped happily away clutching the two halves of the Invicta horse.

Fred knocked on the door to enquire about the pictures. The 'Law of Sod' then entered the equation. Before the days of TTL (through the lens) viewfinders on cameras and when using 'manual wind-on', you could shoot away happily with the lens cap still 'on', which is just what the guy had done. No pictures.

The only record that remains of the incident is the one in the minds of the two guys who were there at the time, but the chimneys which started it all, are still there to be clearly seen. The Last Drop village is a great place to visit. If you do, it is important to remember that the lane concerned is the one to the extreme right of the hotel as you view it from the main road. It now has 'speed bumps' – not that they would have been any deterrent then, mind! About where the second bump is now, is where Bill Greenhalgh jumped.

Were you that young boy who won the two halves of Fred's Invicta plate and, if so, do you still have them? ■

'Nut Roast' and the Red Rose Steam Society

On the edge of Chat Moss in Lancashire, in an area once full of collieries, lies the picturesque village of Astley Green. In the heart of the village stands Astley Green Colliery Museum which, but for the foresight of Lancashire County Council and several leading figures within the community, would have suffered the same fate as the other collieries in the area – total demolition. It is a site that Fred was familiar with and had visited regularly. It has to be said that he particularly enjoyed the fare on offer at the adjacent local chippy and the craic in the local hostelry.

It was the realisation of the uniqueness of the 3300hp twin tandem compound steam winding engine that brought the demolition of the redundant colliery to a halt. Accordingly the museum, which houses Lancashire's only surviving headgear and engine house, now has listed building status. The preservation site and visitor centre is the headquarters of the Red Rose Steam Society, an active body, of which Fred was a keen supporter.

The museum occupies some 15 acres of the old colliery site and is virtually all that is left of the once-great Lancashire Coal Field. The low-lying landscape ensures that the museum's 98ft high impressive lattice steel headgear can be seen clearly from the busy East Lancashire Road (A580). A fitting memorial to days now past, the steam winding engine and its headgear complement the museum's many other industrial exhibits, not least of which is the collection of 28 colliery locomotives, the largest collection of its type in the United Kingdom.

Richard Fairhurst explains why the nuts were well and truly roasted!

The Astley ex-colliery site was chosen by Fred and the film crew as a suitable venue to visit at the beginning of his round-Britain tour. Thus the first real test run of the Aveling & Porter convertible terminated there after a successful and spirited run from Bolton. It was then serviced at the site over the weekend, prior to being low-loaded up to the Lake District, where it was required for more filming. It was on the fascinating coalmine site that Richard Fairhurst renewed his acquaintance with Fred:

I have been fascinated with anything steam or mechanical for many years, probably back to when I was five or six years old. My late grandfather, who was a very patient man and fortunately indulged my childish curiosity, encouraged me or, should I say, put up with my endless questions. He was a great fan of Fred's and so, at an early age, I knew all about the local steeplejack who had restored a steam road roller.

I joined the Red Rose Steam Society when I was 13, went to my first traction engine rally that year and became well and truly bitten by the preservation bug. From then on I have been going to rallies, and a major part of my life now revolves around steam preservation. Like a good many, I bought the early Fred books on steeplejacking and steaming right through my teenage years. By the time I was 15 or so I was probably quite an authority on him. I suppose you could compare it to another youngster worshipping a favourite rugby league player or cricketer. I read and inwardly digested every word.

Born in 1971, I do, of course, understand the need for, and the advantages of, modern technology, but I am also able to appreciate the engineering skills of the past and, like Fred, my hero was Isambard Kingdom Brunel. I joined the Lancashire Traction Engine Club (of which I am now, for my sins, membership secretary and website producer) when I was 18, and that marked a very memorable incident in my life. It was at one of their meetings that I had my first conversation with Fred; there I was, in the same room as the guy I had read so much about.

Around that time I got to know David Lomas, owner of Aveling eight-ton roller No 10753 (NU 3051), when I was still at university and had just turned 21. I began helping David with his engine at rallies and events on most weekends until about 1998. By that time I really wanted a steamer of my own and I set out in earnest to look for one and succeeded. On a very cold November afternoon in 1998 at Astley Colliery, I proudly first steamed the Fowler roller I had just bought, it was then called 'Jenny'. It was then, and still is, my pride and joy.

That was on the Saturday and I slept well that night, with plans to road the machine around the village the following day firmly lodged in my mind. I was up early and soon had 'enough on the clock' to turn the wheels. As I was about to take to the road, who should just happen to turn up at Astley with some friends but Fred. He regularly popped down to Astley, normally calling at the pub opposite, and then having a wander round the site. He always came chatting with the boys working there and was genuinely interested in their projects.

The machine I now own was ordered new on 17 March 1925 by Aberdeen County Council as a DN1, 10-ton, 5hp, compound tar-spraying roller. It was delivered to them several months later on 28 May 1925. When supplied new as a tar-sprayer, it was fitted with Fowler-Woods tar-

Richard Fairhurst

◄ Fred tows the living van up to the road for the first time prior to its run to Astley Green Colliery.

►

◄ In Bolton town centre for the first time with the van in tow, the boys head off at the start of the 'Made in Britain' tour.

◄◄ Alf and Jimmy steer from the back as the van finally reaches the road, Fred on the Aveling.

► Fred takes off the chimney cap so that it can be polished before the big journey gets under way.

►► Fred deep in 'steam talk' with Richard Fairhurst.

spraying gear, a differential, rope drum, fairleads, rim brakes and a full canopy. It was also supplied with two patent gritting machines, and Hecla tar boiler.

The gritters cost an extra £360 each, and the tar-boiler was a further £114-10s. The engine, with a 10 per cent discount, cost the authority £1171, that figure being equivalent to about £40,000 in today's money. During its working life this engine, along with four others supplied by Fowler's, stayed in the Aberdeen area until entering preservation in 1968. All five engines survive today, although two of them are now in 'showman's guise'.

Since the engine was sold into preservation it lived in the Yorkshire area, until moving to Cheshire in the early 1990s, and then finally Lancashire to its present home. When I bought the roller it was a runner, so I never had the work of completely rebuilding it, but I have kept it in tip-top condition and that is something Fred often commented on. He also noticed that I had changed the name to 'Nut Roast' and asked me why I had chosen that 'handle'. He roared with laughter when I told him the reason.

Like all kids with a new toy, I never wanted to put it away. I was forever cleaning and polishing the Fowler; every bit of bright metal was polished on every spare occasion, and still is. I was thinking about a choice of name and couldn't really make my mind up, until one day after the cleaning session it came to me, literally in a flash.

I had been cleaning up the paintwork and I used a light solvent on a rag to wipe over the surfaces. I gave the rag another good soaking and, in doing so, I obviously spilled some of the solvent on my boiler suit. Somebody shouted 'brew up' and passed me a mug of tea, so I stopped work and sat on the boiler barrel in order to enjoy the welcome beverage. I should add it was a very hot boiler barrel.

Big mistake! As I sat there drinking my tea, the heat from the boiler warmed up that part of my boiler suit with which it had contact. A few minutes later, and completely without warning, there was a flash of bright flame as the solvent on the fabric ignited.

I have never taken a boiler suit off so quickly, but unfortunately not quickly enough - hence the name 'Nut Roast'. As I finished telling Fred the tale he started to walk away, but not before exclaiming loudly the title of a 1960s hit song by Jerry Lee Lewis! He never let me forget that incident.

He was a great inspiration to a lot of people, in the steam job in particular and vintage machinery restoration in general, and he raised the level of interest in the subjects by his brilliant TV programmes.

He was an icon for the movement, on which he has certainly left his mark and I, along and with many others, certainly feel the better for having known him. ■

Richard is explaining to Fred the story of the 'Nut Roast' name, but quite where he is up to in the story is not obvious from the position of his hands. Our reporter Sue Mills looks on but, perhaps wisely, she failed to relate what the guys were talking about!

'Made it!' The end of the first day's filming.

'Full service'. The Aveling gets a flue-clean at Astley after its test road run.

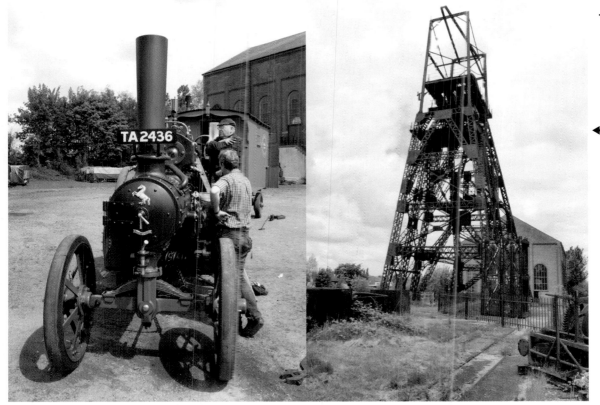

The imposing lattice headgear at Astley is virtually all that is left of the once-mighty Lancashire Coal Field.

A puzzled Fred gives the cylinder block the once-over.

What a relief! Bill Greenhalgh and Fred dispose of some spent ale at The Packhorse,
Bolton on the ocassion of Fred's wedding to Sheila. Bill was Fred's best man.

Bill Richards with the coal mine pump.

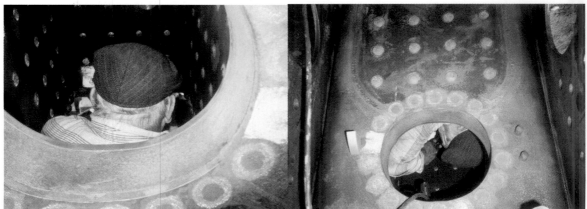

Fred inside the firebox, riveting.

Bill Richards: licensed victualler, mining historian and aircraft mechanic.

'Where's me ten bob?'

Like others of Fred's close acquaintance, Bill Richards is an ex-coal miner and, perhaps more importantly, he is a diligent and ardent collector of artefacts and records connected with the history of that once-great industry. Bill is also involved with engineering restoration and, like a great many who once earned their living underground, he is fascinated by the art of flight. Traditionally, miners have been linked with the flying of racing pigeons but Bill Richards takes his flying a bit further – he assists in the rebuilding of WWII aircraft engines.

Bill is to be found these days behind the bar of the 'Greenfields' private members' club in Westhoughton, near Wigan, which he runs with the help of his wife, Angela, and his family. In the early 1990s he would still have been found driving tunnels underground, working with a tunnelling contractor. For 31 years before that, he toiled at various coal faces far below the county of Lancashire, a part of the world which he dearly loves.

Bill worked as a contractor on the very last tunnel excavated at Parkside Colliery, a heading which opened on to a 'virgin ground' coal face 220 to 250 yards long and which was estimated to have enough quality coal within it to last until 2017, and possibly beyond. There were millions of tons, of which not one saleable shovelful ever reached the surface. The so-called 'modern pit' was sunk in the 1950s and was closed – many say prematurely – after a bitter dispute in 1993. That followed a brave battle in which the miners and their families, with the backing of the NUM, tried in vain to keep the facility open.

Bill needed little persuasion to talk about his friend of many years and how he first became involved with Fred – not, as you might think, in a licensee-and-customer relationship. It was long before that and involved the age-old skill of riveting. This is Bill Richards' tale:

Like a great many friendships, ours started out of need and really at the suggestion of a third party. A mate told me, one night over a pint, that this steeplejack he knew was restoring an old steam roller, and his account of what was occurring, not many miles away from my own front door, fascinated me.

A few nights later the same guy called me over as I was having a pint after work and asked me if we still had blacksmiths working at the pithead. I told him that we did, but added "only just about" as things were looking grim and we were all expecting to be finished up sooner than later. He nodded and said thanks, nothing more was mentioned, and we both returned to our friends.

A week or so later, I was again in the same pub, when my new-found friend came through the door and spotted me. He started waving a piece of paper and gesturing that I should meet him at a quiet corner of the bar. "Do you think the blacksmith's shop will have any of these?" he said, pushing a grubby note under my nose.

That was the first time, albeit unknowingly, that I had ever set eyes upon Fred Dibnah's classic writing style.

There were other signs of Fred on that piece of paper - an oily thumb and fingerprint. It turned out that the guy with the steam engine, who I was told lived in Darcy Lever, was in urgent need of the items sketched on the paper and conforming to the dimensions as noted. It was a request for a stock of good, old-fashioned rivet blanks.

I was later to learn that they were urgently needed to complete the boiler rebuild Fred was undertaking at the time on a steam roller he'd purchased a little time before. I went to the pit the next day and, before going underground, I paid a visit to the blacksmith's shop. The 'smith' was a great man of the old school, and he was very interested in what the rivets were required for, so I explained about this guy in Bolton and his old steam roller.

After I finished my shift I called to see if he had found any of the rivets Fred had asked for. The old guy had gone home, but by the door of his workshop were two hessian sacks tied and one was labelled "Bill Richards x2". I picked up the note and read the words: "Bill, these 'ul do 'im, 10/- to pay". There was a minor problem: if you have ever tried to lift a sack of rivets single-handed into the boot of a car, you will know what I mean. They are bloody heavy! There was also a very neat wooden box stacked alongside the bags with the words "an' this" chalked on it.

Anyway, by following the directions given to me, I went to meet the bloke with the steamer. As you would expect, he was lying under the thing working away, and he slowly crawled out as I shouted a greeting. I showed him the rivets in my boot and he was over the moon, and between us we soon had then stowed safely away in his shed. I was fascinated with the engine and, as you all know, if there is one thing Fred liked it was a receptive audience for the tales of his work. I was definitely that and we got on famously ▶

▲
Maker's name on
the mining pump.

▲
September 2003 and
the convertible
begins to take
shape. Note the
specially laid
railway tracks to
facilitate movement.

and, of course, went on to remain the closest of friends.

But that is not quite all about that meeting. There was the matter of the wooden box which was, in fact, hand-made and looked more like a posh presentation case. I was to learn, by watching him open it, that it contained a brand-new set of air-operated rivet guns, one large and one small, with a full set of 'dollies' (rivet head shaping tools) for each, which on first seeing them caused him, for once, to go speechless. He was like the proverbial dog with two thingies and I reckon he rated those guns back then higher that he would have done the Crown Jewels.

That was back in the late 1960s and Fred went on to use those guns for the rest of his life, a good 10 shillings'-worth. Therein lies a tale. As I left the yard that night, he thanked me for the gear and, as I headed off, I remembered the bit of a label on which the blacksmith had written the price, so I walked back to him.

"Fred," I said, "the old guy wants 10 shillings for the stuff and I will have to pay him when I'm next on shift."

"Fair enough," he said. "It's a bloody bargain, cock. The guns alone are worth 20-times that." Then there was a slight half-smile as he dug into to his overall pocket: "Got no brass on me. You'll be down the yard again; I'll gin it ya then!"

I did go to the yard again. In fact I went many hundreds of times and, right to the sad, premature end of his life, he joked about that bargain we rescued from a pit that was about to close. It was a bargain by anyone's standards and especially for Fred. I paid the blacksmith, and I don't think for a minute that he, in turn, paid the NCB, but dear old Fred never did get around to giving me that 'ten bob'.

One of my main interests is aircraft engines and, in particular, examples from the time of WWII, and Fred was very interested in this work. We were planning to get together and take a restored Rolls-Royce 'Griffin' aero

engine to one of the vintage shows this year (2005) and display it alongside his newly-restored convertible. Sadly, Fred will not now see that happen but maybe it's a project his boys, Jack and Roger, can consider.

Our little engineering society has currently two WWII 'Merlins' on the go and they both came from bomber aircraft. However, our priority project is the restoration of a 1930s-designed Rolls-Royce 'Griffin' engine that last saw service in an RAF Shackleton and was retired only in 1990. I am keen to talk to anyone who is carrying out similar work, as these engines (outside a preserved aircraft, of course) are very rare. The 'Griffin' is a 37-litre power plant as opposed to the 'Merlin', which is only 26 litres so, when fitted to Spitfires, they obviously made the fighters more powerful.

Fred was always keen to talk about aero engines but being, as we know, the all-round engineer, that is not surprising. Another favourite subject of his was mining and, as his last TV series confirms, he liked the company and conversation of ex-miners. On the many occasions he came down to the club for a 'jar of the black stuff' the conversation would often turn to a discussion about the authentic miners' lamps we have around the place and out would come the old mining pictures.

There is one 'Fred' project that I hope will still go ahead and that is the restoration of a diesel-driven mine water-pumping engine, a very rare one that we have stored at Greenfields, and which Fred was planning to restore. I hope now that the Bolton Mill Engine Preservation Society will be able to fit it into their busy programme.

Fred did so much for the industrial preservation movement so I hope others will keep up that very important work in his memory. Like a good many, I greatly valued his comradeship and I am thankful of having so many memories of the time I spent with him. He will be greatly missed. ■

Fred working on the Aveling firebox.

Mine host. Bill at the bar of the Greenfields private members' club.

'On the buses' to

Neil Carney has spent the majority of his adult life as an engineer working on public service vehicles and he took early retirement from his final job as depot engineer at the Wigan bus garage of Greater Manchester Transport to concentrate on his hobby of engineering model making.

Mr Carney is a very accomplished modeller and, in addition, shares a love of all things steam with his wife, Frances. This passion brought them into direct contact with Fred Dibnah who, by all accounts, was already aware of Neil's engineering skills.

From those early meetings the two men developed a comradeship that eventually led to a second career for Neil as a steam restorer and steeplejack's 'grounder'. In the fullness of time he even ventured up to the top of a "quite big 'un" and, as the men's work involvement grew, so did their friendship. The Carneys' daughter, Diane, went on to become godmother to Fred's youngest son, Roger, and even after Neil stopped working for Fred he kept in regular contact. Neil recalls that they were, in fact, lodging away while working on their first restoration job together on the day that Roger was born, 4 June 1990. This is Neil's story:

I first met Fred about 1966 at an early Burtonwood traction engine rally, which was about the time he had just acquired his own roller. At that time we were living and working in our home town of Ormskirk but, in 1969, because of my work, we moved to Bolton. I therefore lost no time in visiting the Dibnah 'works' to check on the progress of the roller I knew Fred was rebuilding.

I recall that he was working on it outside in fairly basic conditions at that time. In fact, if I remember correctly, all he had was a tarpaulin sheet slung between two trees. We kept in touch, but I didn't see a great deal of him until 1989, as it was then that I had taken early retirement and called at the yard to tell him so. Fred lost no time in asking if I might be interested in assisting him with the re-erection of a steam engine belonging to a mill in Wales. This he had removed during the winter of 1988-89 and, having refurbished it in Bolton, it now needed taking back to Caernarfon and reinstalling.

The site was at Glynllifon Park near the village of Llandwrog, and we worked on the project on and off for about nine months. In addition to the engine, we fitted a new boiler rescued from a meat pie factory. At the end of the job the customer had a refurbished engine that worked perfectly. That was towards the end of 1990. I think Fred appreciated my engineering skills and I was able to put them to work effectively during this installation.

We had worked well together, and I think that was why Fred asked if I might be interested in staying with him on the steeplejack side. I was keen to accept, although, I must add, I insisted that the deal would not include climbing and I would only be his 'grounder'. That was to be the beginning of five happy years together, where about half the time was spent on chargeable work, and the rest spent, as I would put it, 'playing in the garden'. Those who've visited there will know fully what I mean. There was always some engineering project to tinker with and I thoroughly enjoyed myself.

A fair amount of the time spent at the yard was dedicated to improving the line shafting and drives associated with Fred's many pieces of machinery. This included connecting a new section of shafting at right-angles to the existing one and driving it by way of a gearbox. I mention this because Fred initially used the gearbox (connected to a belt and pulley) to drive all his machines by using the steam roller. Eventually, of course, the machines were driven by a dedicated steam engine, a unit which had originally been employed to power a mechanical stoker associated with a Lancashire boiler at a cotton mill.

Neil assisting Fred with the flywheel on the convertible.

Neil Carney

'up the ladders'

With regard to chimney work, there was not always a lot for me to do while the actual repair work was taking place 'up top' and it seemed then that a great deal of Fred's time was taken up by pointing. He liked to use special mastic, which he mixed for himself using red lead. This, he maintained, resulted in a better quality job and was in the event easier to use.

Laddering was the real hard graft. The sections would all be prepared a day or two before (ie tying the 'skids' to the ladders). These are the little goalpost-like brackets slightly wider than the ladder, which ensured that it 'stood off' some nine inches from the chimney or tower. The necessary number of ladders was then loaded on the trusty Land-Rover together with 'the dogs'. These were the fixing spikes intended to be driven into a wooden peg, which had first been knocked firmly into a chiselled hole made in the brickwork of the chimney.

To complete the loading, two lashings per ladder (ie a five-foot length of rope with a tied loop at each end)

were also checked on to the vehicle. These sections of rope are required to tie the sections of ladder to the dogs, which will have been fixed to the chimney. A rope to a length totalling a little over twice that of the height of the chimney and a pulley block to be used in conjunction with it would then be added to the cargo.

The full-size rope is then used by the groundman to haul each ladder up to the man at the very top of the previously fixed ladder. In this manner, the chimney is fixed and provides a means by which the steeplejack can safely reach the area intended for his work. On a good day, we could erect up to five ladders in one hour. If the chimney was to be decked out, then it was usual to fix two ladders against it, on opposite sides.

The two tallest chimneys that I worked on with Fred were respectively at India Mills in Darwin and Barrow Bridge in Bolton, the latter being 262ft high. On the Barrow Bridge chimney we used two runs of ladder with 18 sections in each and a section of decking around the ▶

◀ Fred and Neil with the engine reinstalled at Glynllifon Park.

Shoehorning in the ex-pie factory boiler at Glynllifon Park.

his usual way, he just said: "No problem" and set about fixing one in place.

After that I just got on with the job, never bothered about the 70ft drop and happily shuffled back and forth across that plank, because the improvised rail was there. Fred must have noticed this and he made no comment until the end of the job. "Don't know why you wanted that rail, Neil. You never used it once," he observed. And he was quite right. I hadn't.

I was always very busy on the chimney-dropping jobs as my major task entailed keeping the work area free of broken bricks as the boys on the chisels or jackhammers cut them out of the chimney. It was important to have a level working area to make it safe while inserting the props. These were telegraph poles, cut to the exact required length using a chainsaw. The length varied slightly, depending on the thickness of the piece of wood used as a cap piece, which was fashioned to bridge the inner and outer props above the wedges. The wedges were then driven in as pairs, as tight as possible, by using heavy hammers and a lot of muscle power.

To give you some idea of the work involved, the wall thickness of a tall chimney could be up to four-feet, and to drop a chimney like that we would be required to use approximately 16 props and remove 130ft of brickwork. As Fred developed his technique, he took to drilling the support props to aid the burning process. He originally achieved that by using a hand-powered breast drill though, as time progressed, he used power tools for the task.

Fred never considered any alternative to this method of downing chimneys and he never liked or trusted explosives. "You can never be sure where those few bricks which fly out sideways are going. With this method I have a fair idea and total control – well, more or less!"

If I had to sum up Fred's abilities, I think there is one word that covers almost everything and that word is 'ingenuity'. He was a good friend, great guy to work with, a natural engineer and a quick thinker.

One story, in particular, illustrates the way his mind worked. He was returning from a vintage show, miles from anywhere, together with a pal, when the Land-Rover got a back-wheel puncture, and not a pub in sight!

The pair jumped out and examined the problem: it was flat all right. Fred had a spare wheel and its tyre was fully inflated, but what he didn't have was a jack of any kind. That was, except for a 12ft length of 4in x 2in timber, which he had bought at the show to use on a job later in the week.

His thought processes were something like this: "We can lift the vehicle using the timber as a lever and hold it high enough, for long enough, to be able to change the wheel. His puzzled companion agreed with the plan, but asked Fred what he planned to use as a fulcrum?

"No problem," said Fred and, grabbing a spanner from the back of his vehicle, he then forced up a cast-iron grid from the side of the road. We are all familiar with the phrase 'that'll do nicely'. Well it did! ∎

top. The contract called for the pointing of the top 30ft and then recapping the top brickwork.

On the other hand, the India Mills chimney was laddered so some guy could abseil down it to raise money for charity. He insisted on a rope being tied round his waist as he climbed to the top on the ladders (that, in turn, being around a pulley and held firm by someone, as he admitted to being 'not happy' on the ladders). He had abseiled from balloon baskets and was perfectly happy once he got off the ladders, and I recall that he succeeded in raising the necessary cash for the charity concerned.

I did eventually work at height, but not on a massive chimney. It was a water-wheel tower near Todmorden. It was a very impressive stone structure some 70ft high, which had originally housed three waterwheels, one above the other. Our job involved reconditioning the capstones around the edge of the tower, which was about 30ft by 12ft in girth.

Fred had erected a walkway inside the tower about three feet down from the top and I was quite happy working on that. We were renewing the metal straps that tied the stones together and, as the job progressed, the tools we were using got scattered around the job. To make things easier, by his way of thinking, Fred decided to place a couple of extra planks across the middle from one side of the inside of the tower to the other.

I said to Fred: "If you want me to walk across there then let's have one of those spare scaffold poles fixed as a handrail." After all, we were 70ft above the ground. In

On the road with Fred

A tkinson Trailer Hire is a Lancashire company which operate vehicles that many will have seen zipping up and down the country's motorways, but those given to attending vintage shows and steam rallies around the UK will have also noticed the firm's low loader. Inevitably, it would be delivering or collecting someone's cherished steamer to a show site. Consequently, when Fred was asked about a firm that might possibly help moving the convertible between filming locations, there was only one name he gave to the film-makers, that of his long-time friend, Alan Atkinson. This is his story:

It must be every person's ambition to make a living from their hobby. For several months last year I was able to achieve my ambition by combining my love of steam with my job as a haulier. I was asked to transport Fred's recently-restored Aveling convertible tractor around the

UK for what was to become the last BBC series, and I jumped at the chance.

My own involvement with the 'steam job' was via a baptism of fire that dates back to 1975. My brother Richard had helped in the restoration of a very desirable 1925 Wallis & Steevens 'Advance' roller. Unfortunately Richard was killed in an industrial accident shortly after the engine had been restored and I was thrown in at the deep end, so to speak, when I was asked to take his place in completing the restoration and transporting the engine – two things I had not previously been involved with.

The owner had touchingly named the roller 'Friend Richard' in memory of my late brother.

It may have been meant to be – I shall never know – but it happened that the roller came up for sale in 1980 and I bought it and have thoroughly enjoyed

Alan Atkinson

◀ Fred, with a brew, supervises Alan Atkinson and Jack as they lash on the convertible.

◀◀ Almost ready for the off, the boys check that everything in the living van is OK as Fred and Alan pose for the camera.

◀ Alan's mobile café is open and two customers await their early morning cuppa.

rallying it regularly ever since. What is for sure is that I had caught the steam bug as I went on to add a half-scale Atkinson 'Colonial' steam wagon to my collection some years later.

I still take off with the family, given the slightest chance, to rally the two machines around the country. Summer weekends are, of course, all the better if there is some steam involved.

Over the years I had built up a good relationship with Fred, even transporting him and his Aveling roller to the odd rally and promotional event up and down the country. A few years ago, as Fred's second engine was nearing completion, he told me he would like to make a film visiting important places throughout the UK and that he was going to talk to producer David Hall about it.

I told him to put my name down for the transport, never thinking that one day a telephone call from a TV company would answer my prayers. The highlight of the whole affair was the trip to Buckingham Palace when Fred got his 'gong'. We couldn't park up on The Mall but did stop a little way from the front of the big house; we unloaded in Wellington Barracks on Birdcage Walk.

The 'secret of my service' while filming was really very simple, and to those who knew, no secret at all. I always kept a portable gas stove, kettle, water and brew requisites in the cab. While the TV people got set up for the day ahead film-wise, my most important job after lighting up and unloading the engine was to brew up.

Fred would arrive, usually with Alf and Jimmy, and

head straight to the low loader. Picnic chair out and brew in hand, he would then hold court with his public.

As the summer wore on, the whole crew got to know where the brew gear was stored and I ended the location filming with a total of eight beakers lodged in the cab. Oh, yes, and the odd tin of baked beans.

One of the great pleasures during last summer was being able to witness first-hand the affect on between Fred and his two fine boys. Jack and Roger spent many hours both on location and on the road with us and they were very much a part of the team. Whether it was by breaking up wood to light the fire, cleaning the engine, fueling up the coal bunker or getting to drive and fire the Aveling, they were constantly involved.

The fellowship we enjoyed in the evenings after filming will also not be forgotten. Fred was a well-loved figure and, being in his company, we were all treated like royalty wherever we travelled. It was sad to see Fred's health deteriorate throughout the tour but, however unwell he felt, he always had time for his fans.

Over the weekend of 18-19 June 2005 we are to hold a rally at Leisure Lakes, Mere Brow between Preston and Southport to mark the centenary of Rotary International. In order to acknowledge Fred's great contribution to the steam and vintage world we have decided to dedicate the gathering to his memory. The showground is not far from the M6 (J28) at Leyland and, if you have the time call and see us, there will be for sure many people to swap 'Fred' stories with. ∎

Fred with Mike Bossons outside Metropolitan-Vickers' Manchester works. Note young Jack Dibnah on the footplate.

Jim Stevenson, film maker and writer

'Atlas' – Fred's favourite engine

From his very first encounter with traction engines, Fred Dibnah always looked for perfection, and the superb condition of both of his own restored machines bears adequate witness to that belief. However, anyone who knew Fred will tell you that after his first encounter with 'Atlas' he was smitten, and it was indeed love at first sight, with the big Fowler B6 'Super Lion', works number 17105, registered VM 2110.

Fred had seen 'Atlas' at several events and he was forever talking about it. No one would ever have described Fred as a man even remotely obsessed with material possessions but, having encountered 'Atlas', Jim Stevenson, another of Fred's friends who is also a writer and sole proprietor of the film company Moonlight Productions, takes up the story:

I first met Fred in 1974 during a visit to an evening steaming event at the rear of the Red Lion public house in Ellenbrook, Manchester. Neither of us had brought along an engine so we kind of drifted into one another's company and accordingly strolled around looking at the vehicles on show. As many others have intimated, it was not difficult to become friendly with Fred – in fact, quite the opposite was true and I left that evening having promised to keep in touch with him.

During the course of some subsequent refurbishment work to Fred's steam roller, I regularly visited Bolton and I recall, in particular, that I assisted with the refacing of the slide valves and helped with the 'grinding in' of the regulator valve. Some years later I visited the Isle of Anglesey Traction Engine Rally and Fred subsequently told me that he was impressed by the fact that I had 'single-handedly' road-driven my steam roller to the event, a round-trip of over 200 miles. In fact I did that for two years on the run in 1979-80 and my first Anglesey journey became the subject of a book entitled *A Head Full of Steam*. My machine back then was a 1924 Aveling & Porter E-type road roller 'Cinderella', which I restored between 1975 and 1977.

But back to Fred's involvement with 'Atlas'. When, out of the blue, the engine's owner, James Hervey Bathhurst of Eastnor Castle, asked him to carry out some repairs on it, he must have thought his dreams had come true! The Fowler B6 was therefore delivered to his workshops.

Following the work he got to drive 'Atlas' during the making of a film depicting its 'trial' return journey to the Cheshire Steam Fair in 1992 entitled *Travels With an Old World Atlas*, and on that run he was joined on the footplate by Mike Bossons. During the run we made a planned diversion in order to take the loco from Bolton to Trafford Park, Manchester, to visit the premises of engineers Metropolitan Vickers Ltd, who used it to haul heavy loads (often transformers) around the country during the late 1920s.

The big road locomotive featured in a further Moonlight Productions film when it travelled 'light' from its base at Eastnor Castle in Herefordshire to Gloucester and then hauled a 40-ton road train in the reverse direction, over the Malvern Hills. This was in support of a charity event organised by a local radio station.

Fred joined the ensemble for the loaded 'road train' trip when he again piloted the 'Big Un', and that epic 1993 journey was also captured on film, entitled *The Big Road Atlas*. Moonlight Productions has also produced a film in order to commemorate the National Traction Engine Trust's 2004 Golden Jubilee Event, entitled *Going For Gold*. Jim Stevenson's films are still available from Moonlight Productions and he can be contacted on 0161 969 7783.

Derek Rayner is the Technical Editor at *Old Glory* magazine and we are indebted to him for compiling a fact file on the Fowler B6 road loco and some additional information on Fred's convertible.

'Atlas' - a Fowler B6 Super Lion road loco - was new to Norman E Box Ltd, a haulage contractor who had offices in both Manchester and Birmingham. The engine was despatched to that firm from John Fowler & Company's Steam Plough Works in Leeds during May 1928. The engine was fitted with a crane jib attachment (for use with a removable jib) and carried the necessary rope drums etc from new. The lugs for this are still retained on the front of the smokebox.

The B6 spent the next decade moving loads of enormous weight and physical size such as transformers, accumulators, boilers and condensers the length and breadth of the country. This it did not only as a solo machine but also occasionally in conjunction with other engines. The engine later passed into ▶

Fowler road loco 'Atlas' recreates the type of load it would have pulled in its working days, in this case a transformer.

Pickford's Ltd ownership for similar use when Norman E Box Ltd amalgamated with that well-known company in 1930, and eventually, it entered into preservation.

The major part of the engine's initial restoration was carried out by the then-owner, George Trubshaw of Stoke-on-Trent, who carried out the exacting work mostly without outside help. The engine was first 'unveiled' to an admiring public in early July 1984 at the Elvaston Castle rally, near Derby.

■ Fred's newly-unveiled Aveling Convertible Traction Engine, Aveling & Porter works number No 7838, was one of four seemingly identical machines supplied to West Sussex County Council. These were 7836, 7837, 7838 and 7839 respectively. They were of a type described in the Aveling & Porter build records as KND 4hp 'motor tractor & roller combined'.

No 7838 was delivered on 4 December 1912 and was fitted from new with a two-tine scarifier No 1256. This quartet were all thus fitted, and they were dispatched from the works with both a set of rolls for rolling purposes and straked wheels for use in tractor mode.

No 7838 has additional entries in the company's records. It is noted that it was Devon County Council, Fleet No 20 of 29/03/1927. It is also noted that the angle segment (on the front of the smokebox) was dispensed with and a cast iron 'combined' type chimney base with flange for bolting on a saddle (number KND 226) and a new chimney complete were supplied by Aveling to the council. At that stage it was thus definitely in use as a steam roller and there is no doubt about it. Hence it is a convertible engine and therefore it has now been restored in its tractor form.

▶

A TRIBUTE TO FRED DIBNAH

EXCLUSIVE TO READERS OF THIS PUBLICATION
A SPECIAL DVD AND VIDEO FROM THE VIEW FROM THE NORTH

This outstanding three hour collection featuring the best of Fred from the company that produced his programmes for the BBC contains exclusive footage that all of Fred's fans will want. It includes:

THE BBC TRIBUTE
Produced by Fred's long time producer friend David Hall this warm tribute tells Frec's story from his earliest steeplejacking days to filming his last series and receiving his MBE.

FRED DIBNAH'S LAST CHIMNEY
Unique and exclusive record of the felling of Fred's last chimney at the former Park Mill, Royton in May 2004. This 45 minute documentary filmed by The View From The North has not yet been seen on TV and is only available on this special tribute video. It's the first time that Fred's unique approach to chimney felling has been covered in full on film.

MEMORIES OF FRED
The complete, unedited interviews with Fred's friends, old steeplejacking mates fellow steam enthusiasts, personalities and public figures. Over 60 minutes of memories of Fred from those who knew him best.

FRED AT THE PALACE
The complete unedited footage of Fred at Buckingham Palace when he went to receive his MBE. Shot by The View From The North for the final programme in Fred's last series - Made In Britain.

Only available from The View From The North at the special price of £15.95 plus p&p.

THE VIEW FROM THE NORTH

ORDER FORM (BLOCK CAPITALS ONLY)

Title: _____ Initial: _____ Surname: _____

Address: _____

_____

_____

Town: _____ Postcode: _____

Quantity required for this order   DVD _____ VHS _____

Cheques payable to: *The View from the North Ltd*
Send to: The View from the North, PO Box 407, Leeds LS7 9AE

Total DVDs @ £15.95 each: £ _____

Total Videos @ £15.95 each: £ _____

P&P @ £1.25 per item: £ _____

ORDER TOTAL: £ _____

A PHOTOCOPY IS ACCEPTABLE

▶ The engine outside Metropolitan-Vickers' Manchester works.

▶ 'Atlas' is seen setting off from Fred's house in Bolton.

▶▶ 'Atlas' out on the road, adjacent to the Bridgewater Canal at Patricroft, Manchester.

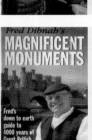

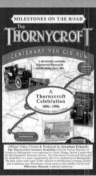

The Fred phenomenon

As the exploits of steeplejack extraordinaire Fred Dibnah became known to a much wider audience by way of his TV and media exposure, photographs and other artefacts of 'Fred memorabilia' naturally became very collectable. As a consequence of Fred's popularity, a large number of books and videos have found their way on the market. As his fame grew, people began to compile collections and, as a result, many thousands of households now have their own 'Fred library'.

While travelling around the country during the filming of his latest TV series, it was commonplace to encounter people clutching books waiting to be autographed and others requesting to have their photograph taken with him. No matter how busy the timetable, Fred always found time to comply with their wishes, often causing frustration among the film crew, as they were naturally acutely aware of the tight schedule.

Unlike the reported attitudes of some media stars, Fred did not consider the public to be 'his public'. They were treated equally and with respect. He looked upon them all as his friends. People who had never met him before would engage him in conversation as familiarly as they would their next-door neighbour. And he would reply in a similar vein. He had this knack of finding common ground with another human being instantly.

Often several quick 'yeah! yeahs!' accompanied by rapid nods of his cloth-capped head, signified that he was intently listening to their offering. Many have alluded to the fact that Fred was a good talker; undoubtedly he was, but what made him special was the fact that he was also a great listener. What they were not to know was that perhaps only 10 minutes earlier someone had asked an identical question of him. Even so, they would walk away knowing that the answer he had given was personal and exclusive to their enquiry. Now that's star quality.

David Devine

A musical interlude

Ask David Devine to tell you what a 'Wigan kebab' is and you will get what is to him a very obvious answer: "Three meat pies on a stick". That's because, although he is a Lancashire man through and through, he is firstly a proud Wigantonian. He is the leading light behind the popular website Wigan World (www.wiganworld.co.uk). That modern news organ has, since its inception, championed the causes of Fred Dibnah and his many acolytes. David Devine can fairly be referred to as a Fred Dibnah archivist and, in keeping with that title, has a barrowload of stories to tell, in addition to a fine collection of photographs. David writes:

It has been my pleasure to have known Fred Dibnah since 1969, and I've been fortunate to accompany him to many events. I have also been mixed up in several escapades, a great many of which involved my late brother, Ken, who Fred often described as a 'frustrated steeplejack!' Ken was, in fact, a virtuoso musician and, in his latter years, a violinist with Manchester's famous Hallé Orchestra. But, if the slightest opportunity presented itself to him, he would go climbing with Fred and, like him, my brother appeared to have no fear of heights.

As we would leave the house to meet up with Fred at a worksite, Ann, my sister-in-law, would elicit from both of us a promise not to do anything dangerous and to keep off chimneys. For years Ken, in particular, broke that promise regularly and got away with it – that is, until the occasion when his photographic skills gave him away.

Having collected a particularly good set of prints from the processor, he got a little carried away and decided to show them to Ann. She studied them and pronounced them as being very impressive, and then her face darkened a little as she noticed that something familiar to her appeared in a shot taken 'looking down the chimney' towards where Fred was working. "Ken Devine!" she exclaimed, "You have been up that chimney or someone else was wearing your shoes!" There, clearly in shot, were Ken's lower legs and shoes. His wife had him 'bang to rights'.

Virtually everyone who ever worked with Fred has a chimney demolition 'funny' and mine, as you would expect, is not a tale from a perfect job. In fact, this particular chimney was in a very restricted situation. Fred had weighed up the job with his usual diligence and we could not have been aware of the problem that awaited us. As the chimney started to fall (in the right direction) one large lump broke away from the top and headed down on its own. It struck and then went through the

roof of a brick-built shed next to the job. No problem, we thought, as the shed was out of use. This part of the factory was derelict.

Wrong! The shed was still being used as a bicycle store and Fred's insurers had to sort out a claim for the damaged bike belonging to a very irate storeman and, in addition, a claim for damage to the roof. Now that was a little out of order as several days later Fred received an enquiry from the firm asking for his best price to knock down that very shed!

The Rev Barry Newth recounted several amusing tales at the 16 November 2004 funeral of our dear departed friend, one of which concerned him and a colleague turning up as promised at a church fete on the steam roller, but they were very late and a little the worse for drink. He kindly did not name Fred's accomplice at that time but, as the saying goes, confession is good for the soul. It was me and, boy, had we had a great session!

In his own way, Fred was very fond of music, so he would chide my brother constantly on the subject of varying musical tastes. On one particular occasion we had been returning to base with a roller, having successfully completed some project or other, the details of which escape me, except to say that we were hungry, thirsty and covered in black soot. That roller used to have a mind of its own and, amazingly, it had a habit of stopping outside the Lever Bridge Inn.

Now we naturally had a few drinks and, while doing so, transferred our dirty fingerprints to a few sandwiches, a couple of pies and the odd bag of crisps. Everything in the world was well and we were all enjoying the conversation and the ambience that was, back then, typical of the traditional British pub when Fred suggested: "What we need now is a sing-song. Come on, Ken, you're the musician. Get on that piano in yon room."

At that point we all picked up our pints and headed for that place especially beloved by Ena Sharples and company in the early episodes of *Coronation Street*, the uniquely British 'snug'.

Ken complained that he had no music so could not play, which cut no ice with anyone. "You're a pro" and "Get on with it" were the typical remarks that I dare repeat. Now, you never know who is in a pub listening to your conversation and, in truth, as the drink goes in you care even less. There was a very smartly dressed elderly man propping up the bar and, on account of the winter weather, he was wearing a long, dark grey overcoat.

He just motioned to get Ken's attention and then, as ▶

One of David Devine's favourite pictures – Fred posing by his Land-Rover in the mid-1980s.

Fred at work, 1981.

Fred on the top
stage of five, 1980.

the film makers would have us believe the archetypal
'wide boy' or Arthur Daley-type would do, he slowly
opened his coat to reveal what looked like an illicit sheaf
of papers in his inside pocket. They were, it turned out, a
collection of sheet music appertaining to popular pub
tunes and even included a couple of hits of the day. That
was it! The sing-song lasted all afternoon and a great
time was had by all. However, Ken needed to be at the
Halle for a concert that night so we eventually dragged
him off the piano and headed for Fred's house, where we
had left the car.

We were, to say the least, a little late and, to make
matters worse, Ken needed to wash and change into his
'zoot suit' for the performance. Now, that gear was in
the back of his car so he grabbed it and, having washed
quickly, he tugged on his posh gear and headed for the
car. We just about had time to make it to Manchester,
but Ken's starter motor thought otherwise, and the thing
would not start.

Fred came to the rescue: "We can go in the Land-
Rover." Which was fine with a by-now very anxious Ken
until he remembered: "Neither of you can drive in that
state." It then transpired that Ken would drive, as he
claimed to be sober, and that Fred would sit with him

and explain the foibles of the gearbox to him as they
went along. I climbed in the back and off we went
leaving instructions for the garage to collect Ken's car.

The plan was that we would have a good feed
and sober up while Ken scraped the strings for an
hour or two and then we would all travel home. But,
as we got to the stage door, my brother asked why we
did not want to see (hear) him play with the Halle.
Well, that was that! Into the Free Trade Hall we went –
our kid in his show gear and us two in our scruff, but
we did have time to dive into the gents and have a
cursory clean-up just before the concert started.

Now that is not entirely the end of this musical story
as, more than two years later, we were in another pub,
this time in nearby Darwen, when Fred spotted the guy
with the overcoat.

He immediately recognised our group and he again
slowly opened his coat while tapping his bundle of
music, which was still in that inside pocket. Ken at that
point suggested that we find another watering-hole and
Fred and I fell about laughing.

Words cannot express how deeply I feel the loss of
Fred but, thankfully, like a good many more, I have a
host of memories to console me. ■

Fred talks to camera while filming at boltmakers Thomas Smith Ltd in Atherton. Alf casts his eye over the furnace.

◀

Alf in his workshop working on his live-steam model wagon.

◀◀

The Three Amigos: Jimmy, Fred and Alf at the Midland Railway Centre walk over to look at a disused mine shaft.

MADE IN BRITAIN
The last TV series

The concept

The idea for what sadly turned out to be Fred's last TV series came mainly from his own desire to visit companies and individuals whose present-day activities reflect the industrial advances that led to the development of steam machinery in general and his Aveling & Porter convertible in particular. The convertible had been an ongoing restoration project for Fred since he purchased the machine in the mid-1970s.

The crew

The series of programmes made by the production company 'The View From The North' was first broadcast on BBC2 in the spring and early summer of 2005. The senior members of the production team had all previously worked with Fred, which led to a cohesive work plan and made the difficult task of location filming easier to achieve.

The producer and director of the series was David Hall and the production manager was Kathryn Hall who in turn was assisted by Kate Siney. The majority of the camera work was in the capable hands of Rob Taylor and the regular soundman was Nigel Chatters. Jon Doyle also directed some of the location shoots and assisted on others, while Steve Shone and Steve Parry took care of the editing.

The cast

In addition to Fred, his two pals, both ex-coalmine workers, toured the country with him. Alf Molyneux and Jimmy Crooks had both worked on the restoration of the Aveling convertible and were also involved with the construction of the 'Mine'. It has to be said that a great many of Fred's friends helped with the aforementioned projects. They are rightly due thanks and can be sure that Fred appreciated their constant help and support, but they are, of course, too numerous to mention individually.

Alf first became involved with Fred following a visit he and Jimmy had made to the site of Wet Earth Colliery in ▶

Alf has paid again! Fred looks on coyly, as Alf has had to pay in the canteen at the Midland Railway Centre. Fred's cash is (he says) locked in the living van.

Fred, Alf and the boys travel along the Cheshire lanes.

the Clifton area of Manchester. After retiring from their jobs as colliery over-men they pursued an interest in the history of that industry. Wet Earth Colliery is of national and international importance, primarily thanks to the activities of James Brindley, the eminent engineer. Brindley's solution to water problems at the colliery remains unique in the annals of coal-mining history.

At Wet Earth they bumped into Alan Davies, who was then the curator of the now-closed Salford Mining Museum. To further their acquaintance, Alf arranged to meet up with Mr Davies later at a local pub. During that meeting another of 'the gang', Bill Richards, introduced Alf to Fred Dibnah and the two men got round to talking about mining. Alf's interests were really aroused when the subject of Fred's Pit Head gear was discussed.

Fred asked him to call by and have a look at the scheme. He did and, in turn, he recruited Jimmy,

Fred is shown the workings of the Anderton Boatlift by engineer Gary Hughes.

Alan Davies and several others to help in the digging of the pit. As Alf tells it, that was the start, and the rest is history. The relationship that developed between the three men during filming was fantastic, and that clearly shows in the resultant programmes. Fred's infectious personality found the perfect soulmate in 'stoic' Alf, whose subtle sense of humour kept the whole crew constantly amused. Jimmy was the quiet man of the group and maybe that was a good thing given that, on a good day, both of the others could talk for England! The ongoing saga of who pays for the tea was always entertaining, and Alf still insists that Fred is related to royalty as, like them, he rarely seemed to carry any money! A real bonus for Fred was the fact that his sons, Jack and Roger, were able to join him for most of the filming and the uplifting effect that had on him was gratifying to behold.

The Journey

The Passion of a Lifetime – First transmitted 8.3.05
The journey took Fred to ancient iron foundries, industrial sites and also little workshops where things are still made today just as they were more than 100 years ago. Fred at the beginning of the tour demolished his last chimney at a textile mill near Oldham. The group were then filmed making preparations to embark on the 'Grand Tour' with the steam traction engine.

Collecting the Coal – First transmitted 15.3.05
Coal, of course, supplied the power for the UK tour but finding the right stuff was a problem as there are no coal merchants left in Bolton. Therefore, an open-cast mine near Wigan was visited. On the first run it was literally an uphill struggle as the engine ran out of steam just a few miles from home. Problems sorted, and the fuel loaded, the boys journeyed to Astley Green Mining Museum. On arrival the trio took a look at Europe's largest steam winding engine and examined closely three discarded Lancashire boilers.

The Source of the Iron – First transmitted 22.3.05
After leaving Lancashire the journey took them to the Lake District, an area not normally associated with industry, but iron ore was once mined on a large scale in Cumbria. On the way, Fred stopped off to meet a friend, Dick Ransome, a fellow-steam enthusiast. Fred and company then enjoyed a sample of the beauty of the Lakes while taking a trip on board a steamboat owned by another friend, Roger Mallinson.
The next stop on the tour was Florence Mine at Egremont, the last deep iron ore mine in Western Europe still in commercial use. Fred took an underground tour, during which he learned about the decline of the iron ▶

◀ Having travelled down the Anderton Lift, Fred sets off for a trip along the Weaver Navigation.

◀ The last occasion on which Fred travelled from Bolton on the convertible. They are heading for the factory of Thomas Smith & Company at Atherton.

◀◀ Setting off to get coal at the start of the journey, the boys travel through Bolton town centre.

▶ On top of the copper mountain, Fred and Alf with Jack and Roger on the engine.

▶ The boys start to climb up to the top of Parys Mountain on Anglesey.

▶▶ Filming is not all glamour: Alf is covered in soot and oil following a trip on the engine in the pouring rain.

▶

ore industry. Next the boys visited Workington Steel Works, now owned by Corus Rail, which was once world-famous for making railway lines using West Cumbrian Iron ore.

Castings – First transmitted 29.3.05
In the next part of the film, Fred and Alf travelled to Scotland, where they were fascinated by the ingenuity of the 'Falkirk Wheel'. They also visited one of the few surviving traditional iron works left in the region. After stopping at the Bo'ness and Kinneil Railway for a few adjustments to the traction engine, they travelled on to Queensferry. The steam roller then became the first such vehicle to cross the Forth Road Bridge under its own power.

Water and Boilers – First transmitted 5.4.05
Crossing the border back into England, Fred visited Ryhope water pumping station in Sunderland, a facility that ceased working in 1967 after 100 years of service. While in the North-East they travelled across the Middlesbrough transporter bridge and took a close look at the way it works. Israel Newton's boiler works in Bradford was the next point of call. Fred considered that a real treat, as the company still carries out boilermaking the traditional way, by using rivets.

The Road to Steel City – First transmitted 12.4.05
Another of Fred's ambitions was to drive a traction engine over the M62 motorway via the imposing Scammonden

Bridge, and the opportunity to do so was taken on the way to visit Sheffield. While in 'steel city' the friends took a tour round a forge and watched 'crucible steel' being made at the Abbeydale Industrial Hamlet.

Mechanics and Riveters – First transmitted 19.4.05
In Yorkshire, Fred and Alf stopped off at Andy Thornton's, a company which make beautiful ornate carvings and Victorian-style wares. Fred tried his hand at carving and then watched a traditional 'ornate glass' cutter at work. On leaving the factory, they had fun scaring a few small children with the steam whistle as they 'roaded off' to Worsborough, near Sheffield, to have a go at making hot forged rivets in the traditional way.

Travelling to Derbyshire, they visited the Midland Railway Centre and toured the workshops in which railway locomotives were being restored and repaired. Fred was delighted to see a hydraulic riveter in action, especially as an old Morris Minor car engine powered it! Thereafter followed a visit to see more friends, the Howard Brothers at Matlock, where their Fowler showman's engine 'Renown', destroyed by fire, was being rebuilt.

Pattern Making – First transmitted 26.4.05
Fred visited David Ragsdale, a skilled pattern maker, who also owns six steam engines. David showed Fred round his traditionally configured workshops and foundry. Steam ▶

Jimmy Crooks joins Fred with three Corus workers. Note that Fred has his flat cap on under that hard hat!

Fred shares his favourite magazine with engineers at the Midland Railway Centre near Ripley, Derbyshire.

Fred with the steam locomotive crew at the Great Central Railway, Loughborough, Leicestershire.

Jimmy Crooks helps out with the making of Alf's model steam wagon.

► The boys arrive by road.

►► A wood-sawing demonstration is filmed at Klondyke.

enthusiasts are renowned for their resourcefulness and a good illustration of that fact is Tom Nuttall, a man who runs a garden centre and museum powered completely by steam, a set-up that greatly impressed Fred.

While in Derbyshire the team took a trip to Ashbourne and visited a traditional clockmaker. The whole workshop was belt-driven, just like Fred's, and it has been a family business since 1826. Fred marvelled at the skills and techniques involved in the delicate processes carried out by the artisans.

Engines at Work – First transmitted 3.5.05
Fred met a few old friends at the North Staffs & Cheshire Traction Engine Club during a visit to their Klondyke base at Draycott-in-the-Clay, Staffordshire. During the day a tree was felled using a steam tractor and steam-driven wood-sawing was demonstrated. In an additional display, the art of 'scarifying' using a restored road roller was shown. All the club's engines were in steam so Fred was naturally in his element, chatting to his mates and enjoying a pint or two!

► Jack with the immaculate Aveling & Porter convertible tractor.

While still in Staffordshire, a visit to meet Len Crane at Bratch Pumping Station was undertaken. Len has spent the last six years restoring a huge triple expansion engine that was once used to pump water around the county.

Once again, steam railways beckoned and this time the team visited the Severn Valley Railway at Bridgnorth, Shropshire, where Fred chatted with the train crews and toured the engineering workshops, but only after sampling the delightful 'bacon butties' in the station buffet. The historic town is built on two levels and, being anxious to see the sights, the crew took the convertible for an extended trundle around the area.

Chains and Copper – First transmitted 10.5.05

After leaving Bridgnorth, Fred, Alf and Jimmy visited the Black Country Living Museum at Dudley in an effort to learn about the mining history of the area. The museum, which deals specifically with the history of an area that was, of course, at the heart of industrial England, was always a favourite location of Fred's. Its popularity may have been enhanced in his view by the attraction on site of a traditional 'chippie', a facility of which the crew took full advantage.

Leaving the English Midlands the grand tour then moved to North Wales, thus giving Fred the opportunity to drive his engine though some stunning scenery. ▶

◀ Fred holds court with a group of like-minded steam people of the North Staffs & Cheshire Traction Engine Club.

▶ Filming in a typical
Lakeland setting
with Fred's friend
Dick Ransome.

The old copper workings at Parys Mountain in Anglesey were visited on a grey, drizzly day, which added to the eerie atmosphere of the site.

It supplied the majority of the world's copper in the 1780s and continued to be a major player in the industry for 100 years.

While in Wales, another railway visit was undertaken: this time the narrow gauge Ffestiniog Railway was the chosen location.

After visiting the Welsh Slate Museum at Llanberis, the team headed back to England – but not before they had driven the Aveling down the famous Llanberis Pass so that, at the end of that journey, Fred could try his hand at the art of slate-splitting. The journey back to the North-West included a visit to the fascinating Anderton Boat Lift in Cheshire, where Fred enjoyed a ride down the fully restored Victorian lift followed by a canal boat trip.

Engineering Workshops – First transmitted 17.5.05
Fred's appreciation of engineering workshops, especially those which use traditional methods, was well-known and two companies whose components were used on the ▶

▶ Jack, Dick Ransome
and Fred chatting
about the
convertible.

▶▶ Jack, Fred and
Jimmy 'tinkering'
with the engine at
Dick Ransome's yard.

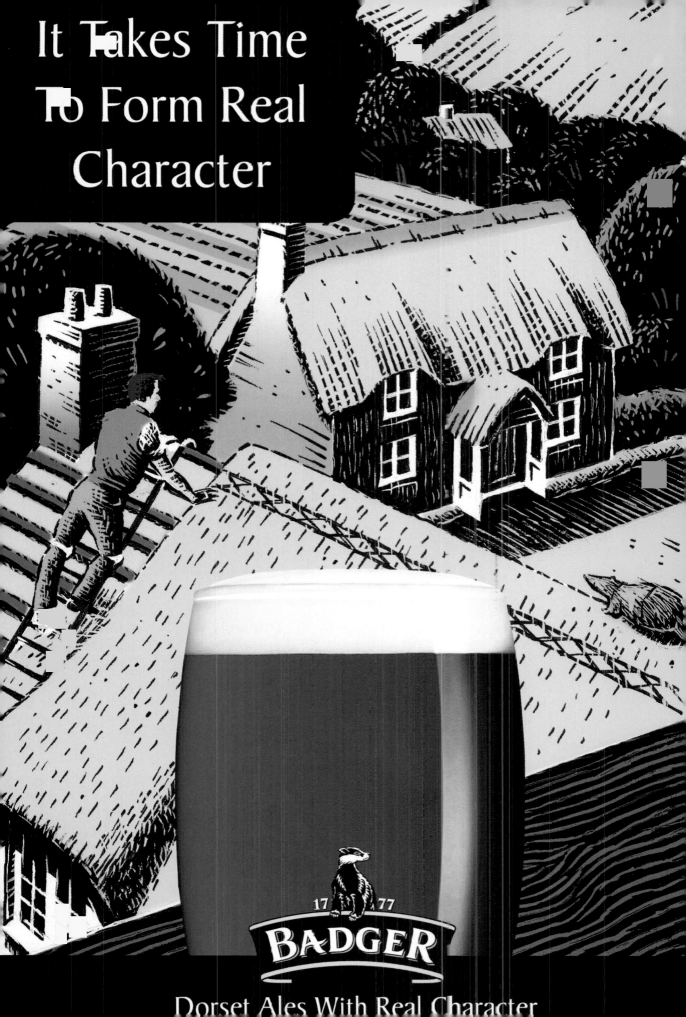

The spirited run down Llanberis Pass.

Aveling rebuild were therefore visited. They were the Budenberg Gauge Co, a German concern which opened a Manchester depot in 1857, and Thomas Smith & Co of Atherton, who supplied Fred with his bolts, rivet blanks and threaded steel bar.

Engineering Excellence – First transmitted 24.5.05
The final part of the journey included another visit to a steam railway and this time the chosen location was the Great Central Railway at Loughborough.

On this occasion Fred was able to drive a steam locomotive during a round-trip on the preserved line.

After leaving the GCR the crew continued south as Fred had business in the capital!

But first they visited Crossness Pumping Station, which was built by Sir Joseph Bazalgette as part of Victorian London's urgently-needed main drainage scheme.

Opened in April 1865, it houses four original rotative beam engines - the greatest collection of such engines in the world.

Fred is on the way to fulfilling an ambition to drive over the M62 on Scammonden Bridge.

Fred in reflective mood while waiting to talk to camera at Thomas Smith's works in Atherton.

Fred gets on with polishing the engine before the run down Llanberis Pass.

Father and son enjoying the sail.

The Trip to the Palace

The highlight of the Great 'Journey' was the visit to Buckingham Palace where Fred received his justly deserved MBE from HM Queen Elizabeth II. The honour was awarded for services to broadcasting and industrial heritage. The presentation of the 'gong' was followed by a celebratory parade around Westminster.

Epilogue

The plans for filming *Made in Britain* included trips to the West Country, South Wales and the Forest of Dean but unfortunately Fred's rapidly deteriorating health prohibited these plans being carried out.

While fighting cancer, Fred's achievement in completing the huge amount of filming, which he did during the spring and summer of 2004, was nothing short of miraculous. His bravery in the circumstances was inspiring and, as such, was a credit to his strength of character and can be taken as a source of inspiration to us all.

What more could you desire: music from an antique cylinder phonograph, summer sunshine and a steamboat?

Looks like Alf is playing 'mother' as the happy group set sail aboard Roger Mallinson's steam boat 'Shamrock'.

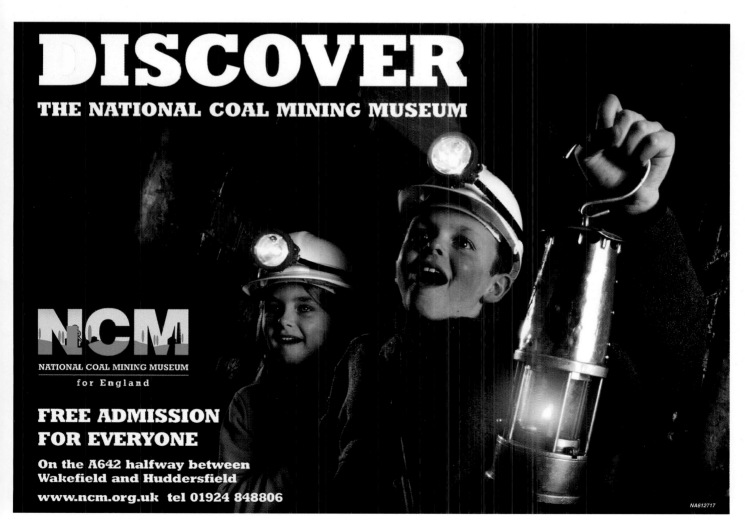

In a rare moment, Fred takes his hat off to the welcoming crowd at the Welsh Slate Museum.

A break between filming at the Severn Valley Railway, from left: Alf, Alan and Fred.

Fred and Alf waiting for the bacon butties in the station buffet at Bridgnorth.

Fred Dibnah in pencils, drawn by his friend Bill Greenhalgh.

Bolton Hospice   20 Oct 2004

I Fred Dibnah request that my funeral be in the form of a procession of Steam Vehicles. My body to be conveyed on an open flat waggon, drawn by my Steam Tractor. to be followed by my Steam Roller & Living Van plus any other Steam Vehicles wishing willing to take part in my last journey.

I have authorised Roger MURRAY to make sure that my wishes are followed through.

SIGNED   Fred Dibnah. MBE   20ᵗʰ Oct 2004.

A proud moment for a brave young man. Fred's elder son, Jack, checks that enough coal is on board the convertible before helping to crew the engine, which is to pull the trailer conveying his dad's coffin.

The day that Bolton stood still

The funeral of Dr Fred Dibnah, MBE
Bolton, Tuesday 16 November 2004

Funerals by their very nature are dour, grey events and, try as they may, the clergy rarely succeed in entirely convincing the assembled mourners that the event is, in fact, a celebration of the dear departed one's life on earth. The occasion of Fred Dibnah's last journey was, without doubt, the exception that proved that rule.

He was an iconic figure to many, both at home and overseas, and he will be greatly missed. To his family he was, of course, much more: a husband, a brother, a father, a grandfather, a cousin, a relative, and it is for those people that his loss will be greatest. He was their kith and kin whom they unselfishly shared, first with his close friends and then with the many who knew and admired him. His funeral day was not an occasion when the family could hide away and mourn in private. It was a very public affair. The family shared their day of grief with so many.

The early morning gloom which, on Tuesday 16 November 2004, pervaded central Lancashire, was to grow by the hour, until it developed into a traditional British rainy day as the poignant events unfolded.

And yet, as Fred's cortege set off from his home at 11.15am and headed for Bolton's Parish Church, the damp and muted conditions seemed appropriate.

From an early hour, many thousands of citizens from that famous old industrial town had lined the route of the funeral procession, where a great many others joined them who had travelled from far and wide to pay their last respects to this glorious son of steam.

Many of the faces of the hushed waiting throng were dampened as their own tears of sadness mingled with the steadily falling rain. The elements had, in their own way, provided a fitting backdrop to the last public act of that town's greatly-loved favourite son.

Fred had requested a Victorian-type funeral – but with steam. This led undertaker John Howarth to comment, when asked by the family to officiate, "Organising this very important event has been a first

for us, but I think it will do him proud."

On the behalf of those who were privileged to attend and, indeed, those millions more who saw the event on TV, may we say that you, Mr Howarth, did exactly that. Some who knew Fred have commented since that, on the day, it was almost as if he were directing the proceedings himself.

Many, through recent contact with Fred and perhaps from their own family experiences, were aware of the ravages of cancer and there was a palpable air of relief among the mourners. A dearly loved friend was no longer a sufferer from a disease that, in one or another of its many forms, touches one-third of the population. He was free of earthly pain and now deservedly at rest.

Fred's life touched many people in differing ways and people worldwide have rightly noted and talked of his passing with sorrow. To the townsfolk of Bolton it was so much more, and deeper: they had lost one of their own. Moreover, in this multicultural part of the Red Rose County, Fred was a 'mate' to people of all colours and creeds and the whole community mourned his passing with equal admiration and respect.

Leading the cortege was the band of 103 Regiment, The Royal Artillery 'Bolton Volunteers' from the town's Nelson Street Barracks. The smartly-dressed, but accordingly sombre musicians were followed by Fred's long-standing pride and joy, his restored steam roller 'Betsy'. Crewing the roller were two of Fred's lifelong pals, Roger Murray and Neil Carney, with Roger, Fred's youngest son, in close attendance.

The living van, so lovingly restored by Fred, was in tow with his faithful old Land-Rover attached. Travelling on the steps of the living van were two friends who additionally had journeyed with Fred to various filming locations during 2004, ex-miners Alf Molireux and Jimmy Crooks. Dear friends and colleagues too numerous to mention individually had gathered on that rainy day in order to say their goodbyes. The townsfolk and their ▶

A family floral
tribute in the
hearse, as Fred
arrives to take his
last journey hauled
by steam power.

The waiting crowd
fall quiet as Fred
arrives outside his
Bolton home.

visitors were to a person in deep mourning.

The newly restored Aveling & Porter and its crew had perhaps the greatest responsibility of all as it was chosen to draw the flat trailer on which Fred was to ride. It is to the youthful steersman of the convertible that much praise for a job well done, under great pressure, must go. Teenager Jack Dibnah did his father, his family and Fred's admirers proud, not only handling the engine with skill but also presenting himself with the utmost dignity.

Michael Webber, a native Boltonian who now resides on the South Coast, yet another of Fred's many friends,

was Jack's partner and it was he who had supplied the flat truck. Fixed upon it were a selection of Fred's steeplejack ladders and ropes. Michael had also secured brackets to hold the coffin firmly in place.

A model of the adopted Bolton symbol, an elephant with a castellated howdah, on loan from the local museum, was fixed at the head of the casket on which Fred's famous flat cap rode forlornly for all to see. Four other steamers, representing Fred's many acquaintances and admirers, followed closely behind.

The band of 103
Regiment, The
Royal Artillery
'Bolton Volunteers'
waits to lead the
cortege.

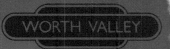

KEIGHLEY & WORTH VALLEY RAILWAY

Steam through the unique beauty of Brontë Country

Every weekend and daily throughout the summer

Special Events run throughout the year including Steam Galas, Day out with Thomas©, Vintage Trains, Dining Trains, Diesel Weekend, Folk & Beer Festival, Santa Steam Specials and Mince Pie Specials

THE KEIGHLEY & WORTH VALLEY RAILWAY PRESERVATION SOCIETY

The Railway Station, Haworth, Keighley,
West Yorkshire BD22 8NJ
Telephone 01535 645214   Fax 01535 647317

Keep up to date with the KWVR 24hr Info 01535 647777   Internet www.kwvr.co.uk

As the immaculate, and perfectly poised, John Howarth led the cortege into the town's Churchgate, the waiting host who, until that point had stood in solemn silence, began to stir. Gradually they caught sight of the vehicle carrying Fred's earthly remains. The silence was broken by, at first, a small ripple of hand clapping, which then rapidly grew into a veritable crescendo and then ceased just as quickly, as the customised 'hearse' came to rest outside the church. The people of Bolton had, in that spontaneous ac,t respectfully said 'thank you' and bade goodbye to Fred.

In truth, double the seats would not have been enough to accommodate all those who wished to partake in the service of remembrance.

The crowded church, a building that in years gone by had benefited from Fred's steeplejack skills, fell silent as his coffin entered to the strains of Julie Covington's rendition of *Don't Cry For Me, Argentina*, a favourite piece of music of Fred's.

For many trying to hold on to their emotions the welcoming words of Canon Michael Williams, Vicar of Bolton, were a timely consolation. How proud Fred would have been to hear his daughter, Lorna, read perfectly the

poignant words of Rabindranath Tagore's poem *Farewell My Friends*, a fitting tribute delivered with tenderness and love. The congregation cleared their throats and, with gusto and feeling, sang *The Lord's My Shepherd*; the vaulted roof of this impressive Lancastrian edifice seemed to echo the fine words of the 23rd Psalm.

The Rev Barry Newth had been associated with Fred and his family for many years and, indeed, was instrumental in awarding a bell tower repair job to him in the early days. The two men remained friends and, fittingly, Barry was at Fred's bedside, in the company of family members, when the end came. Some days before, Roger Murray had visited Fred in Bolton Hospice and, on the bedside table, had discovered a piece of paper on which, in Fred's distinctive hand, was written simply the name Barry Newth. Roger knew that Fred wanted to see again his dear friend.

Barry enthralled and amused the congregation with many fitting tales of Fred's exploits, not least of which recounting the time he had to resort to climbing. Fred had persuaded the terrified vicar to accompany him out on the roof of his church and then coined a one-liner, which later became part of the Dibnah folklore. Fred

Fred's beloved steam roller 'Betsy' hauls his living van, which in turn is coupled to his Land-Rover, into Bolton's Churchgate. The roller is crewed by two of Fred's friends, Nigel Carney and Roger Murray, and Fred's younger son, Roger. Roger Murray was deeply involved with the organisation of the funeral, having been a confidant and aware of Fred's last wishes.

The two friends who accompanied Fred on his latest filming escapades fittingly ride on the living van steps. Nearest the camera is Jimmy Crooks and, on his left, Alf Molineux.

advised Barry thus: "Be careful vicar. One false move and it's half a day out with the undertaker."

He told of the time Fred turned up as promised for a church fete with his beloved steam roller, but very late and a little the worse for drink. He intimated that he naturally got Fred to pay for that misdemeanour with good deeds many times over the years.

David Hall, who for many years had been Fred's film producer and co-author, continued with anecdotal tales from the other side of the camera. It was obvious to all that the two men had become a lot more than just work colleagues – they were friends. Indeed, as he explained, so natural a performer was Fred that the whole production crew benefited from their experiences with him. The problem working with Fred was, said David: "Trying to keep to a schedule which was, to say the least, difficult, given that he would stop to sign every autograph, pose for every photograph, and shake every hand." That was Fred.

Roger Murray was the next to address the assembly and, having arrived in church fresh from the footplate of 'Betsy', wearing his 'blues', there was perhaps no more fitting a way to honour Fred's memory and represent engine men and women everywhere. He spoke touchingly about his visits to Fred in the hospice and, in so doing, shared with all the sadness of those last days. He told of how Fred asked him if he believed in Heaven. And of how they went on to talk of Fred possibly meeting his Victorian heroes and others who had gone before.

At the conclusion of the service, and following the commendation and ministration of Canon Williams, Fred's coffin was taken from the church to the strains of *Carnival of Venice* (the theme from his TV series) and repositioned on the steam-drawn hearse for the journey to Tonge Cemetery. No greater compliment could have been paid to his memory as the heavily falling rain in no way prevented huge crowds from lining the route of his final journey.

At Fred's wishes the attendant engines sounded their whistles in unison as he was lowered to his final resting-place. ■

Note Fred's 'trademark' flat cap on the top of his coffin. Also aboard the trailer is an elephant which has, over time, become associated with the town of Bolton and dates from the time when the town was part of the diocese of Coventry, it being a symbol also associated with that city.

'So be it'

The crew of 'Old Faithful' getting a soaking but still up to the task as they bring up the rear of the cortege that wends its way through the town and on to the cemetery.

'Betsy' outside Fred's home on Radcliffe Road.

The convertible on the way to Fred's last resting-place in Tonge Cemetery.

FAREWELL MY FRIENDS

by Rabindranath Tagore

It was beautiful
as long as it lasted
the journey of my life.

I have no regrets
Whatsoever, save
the pain I'll leave behind.
Those dear hearts
who love and care –
and the strings pulling
at the heart and soul –

The strong arms that held me up
when my own strength
let me down.

At every turning of my life
I came across good friends,
friends who stood by me
even when the time raced by me.

Farewell, farewell, my friends,
I smile and bid you goodbye.
No, shed no tears
for I need them not.
All I need is your smile.

If you feel sad
do think of me,
for that's what I'll like.
When you live in the hearts
of those you love,
remember then,
you never die.

I am writing this having just arrived home after attending Fred Dibnah's funeral. I knew him as a steeplejack, a fellow-Boltonian and a friend. There is little that hasn't already been written or spoken about Fred, about his achievements and his personality but, if you don't mind, I would like to share with you, very briefly, my own thoughts here.

To my mind, there was one particular quality about Fred that set him apart from everyone else: to my eyes he had an unequalled artistic talent. It occurred to me some time ago that I never tired of looking at his Aveling roller. It is a fairly 'ordinary' 10-ton Aveling single but it is different from all the others. It's difficult to say just why - perhaps it's the beautiful flared brass top to the chimney (unique, but 'just right') and the shape and proportions of the canopy. It makes you want to stand and watch it go by.

Similarly, the more recently constructed brick 'mill' chimney in his garden is simply a beautiful shape; you are compelled to look at it. His 'pit head gear' is functional but graceful in its design. Fred was artistic in the truest sense and I think he gained more pleasure from creating these works of art than from almost anything else.

I alighted from the train in Bolton this morning just as the procession passed by. I was a little late so I was walking alongside, trying to get to the church ahead of the cortege. As most of Bolton had turned out, the streets were crowded yet silent. I was walking alongside Fred's Aveling tractor and my friend and I remarked upon how quiet the engine was. There wasn't a breath of steam out of place. All you could hear was the click of the mechanical lubricator; it was all but perfect.

That was Fred's standard, both before and after fame found him. That's why he was an inspiration to everyone in the world of restoration and preservation, regardless of their particular field. He never declared himself to be an engineer – he vociferously admired 'them clever men' – but he had the hands of a craftsman and the rare eye of an artist, which manifested itself in everything he turned his hand to, be it blacksmithing, handwriting, stained glass, riveting or brickwork.

And, yes, he would help anybody. Oh... and he could talk, an' all!

I am sad he's gone. RIP.

Diane Carney

A bronze for Fred
and possibly a memorial workshop?

It is hoped that Graham Ibesson MA (RCA), the sculptor, who was responsible for casting the impressive Eric Morecambe bronze, now standing on the seafront in the legendary comedian's hometown, can be engaged and commissioned to create an effigy of 'Our Fred'. The fund has now been set up and would realistically need to raise a sum in the region of £50k to make the dream a reality.

Retired architect, Bill Greenhalgh, is credited with first suggesting the idea of a statue. He is an active member of the Bolton Civic Trust and as such feels that the town should not be backward in honouring Fred. Television producer, David Hall, the head of the film company The View From The North has also pledged his backing to the project.

Bill Greenhalgh said: "All the statues in Bolton are of people from over a 100 years ago, and while all are appropriate, it would be nice to honour someone from modern times. Who better than Fred to receive such a tribute? He put the town well and truly on the map and

was admired by millions." He went on to add that he has spoken to the proposed sculptor and accordingly can confirm that Mr Ibesson has not only shown interest, but has said enthusiastically that "he would love to be involved".

By the way of a variation on the theme, Bill Greenhalgh has very positive and original thoughts. He explained, "How splendid it would be if the statue could be erected, as suggested, under an enlarged version of the glass shelter which already contains a mill engine built by the local firm Hick Hargreaves Ltd. This could be done in such a way that items of appropriate machinery could be connected by pulleys, therefore hopefully making it a working exhibit".

The mill engine in question was built in 1866 by Hick Hargreaves Engineering of Bolton and was installed at Ford Ayrton & Co a Yorkshire based silk spinning company; where it was in regular use until 1969. The machine carries the works number 726 and is described as an Improved Corliss Engine built to an Inglis & Spencer patent. After its withdrawal from the silk works it was presented to the town by its makers.

The views of Fred's family are of paramount importance and Lorna Dibnah spoke on the behalf of all five of the children.

"I think Bolton Town Centre will be an excellent place for a sculpture in memory of my Dad. In particular, I think it would be fitting to incorporate such a statue within the existing engineering display in Oxford Street.

"For as long as I can remember my Dad had a close working relationship with Hick Hargreaves Engineering. They helped him a great deal during the restoration of his steam roller and he was enthralled with their steam engines and machinery. Over the years he made many close and lasting friendships during his many visits to their works." Fred was sad to see the their old factory close and Lorna recalls, "When they finally moved from the Crook Street site, in 2002, Dad took his steam roller 'Betsy' along to say a fond farewell."

She concluded: "I think that he would be extremely proud to be associated with this important part of Bolton's Industrial Heritage, although I think he would probably be slightly embarrassed by the honour."

Walking the streets of the town and talking to members of the public you gain the opinion that such a statue would be popular and well received. While this is very much a matter for local people, such was Fred's popularity nationwide, and indeed worldwide, that we have given details of the fund set up by the aforementioned Trust at the end of this article.

Of special interest to industrial heritage enthusiasts is an additional proposal, which calls for a special workshop to be set up in the image and style of Fred's old workplace. Utilising the type of machinery associated with him, and as seen being used by him on TV, it would doubtless be a fascinating tribute. The exact location of any such facility would of course have to be decided, but various suggestions have included the Black Country Living Museum in Dudley, the Ironbridge Gorge Visitor Centre in Shropshire or the Manchester Museum of Science & Industry.

Ian Walden is the museum director at Dudley and over the years he became a firm friend of Fred's and indeed hosted the film company in July 2004 during the making of the new TV series. He recalls that Fred's visits to the facility, "Always included a meal of traditional fish & chips from our shop. I often think that Fred would have visited us just for that reason alone!

"While we are all about celebrating the specific industrial heritage connected with the Black Country Fred was, of course, more broadly concerned with the nation's engineering heritage, but there was lots of common ground. Should his family decide to back the setting up of such an exhibit we would be pleased to talk to them in order to establish whether we could be of help."

It is thought that creating such a facility in Bolton

◄ Graham Ibesson's bronze of Eric Morecambe. Could it be Fred next?

would be an option, which the council or others may wish to consider. General opinion is that the site of Fred's ex-home-based workshop, due to size limitations, would not be an entirely suitable location. However, standing in the way of progress at the moment is the all-important fact that Fred's will is, at the time of going to press, 'unproven'.

The mill engine highlighted by Mr Greenhalgh is currently configured as a mobile display, but is of necessity, powered by a small (but concealed) electric motor. He has already prepared the appropriate drawings and has submitted them on the behalf of the Bolton Civic Trust, to the local planning authorities. To facilitate an additional statue (Fred's) and a selection of appropriate machinery the glass-display structure will require enlarging and the estimate for that work is included in the overall cost. The aforementioned display is adjacent to Bolton Town Hall and is in a visitor-friendly location.

With reference to the proposed statue, the local newspaper is inviting comments, by letter to: The Editor, Bolton Evening News, Churchgate, Bolton BL1 1DE or by e-mail to letters@boltoneveningnews.co.uk

Donations can be forwarded to The Fred Dibnah Fund, Lloyds TSB Bank Plc, Hotel Street, Bolton, BL1 1DB.

All cheques should be made payable to The Fred Dibnah Fund. ■

FRED DIBNAH

There'll be many a tear for this fine guy,
A real true king of DIY.
He could build a boiler, line with brick,
Make rusty traction engines tick.
Design as any draughtsman would
Brick and stone and steel and wood.

A champion of a bygone age
When men of vision strode the stage
When coal was king and Empire grand
And chimney stacks bestrode the land.
Steeplejacks in every town
To build and fettle, strap and crown,
These monuments to the nation's wealth
When cash and profit outdealt health.

In his uniform of denim blue
With chain and fob in shiny view
Fred now walks with those men of old
With his half-hunter of polished gold.
Brunel, Newcomen, Telford, too
He'll hold his own and air his view.
Cap and glasses, thumbs in vest,
We liked that, Fred, you've earned your rest.

Derek B Hewartson, Lytham, Lancs.

The author – Keith Langston

Heritage transport specialist photographer and feature writer Keith Langston travelled extensively with Fred Dibnah during the filming of what was to be his last BBC 2 TV series, *Made In Britain*, to record the event for Britain's best-selling transport and industrial heritage magazine, *Old Glory*.

Based in mid-Cheshire, Keith has been associated with the magazine's owning group, Mortons Media Ltd, for a number of years and supplies news and feature material for several of its titles.

After being employed by a local newspaper group, Keith followed other career paths before pursuing in later life a new career in journalism.

Following Fred's untimely death, Keith embarked upon this tribute, drawing not only on his experiences with the Bolton-born steeplejack and TV presenter but, in addition, talking to many folk who numbered themselves among Fred's many friends. Several photographs have been lent especially for use in this tribute by the Dibnah family and others. The publication commemorates the life and times of Fred, who many have rightly described as having been a truly 'Great Briton'.

Letts study aids

Revise Biology

A complete revision course for O level and CSE

Julian Ford-Robertson   MA(Oxon)

Head of Biology Department, Haileybury College, Hertford

Charles Letts & Company Limited
London, Edinburgh, München & New York

First published 1979
by Charles Letts & Company Limited
Diary House, Borough Road, London SE1 1DW

Editor: Linda Reynolds
Design: Ben Sands
Illustrations: Stan Martin

ISBN 0 85097 400 3

Typeset by the Pitman Press, Bath
Printed by Cullum Litho Limited, London

Preface

The principal aim of this book is to provide a concise body of biological facts and ideas in such a form that they can easily be revised. The information is carefully chosen to fit all the GCE 'O' Level and CSE syllabuses in Biology. A unique feature of the book is a table of analysis of all these syllabuses, topic by topic, so that pupils may select for revision only those sections that are necessary for their own particular Examination Board.

The other aims of this book are to both help pupils understand *how to learn* effectively and *how to use their knowledge* effectively in the examination room. Lack of ability in either of these fields is a common cause of failure by otherwise able GCE or CSE candidates. To help prevent such avoidable failure, there is advice on learning techniques and also on question analysis (using questions set by various Examination Boards).

To assist in the learning process each chapter has a test-yourself section by means of which the pupil can test his progress. Answers are provided and are keyed back into the relevant text sections.

While this book has been written principally for a pupil to use on his own, its use does not end there. Teachers should find that the concise yet clear format and the large word-saving diagrams provide a sound framework upon which to base their teaching. The book has the advantage, as a text, of allowing teachers who favour an experimental course to spend less time on note-giving, and the questions provided can be used to monitor progress.

Finally, whether the existing GCE and CSE examination system is replaced by a single nation-wide 16+ examination or not, this book will provide adequate coverage of Biology at this level for many years to come.

Acknowledgements

In the preparation of this book I have been greatly assisted by helpful criticism and advice from C. G. Gayford, BSc, MEd (Science Education), PhD, Postgrad.Cert.Ed., Lecturer in Education at the University of Reading; K. R. C. Neal, MA (Cantab), FIBiol, Head of Biology at Manchester Grammar School and my colleague at Haileybury, P. A. Chamberlain, BSc. Without the artistic expertise of Stan Martin and the patience and understanding of Linda Reynolds, BSc, MSc, and many others at Charles Letts and Company Limited, this examination aid would have had limited value. I am also most grateful to all the Examination Boards who have given permission to reproduce their questions: The Associated Examining Board, Oxford Local Examinations, Southern Universities' Joint Board for School Examinations.

To my wife Anne, and to Ian, Justin and Angus I owe a special debt for their patience, assistance and encouragement.

Julian Ford-Robertson 1979

Contents

Part I

Introduction and guide to using this book

Revise Biology is written especially for those who need help in preparing for their GCE 'O' Level or CSE exams. Within two covers for the first time are all you need for this task:

— advice on **what your syllabus requires**: a table of syllabus analysis (pages 2–7).
—advice on **how to learn**: learning made easier (pages 9–14).
—**what to learn** in readily revisable form: information, lavishly illustrated (pages 15–157).
— means of **assessing your progress**: short test-yourself questions with answers (pages 158–192).
— advice on how to **show the examiner** that you know what he is asking for: an outline of good exam technique, using past GCE questions (pages 193–198).

If you follow this sequence in the use of this book, you will have a good chance of success.

Part I: Using the table of analysis of GCE and CSE syllabuses (pages 2–7). First select from the top of the page your own Examination Board. The key to the initials for the Boards may be found on page 8. Below the name of the Board are details of:

(*a*) the number of theory papers and their length
(*b*) whether there is a practical part to the exam or whether your teacher does this assessment
(*c*) the percentage of marks allocated to compulsory and free-choice parts of the theory papers
(*d*) the content of the course, topic by topic. This information has been divided into numbered sections, not all of which need be studied for your own syllabus.

Select carefully the sections you require by referring to the symbols:

● section required for a syllabus
(●) section required, but with reservations. These reservations may include such things as 'less emphasis than that in the text' or 'this organism suffices for a part of the syllabus, but is not specifically named'.
o optional
Ⓑ option B
Blank: section not required.

The table of analysis must be regarded only as a helpful guide. If you send for your Board's syllabus and for copies of past examination papers (use the addresses on page 8) you will be able to judge more easily what the special features of your syllabus are. Your teacher will also give you advice, particularly on sections marked (●).

Before using the core information, first take care to understand *how* you should revise (pages 9–14). Do not exceed your 'concentration time' (page 12).

Part II: Using the core information. Work through each chapter referring only to the sections you need. Use every memory aid you can, including your own pattern-diagrams.

Part III: Testing yourself. Once you have worked through a chapter turn to the back of the book for the appropriate test-yourself section. Enter the answers in the spaces provided. When you have completed this, turn to the answers (pages 187–192). Each answer is keyed back to sections in Part II. If you have not answered most questions correctly, then turn back to Part II to revise more thoroughly the sections that you have not mastered.

Part IV: Exam technique for biology examinations. The advice given ranges from tips on organising what you should take into the examination room to how to use your time efficiently. In particular this section will help you to answer the questions in the way that will show the examiner that you know the facts.

Table of analysis of examination syllabuses

	A.E.B.	Cambridge	J.M.B.	London	Oxford	O. and C.	S.U.J.B.	W.J.E.C.*	J.M.B. "Science"	O. and C. "Combined Science"	
Level	O	O	O	O	O	O	O	O	$\frac{2}{3}$ O	$\frac{2}{3}$ O	
Number of theory papers	2	2	1	2	2	2	1	1	3	2	
Number of hours for each theory paper	$1\frac{1}{2}$ $2\frac{1}{2}$	2 $\frac{1}{2}$	$2\frac{1}{2}$	$1\frac{1}{4}$ 2	1 2	2 2	$2\frac{1}{2}$	3	$\frac{1}{3}$ $\frac{1}{2}$ $\frac{2}{3}$	$\frac{1}{3}$ $1\frac{1}{2}$	
Practical – paper or assessment (Ass.) or optional (Opt.) (% of total marks)	Photo Qs	1 hr (27%)	Opt.	No	No	2 Qs (20%)	No	No	No	No	
Teacher assessment / Prac. = practical	No	No	No	No	No	No	No	No	No	No	
Theory – % mark, compulsory questions	—	100	50	40	44	40	40	36	70	33	
Theory – % mark, free choice questions	—	0	50	60	56	60	60	64	30	67	
Life											
2.1 Characteristics of organisms; cells	•	•	•	•	•	•	•	•	•	•	2.1
2.2 Organelles – detail	•	(•)	(•)	(•)	•	(•)	(•)	(•)		•	2.2
2.3 How the nucleus controls the cell	•				(•)					•	2.3
2.4 Enzymes	•	•	•	•	•	•			•	•	2.4
2.5 Units of life beyond the cell	•			•					•		2.5
Classification											
3.1 Linnaeus & his classification system					•			•		•	3.1
3.2 Keys								•			3.2
3.3 Plant kingdom					(•)			•		•	3.3
3.4 Animal kingdom					(•)			•		•	3.4
Foods & feeding											
4.1 Food	•	•	•	•	•	•	•		•	•	4.1
4.2 Holophytic, holozoic & saprophytic nutrition	•	•	•	•	•	•	•	•	•	•	4.2
4.3 Mineral salts for mammals & angiosperms	•	•	•	•	•	•	•	•	(•)	•	4.3
4.4 Carbohydrates, fats & proteins	•	•	•	•	•	•	•	•	•	•	4.4
4.5 Vitamins	•	•	•	•	•	•	•	•	•	•	4.5
4.6 Photosynthesis	•	•	•	•	•	•	•	•	•	•	4.6
4.7 Limiting factors	•		(•)	•	•						4.7
4.8 Leaf structure & photosynthesis	•	•	•	•	•	•	•	•	•	•	4.8
4.9 Amino acid synthesis	•	•	•	•	•	•	•		•	•	4.9
4.10 Mineral salt uptake by roots	•	•	•	•	•	•	•	•	•		4.10
4.11 Feeding methods of animals	•		•				(•)				4.11
4.12 Digestion & its consequences	•	•	•	•	•	•	•	•	•	•	4.12
4.13 Experiments with digestive enzymes	•	•	•	•	•	•	•	•	•	•	4.13
4.14 Mammal teeth & jaws	•	•	•	•	•	•	•	•	•	•	4.14
4.15 Mammal alimentary canal	•	•	•	•	•	•	•	•	•	•	4.15
4.16 Herbivores & carnivores – jaws & teeth	•		•	•	•		•	•	•		4.16
4.17 Herbivores & carnivores – gut	•		•	•	•		•	•	•		4.17
4.18 Absorption of food at villi	•	•	•	(•)	•		•	•	•		4.18
4.19 Storage of food	•	•	•	•	•		•	•	•		4.19
4.20 The liver		•			•	•	•	•		•	4.20
4.21 Diet		•		•	•	•	•			•	4.21
4.22 Saprophytes	•	•	•	•	•	•	•				4.22
Water & transport systems											
5.1 Importance of water		•		•	•					•	5.1
5.2 Diffusion, active transport & osmosis	•	•	•	•	•	•	•	•	•	•	5.2
5.3 Water uptake & loss in angiosperms	•	•	•	•	•	•	•	•	•	•	5.3
5.4 Transpiration	•	•	•	•	•	•	•	•	•	•	5.4
5.5 Transport of organic food	•	•	•	•	•	•	•	•	•	•	5.5
5.6 Water uptake & loss in animals	•		•	•	•				•	•	5.6
5.7 Blood systems	•	•	•	•	•	•	•	•	•	•	5.7
5.8 Mammal blood & other body fluids	•	•	•	•	•	•	•	•	•	•	5.8
5.9 Heart, blood vessels & circulatory system	•	•	•	•	•	•	•	•	•	•	5.9
5.10 Changes in blood around the circulatory system	•	•	•	•	•	•	•	•	•	•	5.10
5.11 Lymphatic system	•		•	•	•		•	•		•	5.11
Respiration											
6.1 Breathing, gaseous exhange & cellular respiration	•	•	•	•	•	•	•	•	•	•	6.1
6.2 Internal respiration (aerobic & anaerobic)	•	•	•	•	•	•	•	•	•	•	6.2
6.3 External respiration (gaseous exchange)	•	•	•	•	•	•	•	•	•	•	6.3
6.4 Organisms respiring in water & air	•	•	•	•	(•)	(•)	•	(•)	•	•	6.4
6.5 Bird respiration					•		•			•	6.5
6.6 Mammal respiration	•	•	•	•	•	•	•	•	•	•	6.6
6.7 Gaseous exchange in angiosperms	•	•	•	•	•	•	•	•	•		6.7
6.8 Uses for energy from respiration	•		•		•						6.8
6.9 ATP (Adenosine tri-phosphate)	•				•						6.9
Excretion, temperature regulation & homeostasis											
7.1 Wastes & means of excretion	•	•	•	•	•	•	•	•	•	•	7.1
7.2 Mammal urinary system	•	•	•	•	•	•	•	•	•	•	7.2
7.3 Abnormal kidney function	•		(•)			•		(•)		•	7.3
7.4 Body temperature in organisms	•	•	•	•	•		•	•	•	•	7.4
7.5 Mammal temperature control	•	•	•	(•)	(•)	•	•	•	•	•	7.5

* The W.J.E.C. columns are based on the 1979 syllabuses as the 1980 syllabuses were not available at the time of going to press.

	A.L.S.E.B.	E.A.E.B. North	E.A.E.B. South	E.M.R.E.B. Syll. 1	E.M.R.E.B. Syll. 2	Met.R.E.B. Syll. A	Met.R.E.B. Syll. B	M.R.E.B.	N.R.E.B.	N.W.R.E.B.	S.E.R.E.B.	S.R.E.B. Syll. A	S.R.E.B. Syll. B (Nuffield)	S.W.E.B.	W.J.E.C.*	W.M.E.B.	W.Y. & L.R.E.B.	Y.R.E.B.	
	CSE	CSE	CSE	CSE	CSE	CSE	CSE	CSE	CSE	CSE	CSE	CSE	CSE	CSE	CSE	CSE	CSE	CSE	
	1	2	2	1	1	1	1	1	2	1	2	1	1	2	1	2	1	1	
	2	2 2	¾ 2	2	2	2¼	2¼	2¼	1 2	2	1 1½	2	2	1 2	2½	1½ 2	2	2	
	2 hr (30%)	No	No	1 hr (30%)	Ass. (20%)	1¼ hr (25%)	Ass. (10%)	No	}Ass.	¾ hr (20%)	No	No	No	Ass. (20%)	No	No	Ass. (25%)	No	
	20%	No	20%	20%	10%	No	15%	No	}40%	Prac. (20%)	60%	20%	No	No	No	20%	Prac. (25%)	Yes	
	—	100	40	66	50	—	—	—	100	100	—	—	—	—	70	50	—	100	
	—	0	60	33	50	—	—	—	0	0	—	—	—	—	30	50	—	0	
	●	●	●	●	●	●	●	●	●	●	●	●	●	●	●	●	●	●	2.1
	●										●								2.2
																	●		2.3
	●	●	●	●					●		●	●	●		●		●	●	2.4
						●	●		●		●	●	●		●				2.5
		●	●			(●)	(●)	(●)	(●)		(●)	(●)	●		●				3.1
	●	●				●	●				●	●	●			●		●	3.2
	●		●			●	●	●	●		●	●	●	(●)	●	(●)		(●)	3.3
	●		●			●	●	●	●		●	●	●	(●)	●	(●)		(●)	3.4
	●	●	●	●	●	●	●	●	●		●	●	●		●	●	●	●	4.1
									●	●	●	●	●		●	●			4.2
	(●)	(●)	(●)	(●)	(●)	(●)	(●)	(●)	(●)	●	●	●	●	(●)	(●)	●	(●)	(●)	4.3
		(●)		●	●	●	●	●	●		●	●	●		●	●			4.4
	(●)	●	●	(●)	(●)	(●)	(●)	(●)	(●)	(●)	●	●	●	(●)	●	●	●	●	4.5
	●	●	●	●	●	●	●	(●)	●	●	●	●	●	●	●	●	●	●	4.6
														(●)					4.7
	●	●	●	●		●	●	●	●		●		●	●	●			●	4.8
	●	●	(●)	●		●	●	●	●	(●)	●		●		●	●	●		4.9
	●		(●)			(●)	(●)	●	●		(●)				●	●	●		4.10
	●											●	●				●		4.11
	●	●	●	●		●	●	●	●	●	●	●	●		●	●	●	●	4.12
	●	●	(●)	●	●	●	●		(●)	●	●	●	●		(●)	●	●	●	4.13
	●	●	(●)	●	●	●	●	●	●	●	●	●	●	●	●	●	(●)	●	4.14
	●	(●)	●	(●)	●	●	●	●	●	●	●	●	●	●	●	●	(●)	(●)	4.15
	●					●	●			●		●	●				(●)		4.16
						●	●					●						(●)	4.17
	●	●	●	●	●	●	●	●	●		●	●	●	●	●		●	●	4.18
	●	●	●	●		●	●	●	●	●	●				●	●	●	●	4.19
	(●)	●	(●)			(●)	(●)		(●)		●	●			●		●	(●)	4.20
		●	●	●	●	●	●	●	●		●		●	●	●	●	●	●	4.21
	●	●	●	●	●	●	●	●	●	●	●			●	●	●	●	●	4.22
											●		●						5.1
	●	●	●	●	●	●	●	●	●	(●)	●	●		(●)	●	●	●	(●)	5.2
	●	●	●	●	●	●	●	●	●		●	●	●	(●)	●	●	●	●	5.3
	●	●	●	●	●	●	●	●	●		●	●	●	●	●	●	●	●	5.4
	●	●	●	●		●	●		●	(●)	●	●			●			●	5.5
						●	●	●			●	●	●						5.6
	●	(●)	(●)	(●)	●	(●)	(●)	(●)	●	(●)	(●)	(●)	●	(●)	(●)	●	(●)	(●)	5.7
	(●)	●	●	●	●	●	●	●	●		●	●	●	●	●	●	●	●	5.8
	●		●	●	(●)	●	●	●	●		●	●	●	●	●		●	●	5.9
					●	●			●	(●)	●	●		●			●	●	5.10
				●						●				●			●	●	5.11
	●	●	●	●		●	●	●	●	●	●	●	●	●	●	●	●	●	6.1
	●	(●)	●	●		●	●	●	●	(●)	●	●	●	(●)	●	●	●	(●)	6.2
	●	●	●	●		●	●	●	●		●	●	●	●	●	●	●	●	6.3
	(●)	(●)	●	(●)					●	●	●				●	●	●		6.4
																			6.5
	●	●	●	●		●	●	●	●	●	●	●	●	●	●	●	●	●	6.6
	●	●	●	●		●	●	●	●	●	●	●	●	●	●	●	●	●	6.7
	●					●	●					●	●						6.8
												●							6.9
	●	●	●	●	●	●	●	●	●	●	●	●	●	●	●	●	●	●	7.1
	●	●	●	●	●	(●)	(●)	●	●	●	●	●	●	●	(●)	(●)	●	●	7.2
																			7.3
	●									●					●		●		7.4
	●	(●)	●	●	●	●	●	●	●	●	●	●	●	●	●	●	●	●	7.5

		A.E.B.	Cambridge	J.M.B.	London	Oxford	O. and C.	S.U.J.B.	W.J.E.C.*	J.M.B. "Science"	O. and C. "Combined Science"	
	Level	O	O	O	O	O	O	O	O	⅜O	⅜O	
7.6	Homeostasis			●						●	●	7.6
7.7	Skin functions	●	●	●	●	●	●	●	●		●	7.7
	Sensitivity											
8.1	Sensitivity in plants & animals	●	●	●	●	●	●	●	●	●	●	8.1
8.2	Mammal sense organs	●	●	●	●	●	●	●	●	●	●	8.2
8.3	The eye	●	●	●	●	●	●	●	●	●	●	8.3
8.4	Abnormalities in focusing		●	●								8.4
8.5	The ear	●	●	●	●	●	●	●	●	●	●	8.5
8.6	Insect antennae & eyes			●								8.6
	Co-ordination & response											
9.1	Information, messages & action	●	●	●	●	●	●	●	●	●	●	9.1
9.2	Mammal nervous system	●	●	●	●	●	●	●	●	●	●	9.2
9.3	Nervous impulse	●		(●)								9.3
9.4	Types of nervous system					●						9.4
9.5	Reflex & intelligent action	●	●	●	●	●		●	●		●	9.5
9.6	Instinctive behaviour							●			●	9.6
9.7	The brain	●	●		●	●	●	●	●		●	9.7
9.8	Endocrine system	●	●	(●)	●	●	(●)	●	●		●	9.8
9.9	Nervous & hormonal systems compared	●	●	●	●	●	●	●	●		●	9.9
9.10	Feed-back	●			●	●				●		9.10
9.11	Taxis	●	●	●			●	●		●	●	9.11
9.12	Tropisms	●	●	●	●		(●)	●		●	●	9.12
9.13	Photoperiodism	●			●							9.13
	Suport & locomotion											
10.1	Principles of support	●	●	●	●	●	●	●	●	●	●	10.1
10.2	Skeletons used in water, land & air	●										10.2
10.3	Exo-, endo- & hydrostatic skeletons	●		●			(●)				●	10.3
10.4	Principles of movement	●	●	●	●	●	●	●	●	●	●	10.4
10.5	Earthworm movement	●		●				●			●	10.5
10.6	Insect movement (walking(**W**) & flight (**F**))	●	W	●		W	W				W	10.6
10.7	Mammal movement (tissues)	●		(●)				(●)			(●)	10.7
10.8	Joints	●	●	●	●	●	●	●	●		●	10.8
10.9	Mammal skeleton		●	(●)	●	●	●	●	●		●	10.9
10.10	Insect & mammal skeletons compared	●	●	●	●	●	●			(●)	●	10.10
	Growth											
11.1	Growth in plants & animals	●		●			●	●	●	●	●	11.1
11.2	Growth in angiosperms (primary)				●			●	●	●		11.2
11.3	Secondary thickening							●				11.3
11.4	Factors affecting growth	●		●				●	●			11.4
11.5	Animal growth patterns	●	●	●	●	●	●	●			●	11.5
11.6	Seeds (structure & germination)	●	●	(●)	●	●	●	●	●	ONE	●	11.6
11.7	Growth measurement	●		●				●		●		11.7
	Reproduction											
12.1	Asexual & sexual reproduction compared	●		●	●	●	●	●		●	●	12.1
12.2	Asexual methods of reproduction	(●)	●	●	(●)	●	●	●		●	(●)	12.2
12.3	Winter twig			●	●	●	●	●				12.3
12.4	Perennial, biennial & annual seed-plants	●		(●)	(●)	(●)	(●)	(●)				12.4
12.5	Grafting (**G**) & cutting (**C**)	G		ONE	(●)					ONE	●	12.5
12.6	Sexual reproduction in plants	●	●	●	●	●	●	●	●	●	●	12.6
12.7	Flowers	●	●	●	●	●	●	●	●	●	●	12.7
12.8	Wind & insect-pollination	ONE	●	ONE	●	ONE	●	●	●	ONE	ONE	12.8
12.9	Self & cross-pollination	●	●	●	●	●	●	●	●		●	12.9
12.10	Adaptations for cross-pollination	●										12.10
12.11	Fertilisation & its consequences	●	●	●	●	●	●	●	●		●	12.11
12.12	Fruits	●	●	●	●	●	●	●	●	ONE	●	12.12
12.13	Dispersal of seeds by fruits	ONE	●	●	●	●	●	●	●		TWO	12.13
12.14	Sexual reproduction in mammals	●	●	●	●	●	●	●	●	●	●	12.14
12.15	Placenta	●	●	(●)	●	●	●	●	●	●	●	12.15
12.16	Parental care	●	●	●	●	●	●	●	●	●	●	12.16
12.17	Breeding success in vertebrates compared		●				(●)				●	12.17
12.18	Menstrual cycle	●			●			(●)				12.18
12.19	Contraception	●				●					●	12.19
	Genes, chromosomes & heredity											
13.1	The nucleus, chromosomes & genes	●	●	●	●	●	●	●	●	●	●	13.1
13.2	Genes & characteristics	●	●	●	●	●	●	●	●	●	●	13.2
13.3	Human blood groups: co-dominance		●		(●)							13.3
13.4	Mendel's experiments	●	●	●	●	●	●	●	●	●	●	13.4
13.5	Hints on tackling genetics problems	●	●	●	●	●	●	●	●		●	13.5
13.6	Back-cross test	●		●	●			●	●			13.6
13.7	Ratios of phenotypes	●	●	●	●		●	●	●		●	13.7
13.8	Variation in populations	●	●	●	●		●	●		●	(●)	13.8

* The W.J.E.C. columns are based on the 1979 syllabuses as the 1980 syllabuses were not available at the time of going to press.

A.L.S.E.B.	E.A.E.B. North	E.A.E.B. South	E.M.R.E.B. Syll. 1	E.M.R.E.B. Syll. 2	Met.R.E.B. Syll. A	Met.R.E.B. Syll. B	M.R.E.B.	N.R.E.B.	N.W.R.E.B.	S.E.R.E.B.	S.R.E.B. Syll. A	S.R.E.B. Syll. B (Nuffield)	S.W.E.B.	W.J.E.C.*	W.M.E.B.	W.Y. & L.R.E.B.	Y.R.E.B.	
CSE	CSE	CSE	CSE	CSE	CSE	CSE	CSE	CSE	CSE	CSE	CSE	CSE	CSE	CSE	CSE	CSE	CSE	
(●)	●			(●)				(●)							●			7.6
●		●	Ⓓ		●	●		(●)	(●)	(●)	●	(●)	●	●	●	(●)	●	7.7
●	●	●	●	●	●	●	●	●	●		●	●	●		●		●	8.1
●	●	●	●	●	●	●	●	●	●		●	●	●	●	●		●	8.2
●	●	●	●	●	●	●	●	●	●		●	●	●	●	●	●	●	8.3
			●								●					●	●	8.4
●		(●)	●	●	(●)	(●)	(●)	(●)	●	(●)	●	●	●		●			8.5
			Ⓓ															8.6
●	●	●	●	●	●	●	●	●	●	●	●	●	●	●	●	●		9.1
●	●	●	●	●	●	●	●	●	(●)	●	●	●	(●)	(●)	●	●		9.2
																		9.3
																(●)	(●)	9.4
(●)	●	●	●	(●)	●	●	●	(●)	●	●	(●)	●	●	(●)	●	●	●	9.5
			Ⓓ								●							9.6
	(●)	(●)	●		●	●	(●)	(●)		(●)	(●)			●	●	●		9.7
●	(●)	(●)	●	(●)	●	●	●	(●)		(●)	●	●	●	●	●	●	(●)	9.8
(●)	(●)	(●)	(●)	(●)	(●)	(●)	(●)			(●)	(●)	(●)	(●)	(●)	●	●		9.9
●				●	●	●	●				●							9.10
●	●	●	Ⓓ	●				●			●			●	●			9.11
●	●	●	●	●	●	●	●		(●)		●	●	●		●	●	●	9.12
											(●)							9.13
●	●	●	●		●	●	●	●	●	●	●	●	●	●	●	●	●	10.1
								●	●		●							10.2
(●)			(●)					(●)	(●)		(●)			(●)	(●)			10.3
●	●	●	●	●	●	●	●	●	●		●		●	●	●	●	●	10.4
											●							10.5
			Ⓦ						●						●			10.6
								(●)			(●)							10.7
●	●	●	●	●	●	●	●	●	●	●	●	●	●	●	●	●	●	10.8
●		●	●		●	●	●	●	●	●	●	●	●	●	●	●	●	10.9
●		●	●					●	●		●	(●)			●	●		10.10
			●	●	●	●	●	●	●				●			●	●	11.1
(●)		●	●		●	●	●					●	●			●		11.2
			●															11.3
					●	●								●		●		11.4
	(●)		●	●	●	●	●	(●)	●			●				●		11.5
(●)	(●)	●	●		(●)	(●)		●	ONE		(●)		ONE	●		●	●	11.6
	(●)	●	●	●	●	●	●	●			●					●		11.7
●	●	●	●	●	●	●	●	●	●		●	●	●	●	●	●		12.1
(●)	(●)	(●)	(●)	●	(●)	(●)	(●)		ONE		●	●	●	(●)	●	●	●	12.2
(●)		(●)			●	●								●				12.3
			●											●			●	12.4
					C	C					●	●				G		12.5
(●)				●												●		12.6
●	●	●	●		●	●	●	●	●	●	●	●	●	●	●	●	●	12.7
●	ONE	ONE	●		●	●	●	ONE	●	Ⓓ	●	●	●	●			●	12.8
●		●	●	●	(●)	(●)	(●)		(●)	(●)	●	●	●		(●)	●	●	12.9
			(●)							Ⓓ								12.10
(●)	(●)	(●)	●		(●)	(●)		(●)	●	●	●	(●)	●	●	(●)	(●)	●	12.11
●	●	●	●					●	(●)	Ⓓ	(●)	●	(●)	(●)	(●)	(●)	●	12.12
●	●	●	●	(●)	●	●		●	(●)	●	●	●	●			(●)	(●)	12.13
●	●	●	●		●	●		●	●	●	●	●	●	●	●	●	●	12.14
●	●	●	●		●	●		●	●	●	●	●	●	●	●	●	●	12.15
●	●	●	●		●	●		●	●	●	●	●	●	●	●	●	●	12.16
	(●)							(●)	●		●				●			12.17
	●				●	●					●					●		12.18
			●		●	●					●							12.19
●	●	●	●			●	●	●	●	●	●	●	●	●	●	●	●	13.1
●	●	●	(●)	●	●	●	●			(●)	●	●	(●)	●		●	●	13.2
			(●)	(●)							●	●				(●)		13.3
●	●	●	●	●			●		●	●	●	●	●	●	●	●	●	13.4
		●												●				13.5
																		13.6
		●																13.7
●		●			●	●	●	●			(●)	(●)			●	●	●	13.8

		A.E.B.	Cambridge	J.M.B.	London	Oxford	O. and C.	S.U.J.B.	W.J.E.C.*	J.M.B. "Science"	O. and C. "Combined Science"	
	Level	0	0	0	0	0	0	0	0	⅔O	⅔O	
13.9	Sex determination in mammals	●	●		●	●						13.9
13.10	Sex linkage		●			●						13.10
13.11	Mutation	●					●	●			●	13.11
13.12	Mitosis & meiosis in the life cycle	●	●	●	●	●	●			●	●	13.12
13.13	Mechanism for separating chromosomes	●	●		●	●				●		13.13
13.14	Chromosome behaviour	●	●	(●)	●	●				●		13.14
13.15	Nucleic acids & the genetic code					●						13.15
	Evolution											
14.1	Organic evolution	●	●	●		○	●	●	●	●	●	14.1
14.2	Charles Darwin	(●)	(●)	(●)		○	(●)		(●)	(●)	(●)	14.2
14.3	Summary of the neo-Darwinian theory	●	●	●		○	●	(●)	●	(●)	●	14.3
14.4	Evidence for evolution	●				○			●			14.4
14.5	Other theories of evolution	(●)	(●)	(●)		○	(●)	(●)	(●)	(●)	(●)	14.5
14.6	Artificial selection	●	●								●	14.6
	Ecology											
15.1	The biosphere	(●)	(●)		●	○		●	Ⓐ		●	15.1
15.2	Food chains, food webs, & food cycles	●	●	●	●	○	●	●	Ⓐ	●	●	15.2
15.3	Feeding relationships between species	●	●	●	●	○	●	●	Ⓐ	●	●	15.3
15.4	Stable & unstable ecosystems	●	●		●	○	●	●	Ⓐ		●	15.4
15.5	Soil	●	●	●	●	○	●	●	●	●	●	15.5
15.6	Nitrogen cycle	●	●	●	●	●	●	●	●	(●)	●	15.6
15.7	Carbon cycle	●	●	●	●	●	●	●	●	(●)	●	15.7
15.8	Earthworms & soil	(●)	(●)	●	●	●	●	●	●	●	●	15.8
15.9	Water cycle				●				●	(●)	(●)	15.9
	Man & his environment											
16.1	Ploughing	●	●	●	●	○	●	●	(●)		●	16.1
16.2	Liming & fertilising	●	●	●	●	○	●	●	(●)		●	16.2
16.3	Crop rotation	(●)	(●)	●	●	○	●	●	●		●	16.3
16.4	Pest control				●	○			Ⓑ		(●)	16.4
16.5	Human population crisis (problems)	●			●	○			Ⓑ		●	16.5
16.6	Pollution		(●)		●	○			Ⓑ		●	16.6
16.7	Depletion of resources				●	○			Ⓑ		●	16.7
16.8	Human population crisis (solutions)				●	●	●		Ⓑ		●	16.8
16.9	Predictions for mankind's future				(●)		●		Ⓑ		(●)	16.9
16.10	Types of disease in man	(●)		(●)	(●)	(●)	●	●			(●)	16.10
16.11	Natural defences of the body	●		●	●	●	●	●			●	16.11
16.12	Notable contributors to health & hygiene							●				16.12
	A variety of life											
17.1	Viruses	(●)	●		●			●			●	17.1
17.2	Bacteria	●	●	●	●	●	●	●	(●)	(●)	●	17.2
17.3	*Spirogyra* & algae	●			●	●	●	●	●		●	17.3
17.4	*Amoeba* & protozoa	●	●	●	●	●	●	●	●	(●)	●	17.4
17.5	*Rhizopus* & *Mucor* – fungi	●	●	(●)	●	●	●	●	●	●	●	17.5
17.6	*Hydra*				●	●						17.6
17.7	Earthworm				●	●		●				17.7
17.8	Moss (M) and fern (F)				ONE	F						17.8
17.9	Angiosperms (general structure)	●	●	●	●	●	●	●	●	●	●	17.9
17.10	Parasitic adaptations	●	●		●		●					17.10
17.11	Pork tapeworm	●			●		●					17.11
17.12	*Pythium debaryanum*	OR	(●)		●		OR					17.12
17.13	Dodder											17.13
17.14	Insects (life cycles, external features)	●			●	●	●	●	●		●	17.14
17.15	Locust						●					17.15
17.16	House-fly	OR	●		OR		OR					17.16
17.17	Large cabbage white butterfly							●	●			17.17
17.18	Honey bee				●			●				17.18
17.19	Importance of insects to man				(●)		●				●	17.19
17.20	Bony fish	(●)		(●)	●			●	●		(●)	17.20
17.21	Three-spined stickleback								●			17.21
17.22	Frog		(●)	(●)	●			●				17.22
17.23	Birds – flight (F) & reproduction (R)	F	R	F		●		●			F	17.23
17.24	Mammal characteristics				●	●	●		●		●	17.24
17.25	Rabbit					●			(●)	(●)	(●)	17.25

* The W.J.E.C. columns are based on the 1979 syllabuses as the 1980 syllabuses were not available at the time of going to press.

A.L.S.E.B.	E.A.E.B. North	E.A.E.B. South	E.M.R.E.B. Syll. 1	E.M.R.E.B. Syll. 2	Met.R.E.B. Syll. A	Met.R.E.B. Syll. B	M.R.E.B.	N.R.E.B.	N.W.R.E.B.	S.E.R.E.B.	S.R.E.B. Syll. A	S.R.E.B. Syll. B (Nuffield)	S.W.E.B.	W.J.E.C.*	W.M.E.B.	W.Y. & L.R.E.B.	Y.R.E.B.	
CSE	CSE	CSE	CSE	CSE	CSE	CSE	CSE	CSE	CSE	CSE	CSE	CSE	CSE	CSE	CSE	CSE	CSE	
	●		●					●							●		●	13.9
																(●)		13.10
(●)		●	●							(●)	●	●			●			13.11
●	●		●	●	●	●	●	●	●		●	●				●		13.12
			●								●	●			●			13.13
			●								●				●			13.14
			(●)									●						13.15
	●		●	(●)	●	●	●	●	●	●	●	●	●	●	●	●	●	14.1
											(●)	(●)	●			●		14.2
	(●)					●	●			●	●	●	(●)	●	(●)		●	14.3
	(●)		●	(●)			●	●			(●)	●	●		(●)	●		14.4
											●	●						14.5
			(●)	●	●		●			Ⓑ Ⓓ	●	●			●	●		14.6
(●)	(●)		Ⓒ					●										15.1
●	●	●	●	●	●	●	●	●	●	●	●	●	●	●	●	●	●	15.2
●	●	●	●	●	●	●	●	●	●		●	●		●	●	●	●	15.3
●	●		Ⓒ		●	●	●	●	●			●	●			●		15.4
●	●	●	●	●	●	●		●	●	●	●	●	●		●		●	15.5
●	(●)		●		●	●				(●)	●	(●)	●				●	15.6
●	●		●		●	●				●	●	(●)	●				●	15.7
		●							●		●						●	15.8
●			●							●	●						●	15.9
●		●										●						16.1
●	●	●			●	●				●		●					(●)	16.2
●	(●)	●	(●)		(●)	(●)				(●)	(●)						(●)	16.3
●	●				●	●					(●)	(●)	●			(●)		16.4
●	●								●							●		16.5
●	●		Ⓐ Ⓒ	●	●	●		●	●	(●)		●	●	●	(●)	●	●	16.6
●	(●)		Ⓐ	(●)	(●)	(●)		(●)					(●)	(●)			(●)	16.7
●	●		Ⓐ													●	(●)	16.8
(●)	(●)																(●)	16.9
	●	●	Ⓐ		●	●	●	(●)		Ⓑ	●	●	●	(●)	●	●	●	16.10
	●	●	Ⓐ		●	●	●	(●)		Ⓑ	●	●	●	(●)	●	●	●	16.11
					●	●	(●)			Ⓑ	(●)	(●)	●	●	●	●	●	16.12
	(●)	●	Ⓐ		(●)	(●)				Ⓑ	●	(●)	●		●	●	●	17.1
	(●)	●	Ⓐ		(●)	(●)				Ⓑ	●	●	(●)	●	●	●	●	17.2
																	●	17.3
(●)	(●)	(●)		(●)	(●)	(●)				●					(●)	(●)	●	17.4
(●)	●	(●)	(●)	(●)	(●)	(●)	(●)		●	(●)	(●)	(●)		(●)	●		●	17.5
												(●)					●	17.6
												●					●	17.7
											●	M					(●)	17.8
●		●	●	●	●			●	●	●	●		●			●	●	17.9
										(●)		(●)		(●)		●	(●)	17.10
																(●)	(●)	17.11
							ONE							ONE		(●)	OR	17.12 / 17.13
(●)		(●)			●	●		(●)			●	●	●			●		17.14
			(●)								●	●				(●)		17.15
	●	●					ONE				●		ONE			OR		17.16
			●									●						17.17
					(●)													17.18
										Ⓓ	●	(●)	●		(●)	(●)		17.19
			(●)		●	●		●				●				Ⓓ		17.20
			(●)									(●)						17.21
			(●)			(●)			(●)		(●)	●						17.22
					●	●			●			R				F		17.23
●		●			●	●	●			●	●		●		●		●	17.24
					(●)	(●)	(●)										(●)	17.25

GCE Boards

A.E.B.	Associated Examining Board Wellington House, Aldershot, Hampshire GU11 1BQ
Cambridge	University of Cambridge Local Examinations Syndicate Syndicate Buildings, 17 Harvey Road, Cambridge CB1 2EU
J.M.B.	Joint Matriculation Board Manchester M15 6EU
London	University Entrance and School Examinations Council University of London, 66–72 Gower Street, London WC1E 6EE
Oxford	Oxford Local Examinations Delegacy of Local Examinations, Ewert Place, Summertown, Oxford OX2 7BX
O. and C.	Oxford and Cambridge Schools Examination Board 10 Trumpington Street, Cambridge; and Elsfield Way, Oxford
S.U.J.B.	Southern Universities' Joint Board for School Examinations Cotham Road, Bristol BS6 6DD
W.J.E.C.	Welsh Joint Education Committee 245 Western Avenue, Cardiff CF5 2YX

CSE Boards

A.L.S.E.B.	Associated Lancashire Schools Examining Board 77 Whitworth Street, Manchester M1 6HA
E.A.E.B.	East Anglian Examinations Board The Lindens, Lexden Road, Colchester, Essex CO3 3RL
E.M.R.E.B.	East Midland Regional Examinations Board Robins Wood House, Robins Wood Road, Apsley, Nottingham NG8 3NH
Met.R.E.B.	Metropolitan Regional Examinations Board Lyon House, 104 Wandsworth High Street, London SW18 4LF
M.R.E.B.	Middlesex Regional Examining Board 53–63 Wembley Hill Road, Wembley, Middlesex HA9 8BH
N.R.E.B.	North Regional Examinations Board Wheatfield Road, Westerhope, Newcastle upon Tyne NE5 5JZ
N.W.R.E.B.	North West Regional Examinations Board Orbit House, Albert Street, Eccles, Manchester M30 0WL
S.R.E.B.	Southern Regional Examinations Board 53 London Road, Southampton SO9 4YL
S.E.R.E.B.	South East Regional Examinations Board Beloe House, 2/4 Mount Ephraim Road, Royal Tunbridge Wells, Kent TN1 1EU
S.W.E.B.	South Western Examinations Board 23–29 Marsh Street, Bristol BS1 4BP
W.J.E.C.	Welsh Joint Education Committee 245 Western Avenue, Cardiff CF5 2YX
W.M.E.B.	West Midlands Examinations Board Norfolk House, Smallbrook Queensway, Birmingham B5 4NJ
W.Y. & L.R.E.B.	West Yorkshire & Lindsey Regional Examining Board Scarsdale House, 136 Derbyshire Lane, Sheffield S8 8SE
Y.R.E.B.	Yorkshire Regional Examinations Board 31–33 Springfield Avenue, Harrogate, North Yorkshire HG1 2HW

1 Academic success

1.1 INTRODUCTION

Successful students are those who can organise their work. In particular, they must be able to work effectively on their own. If you are to be successful you need determination to succeed, a work plan fitted to a time schedule and determination to keep to that schedule. Unfortunately, few students are told *how* to devise that plan and carry it out – that is where this book comes in.

This chapter contains some advice that will help you to succeed in school. It also gives reasons for this advice. The rest of the book concerns itself with presenting biological facts in a form that makes it easy to revise.

The first three steps in the learning process are planned by your teacher who knows the sort of exam you will be sitting (stage 5 in Fig. 1.1) and plans accordingly. Where so many students fail, needlessly, is at stage 4 (revision) – because they do not know how to go about it. **Revision** is what this book is all about – leave out stage 4 in the diagram below and you have F for failure.

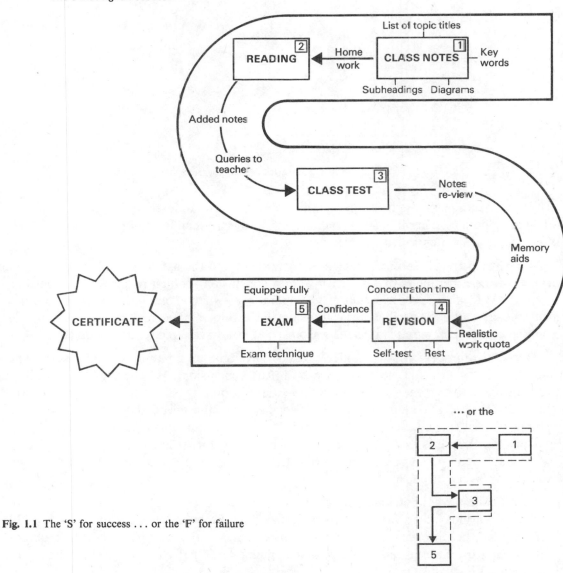

Fig. 1.1 The 'S' for success . . . or the 'F' for failure

1.2 THE LEARNING PROCESS: PATTERNS IN THE MIND

In science you learn from experiments – your own or those reported by others. It is well known that students tend to remember far better the 'facts' they have learned by doing experiments themselves. Unfortunately there is not enough time to learn everything this way, so that the rest has to be learned by reading and listening.

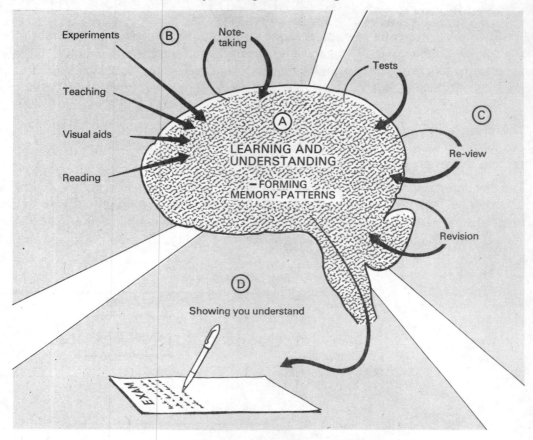

Fig. 1.2 From learning to showing you understand

Why is learning through reading and listening harder than learning by experiment? Why are good annotated diagrams often so much easier to learn than line upon line of words? Why is a good teacher such a help in learning?

Experiments: doing these needs personal involvement and the use of several senses. Then, at the end of the experiment, one must arrive at a conclusion – which requires some reasoning. In a word, the whole process requires *understanding* – understanding the **aim** of the experiment, the **method** to be used and how to record the **results** in a meaningful way. And the final step, the **conclusion,** requires reasoning from what you have already understood.

During this process you will notice that you have built up a pattern of knowledge – like a jig-saw – lacking just one piece to complete it (the conclusion). Having completed it, if you were a professional scientist, you would find yourself doing yet another jig-saw, and another, and so on. However there is one vital difference between the scientist's jig-saw game and the jig-saws you do for amusement. The scientist's pieces are interchangeable between *different* jig-saws (Fig. 1.3). It is as if his jig-saws all interlocked in three dimensions. On a simpler level you probably realise that you can play noughts and crosses in three dimensions and not just in two, as on a piece of paper.

But of course you know this from your own everyday experience. When someone says the word 'cat' various other words will spring to mind. Perhaps 'claws', 'fluffy', 'leopard' or 'witches', and these words themselves will bring to mind further words. In short, **learning is a process requiring patterns to be built up in the mind:** relate what you have just learned to what you already know and the facts will stick – because you *understand*.

Reading: in contrast to experimenting, when reading you are using only one of your senses – sight – and you are not *involved*, as you are in an experiment, unless you make a mental effort. Nor do you feel the same sense of discovery. Worst of all, the information is presented as a series of facts. In well-written books the facts *are* written to form patterns; but

3-DIMENSIONAL JIG-SAW OF FACTS

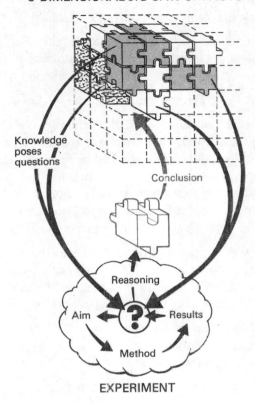

Fig. 1.3

it is you, the reader, who has to concentrate hard enough to pick them out. If you can do this and fit your newly acquired jig-saw of facts into the system of jig-saws already in your brain, you have learned to learn by reading. This is initially much harder to do than by experiment.

Pictures and diagrams: one method of learning from books goes half-way towards experimental learning. Do you enjoy strip cartoons? At any rate you will agree that they are easy reading and convey much more than the few words appearing with the pictures. Pictures and diagrams, like words, require eyes alone to see them. But, unlike words, pictures build up patterns in the brain more readily and understanding is more immediate. So, well-constructed diagrams are an invaluable learning aid. If you learn the art of diagram-drawing you will reinforce both your memory and your understanding. Ultimately you should be able to construct your own original topic-summary diagrams, and there is a definite stage in the learning process when you should do this (see Section 1.4).

Teachers: have you ever thought about the role of teachers in the learning process? They attempt to activate more senses in you than just your hearing. By showing films and slides, by drawing diagrams or asking your opinions and by giving you definite learning objectives, they try to keep you personally involved. It is for you to respond – if you are going to learn. Amidst it all you must carefully latch onto the *pattern* of facts that the teacher explains. A teacher usually explains what the *whole* lesson is to be about during the first few minutes. Listen hard to that outline and the rest of the lesson will be easier to absorb. The outline is the basic skeleton upon which the teacher will build up the flesh and features of his subject, as the lesson proceeds. If you miss the description of the skeleton, the subject may turn out to be a monster for you!

1.3   CAPTURING FACTS

1　Class notes: your teacher has probably advised you on how to make these. For easy revision it is essential that they include:

(*a*) a topic list referring to numbered pages in your notebook

(*b*) clear, underlined topic titles and sub-titles

(*c*) underlined 'key words'

(*d*) clear diagrams with titles

(*e*) space for topic-summary diagrams made during revision.

2   Reading texts: your teacher may advise you what to read. Realise too that a text has an index at the back; use it to look up things for yourself. At this stage many students get bogged down because they read slowly and give up. If you are someone with this problem, try this:

The cat sat on the mat.

Because of the way you were taught to read, for example 'c-a-t' or 'cat' you have been 'brainwashed' into thinking that you can only read one word at a time. Now bring your head back further from the page. Notice that now you can have more than one word in focus at a time – without having to move your eyes at all. With practice you will find that not only 'cat' is in focus but also 'The' and perhaps even 'sat' as well. It does need practice but soon you will find that the whole of 'The cat sat on' is in focus at one glance and that you can take it *all* in. Four words instead of one at each glance – four times your original reading speed!

Time how long it takes you to read a page now. Repeat the test after each week of practising the new method. Some people can read 800 words per minute with ease, understanding as they go. No wonder this method is called speed-reading! Reading the text should be done after you have been taught the topic – say during home-work. Your reading:

(*a*) reinforces in your mind the facts recorded in class notes

(*b*) allows you to add extra bits to your notes

(*c*) should clear up misunderstandings.

Ask your teacher if you still do not understand something.

3   Class tests: these are designed to help you to recall facts and to reason from them. In this process you and the teacher are on the *same* side; together you will succeed. The teacher is *not* putting you to the torture. Tests:

(*a*) help you to assess your progress (should you work harder?)

(*b*) help the teacher to clear up your difficulties (adjust your notes?)

(*c*) help you to remember facts better

(*d*) give you exam practice.

1.4   RETAINING FACTS

Revision: this is the vital last stage in the learning process, the stage when you are finally on your own. You must understand clearly how to go about it. Look at the graph in Fig. 1.4.

All of us have different **'concentration times'**. How long is yours? Go to a quiet working place indoors, without distractions, and note the time. Read a part of your text-book that is new to you, making a determined effort to take in all you read. When your mind begins to

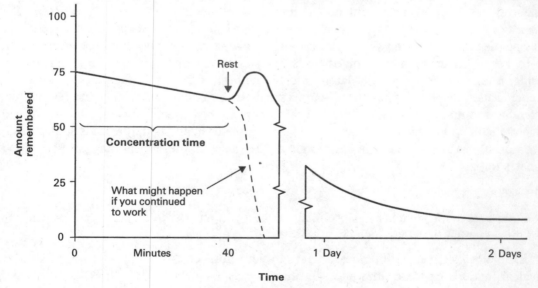

Fig. 1.4 Concentration time graph

wander, look again at your watch; you are at the end of your concentration time. It should be around 20–40 minutes and will differ according to the amount of sleep you have had, what else is on your mind, and even on the subject matter. Never revise for longer than your concentration time. If you do, you will waste your time. You may still be reading but you will not understand. So **rest** for five minutes.

After the rest, surprisingly enough, the facts you read in the text-book will come back to you more easily still. During the rest, the brain was 'organising' the facts you took in. Note-taking would have assisted this organising process. Unfortunately most of these facts go into what is called your 'short-term memory'. Within 48 hours you will retain as little as 10% of what you thought you knew so well. Don't be depressed. You can push these facts into your 'long-term memory', which is essential for exam purposes, by **reviewing**.

Reviewing is a *quick* re-read of your notes, taking only a few minutes. If your notes are disorganised you will not gain much. But with clear summaries, such as you will find in this book, you should dramatically increase the number of facts going into your long-term memory. Do this re-reading after a week and then again two weeks later after having learned the topic for the first time in class. Figure 1.5 shows the sort of result that can be obtained by thorough reviewing and revision.

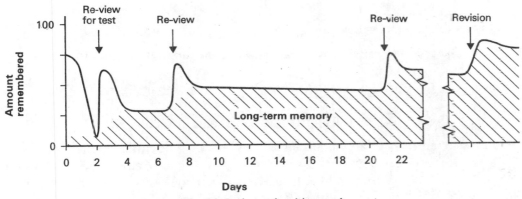

Fig. 1.5 Review and revision graph

Revision is just an extension of reviewing. If you have followed the learning plan so far, there will be relatively little to do. During revision whole chunks of your notes will not need to be read because sub-titles and key-words alone will trigger off a mass of facts already in your long-term memory. For the rest of the plan, follow these principles:

(*i*) Months ahead of the exam, plan how much to revise each week.

(*ii*) Have a regular time for work and stick to it.

(*iii*) With your concentration time in mind, plan a *realistic* amount of work for each 20–40 minute session. You must get up from your task with a sense of achievement, i.e. that you have completed what you set out to do. Otherwise you will get depressed 'at the hopelessness of it all'.

(*iv*) Take those 5 minute breaks. But do not exceed them.

(*v*) Use the memory aids and summary diagrams in this book to help you.

(*vi*) Check your knowledge by using the test-yourself sections on each chapter (pages 158–186).

Memory aids

(*i*) Repetition   (*ii*) Mnemonics   (*iii*) Pattern-diagrams

(**i**) **Repetition:** By chanting something over and over again you can learn it 'parrot-fashion'. Many people learn their times-tables or poetry in this way. The method has its uses. But though you can remember in this way you do not necessarily *understand*.

(**ii**) **Mnemonics:** These are words, sentences or little rhymes chosen from everyday language to help you to remember technical words that you find difficult to memorise. This book provides you with a few examples; but you may be able to do better. Make your own mnemonics funny, outrageously absurd – even rude – if you are going to remember them. Dull mnemonics are difficult to remember. The words you choose must be sufficiently similar to the technical words to remind you of them. For example:

'How do I remember the words on the Royal Garter when I don't know enough French?' Look at Fig. 1.6 and try:

On his way he madly puns.

Fig. 1.6 The Royal Garter

'How can I remember the characteristics of living things – which I *do* understand but may not be able to remember fully in an exam?' Try **Berlin God sees** and turn to Section 2.1. This example uses initial letters of the key words only.

'How do I remember the principal regions of the vertebral column?'

Try **The servant   attacks with saw and axe the lumber   stack and cord**

against   Cervical (atlas, axis) Thoracic   Lumbar Sacral   Caudal

and turn to Fig. 10.10. You will find another mnemonic in Section 3.1.

(iii) **Pattern-diagrams:** these are important or 'key' words written down and joined up with lines according to their connections with each other. You have already seen two examples (Figs. 1.1 and 1.2). When you have finished revising a topic always try to summarise it in this way. You will be surprised how easy it is. And why? Because, you will remember (Fig. 1.3), your mind thinks in patterns and not in lists. When you come to the exam you will be able to remember your pattern-diagrams and even create new ones when planning your answers to essay questions (see page 194).

Part IV of this book (pages 193–198) contains valuable advice on how to do your best in the exam. It also tells you about the types of question you might expect to find in an exam and gives hints on how to answer them.

Part II Core material, chapters 2–17

2 Life

2.1 CHARACTERISTICS OF ORGANISMS

Living things are called **organisms**. Three large groups of organisms are the **green plants**, e.g. grass; **non-green plants**, e.g. mushrooms; and the **animals** (see Sections 3.3 and 3.4). All organisms perform *all* the 9 'vital functions' at some time during their existence; and their bodies are made of cells. Some organisms remain, for a time, **dormant** (inactive), e.g. as seeds, spores or cysts. These bodies appear not to perform vital functions but are activated by suitable stimulation.

10 characteristics of organisms   (*Mnemonic:* BERLIN GOD SEES)

Breathing (= Respiration)
Excreting
Reproducing
Locomotion (= Moving)
Irritability (= Sensitivity and response)
Nutrition
Growing
Osmoregulation
Death
Cells

B   **Respiration:** release of energy within cells from food so as to power other vital functions. In most organisms, requires oxygen and releases carbon dioxide and heat. (See Chapter 6.)

E   **Excretion:** removal of waste products from **metabolism** (all the chemical reactions with the body). (See Chapter 7.)

N.B. Do not confuse this with 'egestion' (Removal of **indigestible** matter – which has thus never entered cells to be metabolised).

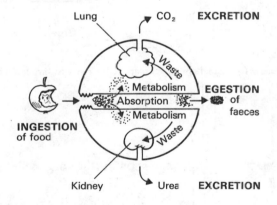

Fig. 2.1 The distinction between excretion and egestion

R   **Reproduction:** formation of more individuals either from one parent (asexually) or two (sexually). (See Chapter 12.)

L   **Movement:** an animal moves its whole body, using limbs or their equivalent. A plant 'moves' only by growing parts of itself towards or away from influences important to it. (See Sections 9.11 and 9.12.)

I   **Sensitivity and response:** areas receptive to influences (**stimuli**) in the surroundings (**environment**) are stimulated so that they send messages to other parts which respond, e.g. by movement, growth or secretion. (See Chapter 8.)

N   **Nutrition:** intake of food materials from the environment for building up and maintaining living matter. (See Section 4.2.)

G   **Growth:** cells divide and then get larger again by adding more living material (made from their food) until they repeat the process. (See Chapter 11.)

O   **Osmoregulation:** maintenance of the water content of cells at a suitable level. (See Section 5.6.)

D   **Death:** when metabolism ceases completely.

C   **Cells:** the simplest units of life. All cells, when young, have at the very least 3 parts: a *membrane* enclosing jelly-like *cytoplasm*, in which lies a *nucleus* which controls its life. (See Section 2.2.) These three parts make up *protoplasm* (living matter). The cell wall secreted outside the protoplasm by plant cells only, is non-living. Cells cannot live without supplies of energy, food, water and O_2 and a suitable environmental temperature and pH.

Cells from animals and green plants show differences, as seen in Fig. 2.2.

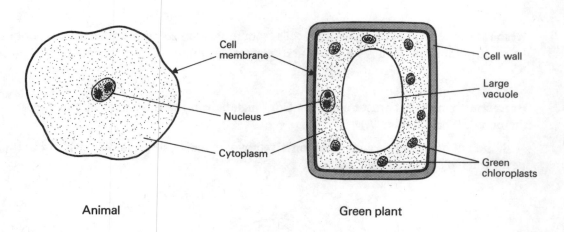

Animal   Green plant

Fig. 2.2 Generalised animal and green plant cells as viewed through a light microscope

2.2   ORGANELLES

Cells examined with an electron microscope show further **organelles** (parts with special functions) as seen in Fig. 2.3.

(*a*) **Cell wall**

Made of cellulose.

Freely permeable (porous) to all kinds of molecules.

Supports and protects the cell.

Supports non-woody plant organs, e.g. leaves, by turgor pressure (water pressure within vacuole distending cell wall).

Osmoregulates by resisting entry of excess water into cell.

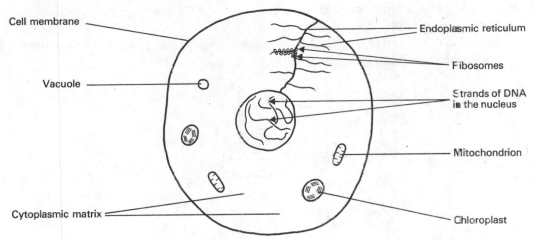

Fig. 2.3 Generalised animal cell as viewed through an electron microscope

(b) **Cell membrane**

Exterior of all protoplasm.

Very thin layer of protein and oil.

Freely permeable to water and gases only.

Selectively permeable to other molecules (e.g. allows foods in but keeps unwanted molecules out).

(c) **Endoplasmic reticulum (E.R.)**

Maze of fine tubes, made of cell membrane material, throughout the cytoplasm.

Allows transport of materials across cell.

Allows export of materials out of cell, e.g. digestive enzymes.

(d) **Ribosomes**

Minute bodies in thousands; most attached to membranes of E.R.

Assemble proteins under 'instructions' from nucleus.

(e) **Vacuoles**

Spaces for various functions, e.g. food storage, osmoregulation.

(f) **Chloroplasts** (for photosynthesis)

Large bodies containing chlorophyll (green).

Chlorophyll converts sunlight energy into chemical energy (ATP).

ATP is used to combine CO_2 with H_2O, making glucose; by-product is O_2.

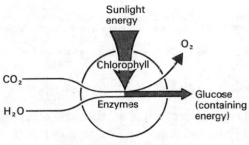

Fig. 2.4 Photosynthesis

(*g*) **Mitochondria** (for internal respiration)

Absorb O_2 and glucose.

Break down glucose to CO_2 and H_2O. This releases energy from glucose bonds to form ATP (for use in other vital functions, e.g. growth).

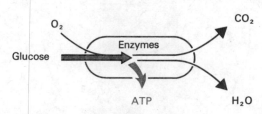

Fig. 2.5 Internal respiration

(*h*) **Cytoplasmic matrix**

Supports organelles.

Consistency of raw egg-white.

Up to 80% water; remainder mainly protein.

(*i*) **Nucleus**

Stores and passes on cell 'information'.

Contains many long strands of DNA (invisible).

When cell divides, DNA coils up to form chromosomes (visible). (See Section 13.1.)

Segments of DNA are called **genes**.

Genes are responsible for characteristics of organisms, e.g. blood group and eye colour.

2.3   HOW THE NUCLEUS CONTROLS THE CELL

DNA makes RNA and RNA makes proteins. (See Fig. 2.6.)

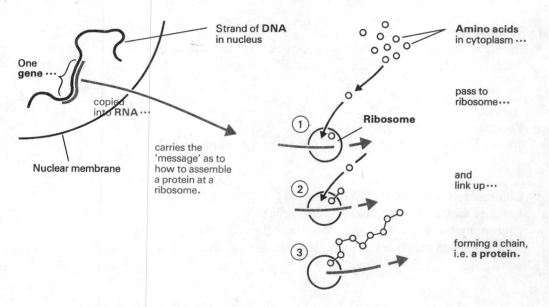

The protein may be an enzyme. Enzymes are catalysts 'controlling' cell metabolism. Thus the nucleus, via RNA, ribosomes and enzymes, 'controls' the cell.

Fig. 2.6 How the nucleus controls the cell

2.4   ENZYMES

Enzymes are protein catalysts which catalyse *all* chemical reactions (metabolism) of the body, e.g. respiration, photosynthesis, and digestion. Without enzymes, reactions would not go fast enough for life to exist.

Each enzyme works at a preferred *temperature* (boiling stops its action for good; cooling only slows its action) and at a preferred *pH*, e.g. pepsin works only in acid conditions. (See Section 4.13.)

Each enzyme is specific in action, e.g. ptyalin digests starch only, never protein. (See Section 4.13.)

2.5 UNITS OF LIFE BEYOND THE CELL

Just as inorganic molecules are built up into organic molecules; which in turn are built into organelles (see Section 2.2), so cells are sub-units of organisms. There is a great variety of types of cell. (See Sections 4.8, 5.5, 5.8, 9.2, 10.7, 12.14.)

Tissues are groups of cells, usually of the same type, specialised to carry out certain functions, e.g. muscle, nerve, epithelium, xylem, bone.

Organs are made up of tissues co-ordinated to perform certain functions, e.g. eye, leaf, kidney.

Organ systems are groups of organs which combine to perform their functions, e.g. gut, endocrine system, nervous system.

Organisms, depending on their complexity, may each be just one cell, e.g. a bacterium, or *Amoeba*, or millions of cells with a variety of functional units as above, e.g. an oak tree or man. An organism which reproduces sexually is not much use on its own, unless it self-fertilises. The basic unit of reproduction is thus usually a **breeding pair**. From this stem **populations** – as small as herds or as large as hundreds of herds occupying an island or a continent. A number of populations forms a **species** (see Fig. 2.7). Populations of different species living in balance in nature are called **communities**. Communities form part of **ecosystems** in the **biosphere**. (See Section 15.1.)

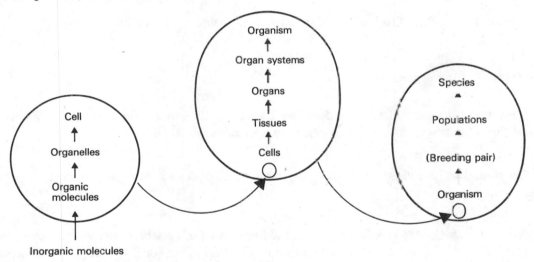

Fig. 2.7 Units of life

3 Classification

3.1 LINNAEUS AND HIS CLASSIFICATION SYSTEM

Carl Linnaeus of Sweden in 1735 introduced the basis of modern **taxonomy** (classification):

All species are given two names in Latin – the **binomial system** of naming:

(*a*) genus name, written first, with an initial *capital* letter, e.g. *Homo* (man).
(*b*) species name, written second, with a *small* initial letter, e.g. *sapiens* (modern).

The binomial ought to be printed in italics but is underlined when handwritten or typed by scientists, e.g. <u>Panthera</u> <u>tigris</u> (tiger).

Species: a group of organisms with a very large number of similarities in structure and physiology, capable of breeding to produce fertile offspring.

Genus: a group of organisms with a large number of similarities but whose different sub-groups (species) are usually unable to inter-breed successfully.

Taxons: just as species are sub-groups of genera, so genera are grouped together into larger and larger groups forming a **hierarchy of taxons** (groups), each group including as many *similarities* as possible. The largest taxon is a kingdom, the smallest a species. The lion can be classified as follows:

Kingdom	Animalia	– as opposed to plants.
Phylum	Vertebrata	– animals with backbones (fish, amphibia, reptiles, birds and mammals).
Class	Mammalia	– hairy, warm blooded, suckle young on milk.
Order	Carnivora	– mainly flesh-eating group (cats, dogs, bears, seals).
Family	Felidae	– cats.
Genus	*Panthera*	– large cats (includes tiger; leopard, *P. pardus*).
Species	*leo*	– lion only.

Mnemonic: **K**adet, **P.C.**, **OF**ficer, **G**eneral in**S**pector (promotion in the Police force).

Advantages of the system

1 Universal: Japanese, Bantu or Russian biologists all understand that *Felis domestica* means 'house cat' without having to resort to a dictionary.

2 Shorthand information: one word, e.g. mammal, conveys a mass of information to all biologists. (See Section 17.24.)

3 Reflects evolutionary relationships: e.g. the five classes of vertebrate are very different (see Section 3.4), yet all have a common body plan. The basic plan (in Fish) (see p. 23), was improved upon, permitting land colonisation (Amphibia) and exploitation (Reptiles and Mammals), and even conquering of the air (Birds). The classification of vertebrates thus probably reflects the evolutionary process.

3.2   KEYS

Keys are a means of identifying organisms in *local* situations, e.g. in stream or woodland. The user of the key selects one of two contrasting descriptions, choosing the one that fits the organism being identified. The chosen description leads to a number, alongside which are further descriptions from which to choose. The final choice leads to the organism's name.

Example: Choose one of the organisms in Fig. 3.1 on the next page and use the key below the diagram to identify it.

Fig. 3.1

With wings	**1**	(*Now look at descriptions by* **1** *below*)
Without wings	**2**	(*Now look at descriptions by* **2** *below*)

1 { Two legs   C – Bat
    Six legs   B – Butterfly

2 { With legs   A – Woodlouse
    Without legs   **3** (*Now look at description by* **3** *below*)

3 { With eyes   D – Fish
    Without eyes   E – Earthworm

In the example above, use of internal characteristics (e.g. vertebrae) or confusing ones (e.g. hairiness) would delay identification – some butterflies are as hairy as bats!

Your key of the organisms above could be different but still be 'correct' – if it works.

3.3   PLANT KINGDOM

Classification of the main members of the plant kingdom can be seen on page 22 overleaf.

3.4   ANIMAL KINGDOM

Classification of the main members of the animal kingdom can be seen on page 23 overleaf.

THE PLANT KINGDOM

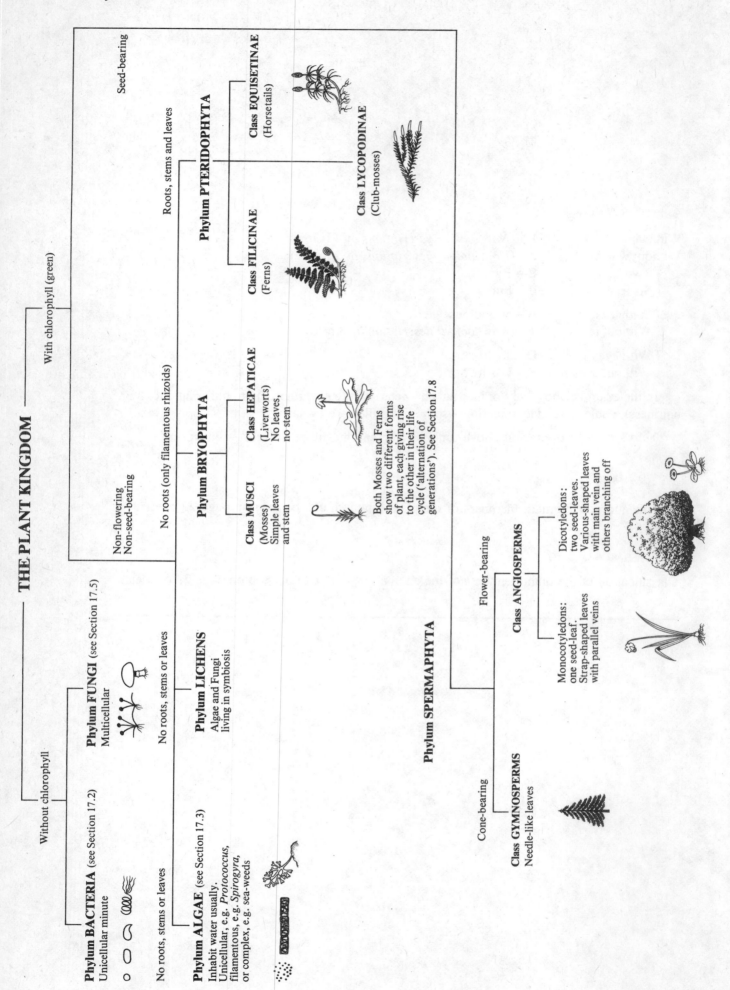

Without chlorophyll

- **Phylum BACTERIA** (see Section 17.2)
  Unicellular minute
  No roots, stems or leaves

- **Phylum FUNGI** (see Section 17.5)
  Multicellular
  No roots, stems or leaves

- **Phylum LICHENS**
  Algae and Fungi living in symbiosis

With chlorophyll (green)

Non-flowering
Non-seed-bearing

No roots (only filamentous rhizoids)

- **Phylum ALGAE** (see Section 17.3)
  Inhabit water usually.
  Unicellular, e.g. *Protococcus*, filamentous, e.g. *Spirogyra*, or complex, e.g. sea-weeds

- **Phylum BRYOPHYTA**
  - **Class MUSCI** (Mosses) Simple leaves and stem
  - **Class HEPATICAE** (Liverworts) No leaves, no stem

  Both Mosses and Ferns show two different forms of plant, each giving rise to the other in their life cycle ('alternation of generations'). See Section 17.8

Roots, stems and leaves

- **Phylum PTERIDOPHYTA**
  - **Class FILICINAE** (Ferns)
  - **Class EQUISETINAE** (Horsetails)
  - **Class LYCOPODINAE** (Club-mosses)

Seed-bearing

- **Phylum SPERMAPHYTA**

  Cone-bearing
  - **Class GYMNOSPERMS**
    Needle-like leaves

  Flower-bearing
  - **Class ANGIOSPERMS**
    - Monocotyledons: one seed-leaf. Strap-shaped leaves with parallel veins
    - Dicotyledons: two seed-leaves. Various-shaped leaves with main vein and others branching off

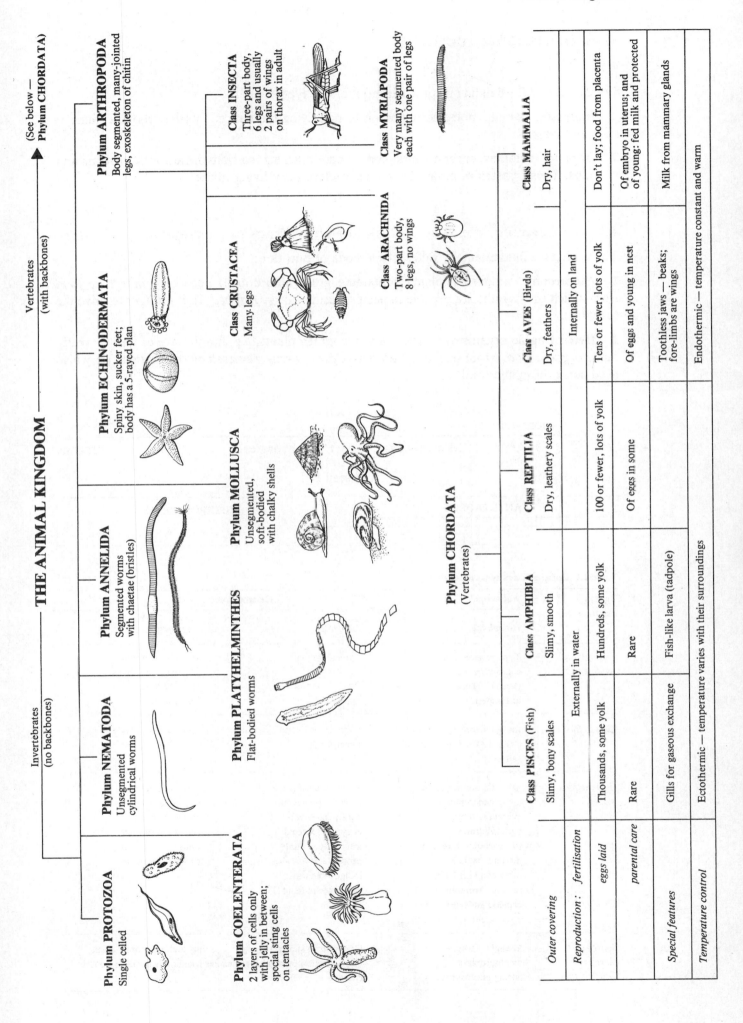

THE ANIMAL KINGDOM

Invertebrates (no backbones)

Vertebrates (with backbones)

(See below — Phylum CHORDATA)

Phylum PROTOZOA
Single celled

Phylum COELENTERATA
2 layers of cells only with jelly in between; special sting cells on tentacles

Phylum NEMATODA
Unsegmented cylindrical worms

Phylum PLATYHELMINTHES
Flat-bodied worms

Phylum ANNELIDA
Segmented worms with chaetae (bristles)

Phylum MOLLUSCA
Unsegmented, soft-bodied with chalky shells

Phylum ECHINODERMATA
Spiny skin, sucker feet; body has a 5-rayed plan

Phylum ARTHROPODA
Body segmented, many-jointed legs, exoskeleton of chitin

Class CRUSTACEA
Many legs

Class INSECTA
Three-part body, 6 legs and usually 2 pairs of wings on thorax in adult

Class ARACHNIDA
Two-part body, 8 legs, no wings

Class MYRIAPODA
Very many segmented body each with one pair of legs

Phylum CHORDATA
(Vertebrates)

		Class PISCES (Fish)	Class AMPHIBIA	Class REPTILIA	Class AVES (Birds)	Class MAMMALIA
Outer covering		Slimy, bony scales	Slimy, smooth	Dry, leathery scales	Dry, feathers	Dry, hair
Reproduction:	fertilisation	Externally in water	Externally in water	Internally on land	Internally on land	Internally on land
	eggs laid	Thousands, some yolk	Hundreds, some yolk	100 or fewer, lots of yolk	Tens or fewer, lots of yolk	Don't lay; food from placenta
	parental care	Rare	Rare	Of eggs in some	Of eggs and young in nest	Of embryo in uterus; and of young: fed milk and protected
Special features		Gills for gaseous exchange	Fish-like larva (tadpole)		Toothless jaws — beaks; fore-limbs are wings	Milk from mammary glands
Temperature control		Ectothermic — temperature varies with their surroundings	Ectothermic — temperature varies with their surroundings	Ectothermic — temperature varies with their surroundings	Endothermic — temperature constant and warm	Endothermic — temperature constant and warm

4 Foods and feeding

4.1   FOOD

Food (material for building up protoplasm) is of two types:

1   Inorganic: (simple molecules common to non-living matter), e.g. carbon dioxide, mineral salts and water.

2   Organic: (complex, carbon-containing compounds), e.g. carbohydrates, fats, proteins and vitamins. These classes of molecules are characteristic of living matter.

4.2   HOLOPHYTIC, HOLOZOIC AND SAPROPHYTIC NUTRITION COMPARED

There are two fundamentally different methods of nutrition:

1   Autotrophic organisms (plants containing green chlorophyll) need *only inorganic food* from which they synthesise organic molecules, using *energy trapped from sunlight* to drive the reactions.

2   Heterotrophic organisms (animals and non-green plants, e.g. fungi) have to feed on ready made *organic food*. From this food they derive their *energy, released by respiration*. They also need some inorganic food.

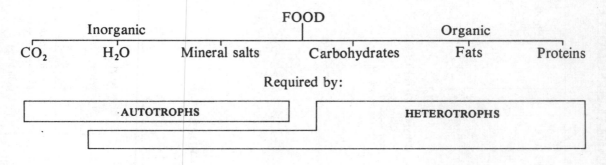

Table 4.1 Comparison of types of nutrition

Type of nutrition	Autotrophic	Heterotrophic	
	Holophytic	*Holozoic*	*Saprophytic*
Examples of organisms	Typical green plants e.g. *Spirogyra* (Sec. 17.3) and angiosperms	Typical animals e.g. *Amoeba* (Sec. 17.4) and mammals	Bacteria and fungi of decay e.g. *Mucor* (Sec. 17.5) and mushrooms
Type of food	Inorganic only: CO_2, H_2O and mineral salts	Organic, H_2O and mineral salts	Dead organic, H_2O and mineral salts
How the food is used	(*i*) CO_2 and water are combined in **photosynthesis** to make carbohydrates (*ii*) carbohydrates are modified and also often combined with salts to **form other organic molecules**, e.g. protein	Food organisms are killed; *ingested* into a **gut**; *digested* by enzymes secreted internally; soluble products *absorbed*; indigestible waste *egested* (eliminated)	Dead organisms or excreta are digested by enzymes secreted **externally** onto them; soluble products absorbed
Source of energy for vital functions	**Sunlight** – trapped by chlorophyll during photosynthesis	Cannot trap sunlight energy since they lack chlorophyll. Rely on **respiration** of organic molecules (the bonds of which contain energy)	

Organic food can be obtained from living organisms (**holozoic** nutrition) or from dead matter (**saprophytic** nutrition). (For other variations see Section 4.11.)

Thus the kinds of organism practising these three forms of nutrition provide food for each other:

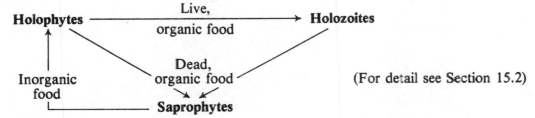

(For detail see Section 15.2)

The principles outlined in Table 4.1 are best studied in detail by reference to simple organisms such as those named (see Sections 17.3–17.5). Complex organisms, however, have complex requirements and uses for the molecules they absorb. This is taken into account below.

INORGANIC FOOD

1   Water (see Section 5.1)   **2   Mineral salts.**

4.3   MINERAL SALTS FOR MAMMALS AND ANGIOSPERMS

(Angiosperms are flowering plants)

Table 4.2 Mammal requirements (especially man)

Element	Good sources	Uses	Deficiency effects
Ca	Milk; cheese; bread (chalk added by law)	Bones and teeth are about ⅓ calcium phosphate	Brittle bones and teeth
P	Milk	Bones and teeth; ATP the energy molecule (Sec. 6.9); nucleic acids–genes and their functions (Sec. 3.5)	As above
Fe	Liver, egg yolk	Part of haemoglobin, the oxygen-carrying molecule	Anaemia (lack of red blood cells)
I	Sea foods, Table salt (iodised by law)	Part of thyroxin, the hormone controlling metabolic rate (Sec. 9.8)	Goitre – thyroid swelling in adults
F	Toothpaste or tap water that have been fluoridated	Ensures hard tooth enamel, therefore less tooth decay (caries)	Dental caries more likely
Na	Table salt (NaCl)	A correct balance of these is required, particularly for proper function of nerves and muscles	
K	Plant food		

Table 4.3 Angiosperm requirements (See Section 4.10)

Element	Sources	Uses	Deficiency effects
N	Nitrates	Protein and nucleic acid synthesis	Poor growth – little protoplasm made
S	Sulphates		
P	Phosphates	ATP (energy molecule) in photosynthesis and respiration; nucleic acid synthesis	Poor growth – little energy for synthesis of protoplasm

Table 4.3 – (*cont'd*)

Element	Sources	Uses	Deficiency effects
K	Potassium salts	Functions not clear	Poor growth – dehydration
Ca	Lime ($CaCO_3$)	'Gum' (middle lamella) between adjacent cell walls	Faulty cell division
Fe	Iron salts	Enzymes for making chlorophyll	Pale leaves (chlorosis)
Mg	Magnesium salts	Part of chlorophyll molecule	Pale leaves (chlorosis)

Trace elements include Zinc (**Zn**), Copper (**Cu**) and Manganese (**Mn**). Required in very minute quantities for healthy growth (larger quantities are often poisonous).

Although green plants absorb mineral salts as ions, man does not always give them to his crops by way of inorganic fertilisers (see Section 16.2). Organic fertilisers, such as dung, also yield salts, once they have been broken down by bacteria and fungi (see Sections 15.6, 17.2, 17.5).

ORGANIC FOOD

1 Carbohydrates, fats and proteins   2 Vitamins

4.4   CARBOHYDRATES, FATS AND PROTEINS

Table 4.4 Carbohydrates, fats, oils and proteins

	Carbohydrates	*Fats* (solid), *oils* (liquid)	*Proteins*
Elements	C, H, O Ratio of H:O is 2:1 (as in H_2O)	C, H, O Ratio of H:O is very high, i.e. very little O	C, H, O, N, often S
Examples	Glucose, $C_6H_{12}O_6$ Sucrose, $C_{12}H_{22}O_{11}$	Mutton fat: ($C_{57}H_{110}O_6$)	Haemoglobin, ptyalin, insulin
Units	Mono-saccharides (simple sugars, like glucose)	Glycerol + fatty acids	Amino acids
	These units are the only forms in which these three classes of food are absorbed after digestion (*hydrolysis*). The units can be reassembled into larger molecules again by *condensation*, e.g. when food needs to be stored (see Section 4.12).		
Larger molecules	Di-saccharides (2 units) e.g. sucrose, maltose Poly-saccharides, e.g. starch, glycogen, cellulose		Di-peptides (*two* linked amino acids) Poly-peptides (*many*) Peptones (*very many*) Proteoses (*very very many*)
Chemical tests	1 Blue **Benedict's** solution* + **reducing sugar** $\xrightarrow{\text{boiled}}$ *orange* precipitate	1 **Translucency:** when warmed on paper, makes paper permanently translucent ('grease spot')	1 Colourless **Millon's** solution + protein $\xrightarrow{\text{boiled}}$ *brick-red* clotted protein

Table 4.4 – *(cont'd)*

	Carbohydrates	*Fats* (solid), *oils* (liquid)	*Proteins*
Chemical tests (cont'd)	**2** Colourless conc. **HCl** + **sucrose** $\xrightarrow{\text{boiled for 10 minutes}}$ *urine-coloured* solution **3** Brown **iodine** solution + **starch** $\xrightarrow{\text{must be cold}}$ *blue-black*	**2** Red **Sudan III** stains fats intensely, so fat layer floating on watery food extract looks dark red	**2** Colourless 40% **NaOH** + protein extract, add 2 drops blue **CuSO₄** → *mauve* Biuret colour (Biuret test)
Functions	**Energy supply** when respired: 17 kJ/g. Used first. Stored as *starch* (green plants) and *glycogen* (animals, colourless plants). Transported as sugars **Structural:** cellulose cell walls **Origin of other organic molecules:** e.g. sugar + nitrate → amino acid	**Energy supply** when respired: 39 kJ/g. Used after carbohydrates. Important in flying, migrating and hibernating animals. (More energy per unit mass than glycogen) **Heat insulation:** subcutaneous fat in mammals **Waterproofing:** of skin, fur, feathers **Buoyancy:** e.g. fish larvae in the sea	**Energy supply** when respired: 17 kJ/g. Important in carnivores otherwise only respired extensively in starvation **Movement:** *muscles* contract; *tendons* connect muscles to bones; *ligaments* connect bone to bone at joints — all are protein **Catalysts:** *enzymes* make metabolism reactions possible (see Section 2.4) **Hormones** regulate metabolism (see Section 9.8). Many, e.g. insulin, are protein

* *Note:* **Fehling's** solutions I and II, if mixed to give a *royal blue* solution, give similar results to Benedict's solution.

4.5 VITAMINS

Vitamins: organic substances (of a variety of kinds) required in *minute* amounts to maintain health of heterotrophs. Autotrophs make all they need.

Lack of a vitamin in the diet results in a *deficiency disease*, e.g. scurvy. A vitamin for one organism is not necessarily a vitamin for another, e.g. man suffers scurvy from lack of vitamin C but rats do not because they synthesise their own.

Fat-soluble vitamins (**A, D, E, K**) are ingested in fats and oils.

Water-soluble vitamins (**B, C**) are present in other materials.

Table 4.5 Vitamins

Vitamins	*Good sources*	*Functions*	*Deficiency diseases*
A	Vegetables, butter, egg yolk Liver oils, e.g. cod-liver oil	1 Healthy epithelia 2 Part of 'visual purple' in rod cells of retina (Sec. 8.2)	Susceptibility to *invasion by disease organisms* Poor night-vision
D *'sunshine vitamin'*	Butter, egg yolk. (Can be synthesised in the skin from oils irradiated by ultra-violet light)	Regulation of calcium and phosphate absorption from gut and their deposition in bone	*Rickets:* poor bone formation, weak and often deformed, e.g. 'bow legs' in children

Table 4.5 – *(cont'd)*

Vitamins	Good sources	Functions	Deficiency diseases
E	Butter, wholemeal bread	Not important to man. (Rats: in reproduction)	Male rat sterility; death and resorption of embryos
K	Cabbage, spinach. Made abundantly by bacteria in intestine	Aids blood clotting	Longer bleeding time
B_1 (*Thiamine*)	Wholemeal bread	Efficient respiration	*Beri-beri:* inflamed nerves; and swollen heart muscle
B_2 complex (*9 vitamins*)	Yeast and 'Marmite' (= yeast extract) — Liver	A variety of roles in metabolism	Skin, eye lesions (riboflavin); *pellagra:* gut problems, paralysis etc. (nicotinic acid)
B_{12} (*Cobalamine*)	Liver	Aids formation of red blood cells	*Pernicious anaemia:* lack of red blood cells
C 'Sailors' *vitamin'*	Citrus fruit, milk and *fresh* vegetables (destroyed by cooking)	Tissue-damage repair	*Scurvy:* capillary bleeding, poor healing of wounds

HOLOPHYTIC NUTRITION

Unique features: uses only inorganic food molecules to photosynthesise sugars and synthesise amino acids.

4.6 PHOTOSYNTHESIS

Photosynthesis: makes sugars and the by-product oxygen, from CO_2 and water using the energy of sunlight, trapped by chlorophyll. Occurs in chloroplasts (see Section 2.2). Two stages:

(*a*) **photolysis** – water is split to give

  (*i*) oxygen gas (by-product) ⎫ only in the *light*
  (*ii*) hydrogen for reducing CO_2 ⎭

(*b*) **reduction** – of CO_2 to form sugars, e.g. glucose.

Evidence: if heavy isotope of oxygen, ^{18}O, is used to 'label' water fed to plants, all the O_2 given off is ^{18}O and none is normal oxygen, ^{16}O. If the CO_2, and not the water, fed to the plants is labelled with ^{18}O, *none* of the O_2 given off is ^{18}O. Therefore all the O_2 by-product comes from water and not CO_2. (This also proves the need for water in photosynthesis.)

To take account of this, the **overall equation** for photosynthesis must be:

$$6CO_2 + 12H_2O \xrightarrow[\text{Chlorophyll}]{\text{Sunlight energy}} \underset{\substack{\text{Glucose}\\ \text{(storing sun-energy)}}}{C_6H_{12}O_6} + 6O_2 + 6H_2O$$

Similarly, if CO_2 'labelled' with ^{14}C is fed to a plant, the ^{14}C ends up in glucose.

Fate of glucose:
(*a*) condensed to sucrose – for *transport* elsewhere
(*b*) condensed to starch – for *storage* in leaf (transported away as sucrose by night). (Basis for leaf starch-test.)
(*c*) used in *respiration,* or *amino acid synthesis* (see Section 4.9)
(*d*) condensed to cellulose – making *cell walls.*

Evidence for the four factors necessary for photosynthesis
1 **Test leaves for starch** (Fig. 4.1). Plant must be de-starched before the experiment by keeping it in the dark for 48 hours.

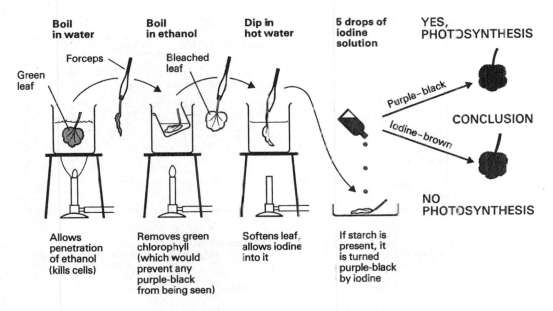

Fig. 4.1 Testing leaves for starch

2   Test the need for: ① **Sunlight.** ② **Carbon dioxide.** ③ **Chlorophyll** (Fig. 4.2).

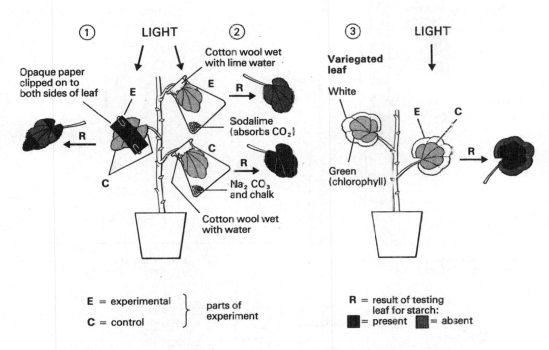

Fig. 4.2 Testing the need for ① sunlight, ② carbon dioxide, ③ chlorophyll in photosynthesis

④ **Water** – impossible without use of ^{18}O isotope experiment (see 'photolysis' above) because denying the plant water kills it anyway.

4.7   LIMITING FACTORS

In a physiological process (such as photosynthesis) any factor which is in short supply, so that it reduces the rate of the process from its possible maximum, is said to be the limiting factor. Thus with plants photosynthesising outdoors, *light* is limiting at dusk; CO_2 during most of the day; *water* probably never. *Temperature* can also be limiting (too cold – reactions too slow; too hot – destroys enzymes). *Factors closing stomata* are limiting by reducing flow of CO_2 into leaf. *Lack of Mg* in soil limits the amount of chlorophyll made in the leaf (see Fig. 4.3).

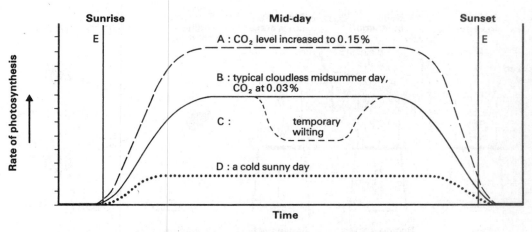

At each plateau on the graphs, a factor is limiting photosynthesis.
A and B : probably CO_2 in air.
C : CO_2 reaching chloroplasts.

D : temperature.
E : at dawn and dusk : light.

Fig. 4.3 Limiting factors for photosynthesis

Rate of photosynthesis in a water plant, e.g. *Elodea*, can be estimated by counting the *number of bubbles* per unit time coming from a cut stem. Alternatively, trap bubbles and measure *volume* per unit time in a capillary tube (see Fig 4.4).

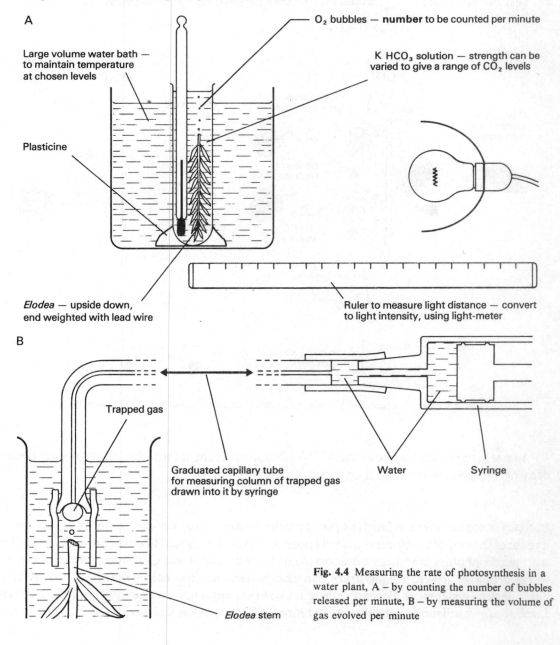

Fig. 4.4 Measuring the rate of photosynthesis in a water plant, A – by counting the number of bubbles released per minute, B – by measuring the volume of gas evolved per minute

4.8   LEAF STRUCTURE AND PHOTOSYNTHESIS

LEAF STRUCTURE

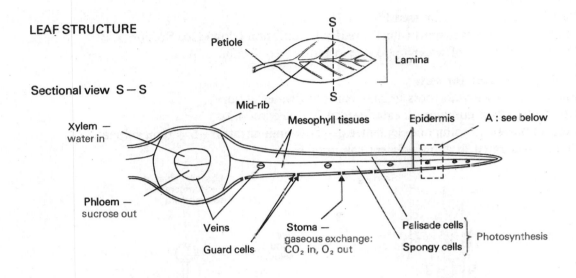

Sectional view S — S

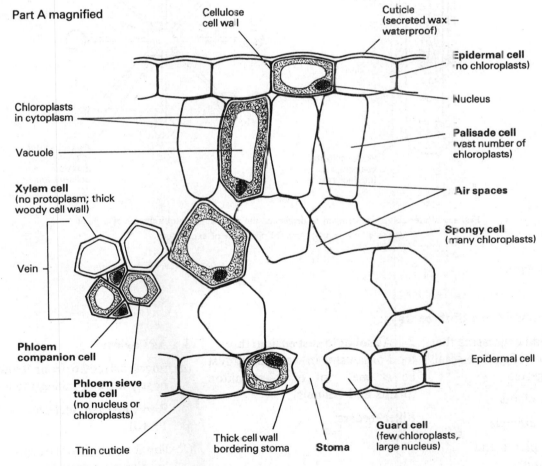

Fig. 4.5 Leaf structure

4.9   AMINO ACID SYNTHESIS

Dependent on photosynthesis.
Nitrates combine with sugar products to form amino acids.
Green plants alone can do this, at root and shoot tips (growing regions).
Amino acids are condensed (see Section 4.12) to form protein.

4.10   MINERAL SALT UPTAKE BY ROOTS

Absorption of salts
Mainly at root tips.
Partly at root hair region (see Fig. 11.1).
Mainly by active transport (quick), partly by diffusion (slow) (see Section 5.2).
Quite independent of water uptake by osmosis (see Section 5.2).

Evidence for need for salts
Plants are grown with roots in salt-solutions ('water culture').
Control solution contains all salts needed (see Section 4.3).
Test solutions each omit one element, e.g. −N = omit nitrates; −S = omit sulphates.
Solutions aerated to allow efficient salt uptake.

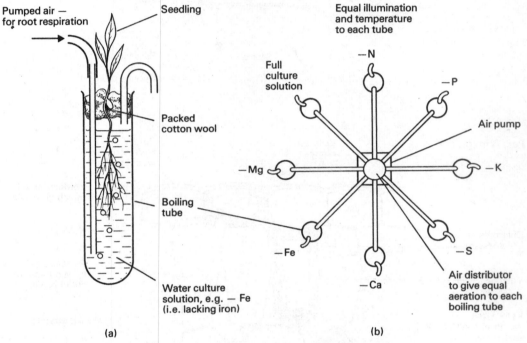

Fig. 4.6 Water culture experiment to determine the mineral salt requirements of a plant:
(a) side view of one tube, (b) plan view of experiment

HOLOZOIC NUTRITION

4.11   FEEDING METHODS OF ANIMALS

Animals obtain food in one of three ways:

1   As solids: food-organisms that have to be chewed (Fig. 4.7) small enough to be ingested.

Herbivores – eat plants

Carnivores – eat animals

Omnivores – eat plants and animals

2   As solids in suspension: tiny food-organisms in water that must be strained out of it – plankton (plants and animals)

Filter-feeders

3   As liquids:

(*a*) juices extracted from living hosts, without killing them.

Parasites (see Section 17.10)

(*b*) liquid nutriment produced by digesting dead food externally and then sucking it up

Saprozoites, e.g. housefly (Fig. 4.10)

Adaptations necessary for each feeding method
1   Herbivores: food does not run away, but large quantities must be gathered since food is relatively poor in quality. Herbivores include locusts, deer and sheep.

2   Carnivores: have to capture and overcome prey, e.g. by cunning (dogs), traps (spiders' webs), poisons (cobras) and sharp weapons (claws, teeth). (See Fig. 4.14.)

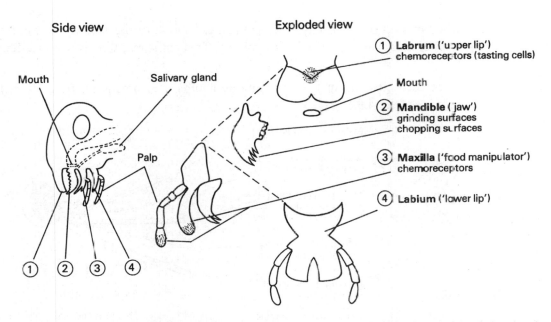

Side view   Exploded view

Mouth   Salivary gland

Palp

① ② ③ ④

① **Labrum** ('upper lip')
   chemoreceptors (tasting cells)

— Mouth

② **Mandible** (jaw')
   grinding surfaces
   chopping surfaces

③ **Maxilla** ('food manipulator')
   chemoreceptors

④ **Labium** ('lower lip')

Fig. 4.7 Mouthparts of a chewing insect, e.g. locust (herbivore), cockroach (omnivore), ground beetle (carnivore)

3 Omnivores: adaptations for feeding are intermediate between those of herbivores and carnivores, e.g. human teeth. Often very successful animals since they vary their food according to availability, e.g. cockroaches, rats, pigs and man. ·

4 Filter feeders: require sieves. (Figs. 4.8a and 4.8b.) Baleen whales trap 'krill' (shrimps) on frayed edges of whale-bone plates hanging down in mouth cavity, open to the sea as they swim.

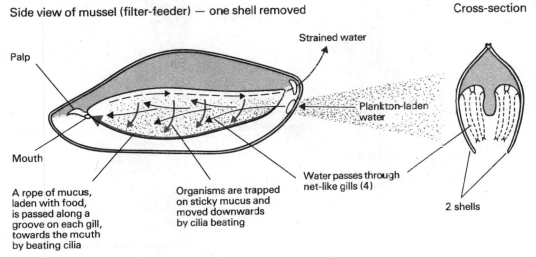

Side view of mussel (filter-feeder) — one shell removed   Cross-section

Palp

Strained water

Plankton-laden water

Mouth

Water passes through net-like gills (4)

A rope of mucus, laden with food, is passed along a groove on each gill, towards the mouth by beating cilia

Organisms are trapped on sticky mucus and moved downwards by cilia beating

2 shells

Fig. 4.8a Filter feeding in mussels

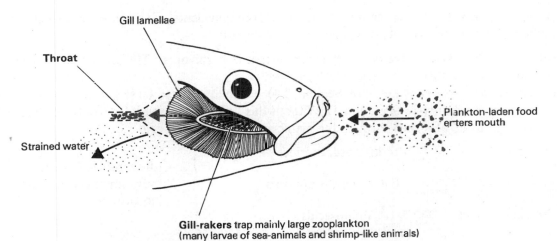

Gill lamellae

Throat

Plankton-laden food enters mouth

Strained water

Gill-rakers trap mainly large zooplankton
(many larvae of sea-animals and shrimp-like animals)

Fig. 4.8b Filter feeding in herring (one gill of its four pairs displayed)

5   Parasites: Endo-parasites bathe in nutritious liquids, e.g. blood or digested food in gut of host, absorbing food directly through 'skin' – no gut, e.g. Trypanosome, tape-worm (see Section 17.11).

Ecto-parasites pierce their host to suck out nutritious liquids, e.g. mosquito, flea, (blood); aphid (phloem sap). (See Fig. 4.9.)

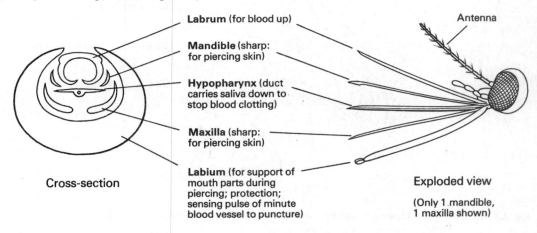

Fig. 4.9 Mouthparts of female mosquito – for piercing skin and sucking blood

6   Saprozoites: need no jaws, only tubes for saliva (down) and liquid food (up), with pumps (see Fig. 4.10).

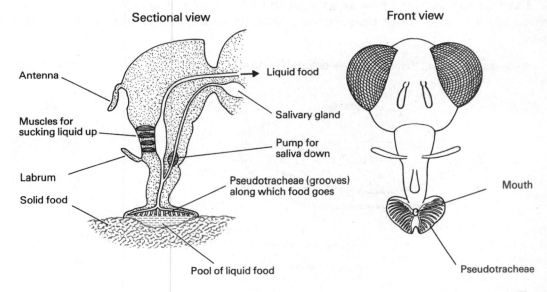

Fig. 4.10 Mouthparts of a housefly – for sucking liquid food (digested externally)

4.12   DIGESTION AND ITS CONSEQUENCES

All animals **ingest** food via the mouth into a gut (or equivalents). Exceptions: parasites which bathe in food. In the gut, food is **digested** in two ways:

(*a*) *physically* – by chewing or grinding (important in herbivores). This increases the surface area of food, making it easier for (*b*) below.

(*b*) *chemically* – by enzymes (see Section 2.4) which hydrolyse large molecules into their small basic units (see Section 4.4). Without this, large food molecules would not be small enough to be **absorbed** through the membranes of gut cells: e.g.

$$\text{Starch} + \text{Water} \xrightarrow[\text{enzymes}]{\text{Hydrolysing}} \text{Monosaccharides}$$

$$\text{Fat} + \text{Water} \xrightarrow[\text{enzymes}]{\text{Hydrolysing}} \text{Fatty acids} + \text{Glycerol}$$

$$\text{Protein} + \text{Water} \xrightarrow[\text{enzymes}]{\text{Hydrolysing}} \text{Amino acids}$$

these molecules are now small enough for absorption

Absorbed food is then **assimilated** (used or stored) into the body. Storage occurs when enzymes condense the small units of foods into large molecules (reverse of hydrolysis). For example:

$$\text{Amino acids} \xrightarrow[\text{enzymes}]{\text{Condensing}} \text{Protein} + \text{Water}$$

Indigestible food is **egested** (eliminated) through the anus or equivalent. Most animals have no enzymes to digest cellulose – hence special adaptations of herbivores. (See Section 4.17.)

4.13 EXPERIMENTS WITH DIGESTIVE ENZYMES

Each enzyme works best at a certain temperature and pH (these are its 'optimum' conditions). Outside these conditions enzymes may cease to work or may even be destroyed.

Example 1   Investigating the effect of temperature on digestion of starch by salivary amylase (ptyalin).

Method:

1   Add 5 cm³ of 1% starch solution to each of 5 boiling tubes and 1 cm³ of saliva diluted with water to 4 test tubes as shown in Fig. 4.11a.

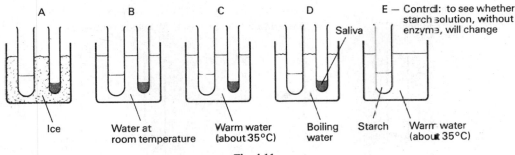

Fig. 4.11a

2   Leave the starch and the enzyme for at least two minutes, to gain the temperature of the water bath.

3   Pour the saliva into the boiling tube next to it, so mixing it with the starch. Note the time immediately.

4   Using a dropper, test one drop from each boiling tube with iodine, as shown in Fig. 4.11b.

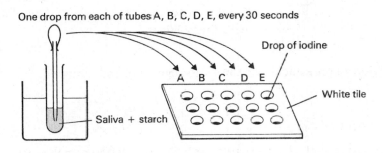

5   Note the time when each drop no longer turns the iodine blue-black (i.e. starch is digested). Do not test for longer than 15 minutes.

Results:
A – still blue-black after 15 minutes
B – changes to brown at 8 minutes
C – changes to brown at 2 minutes
D – still blue-black after 15 minutes
E – still blue-black after 15 minutes

6   Now put the boiling tubes from A and D into the warm water bath C and test them with iodine after 5 minutes (once only).

Results:

A – brown colour
D – blue-black

Conclusions:

1   Digestion proceeds faster at warm temperatures than at cold (A, B, C).

2   At low temperatures, the enzyme is inactive but not destroyed (A, step **6**).

3   At water's boiling point, the enzyme is destroyed (D, step **6**).

Example 2   Investigating the effect of pH on digestion of egg albumen (protein) by pepsin.

Method:

1   Put in each of 6 tubes a 5 mm cube of cooked egg white and a thymol crystal (to prevent bacteria digesting the egg). Then add 2 cm³ of M/10 solutions to affect the pH. as shown in Fig. 4.12.

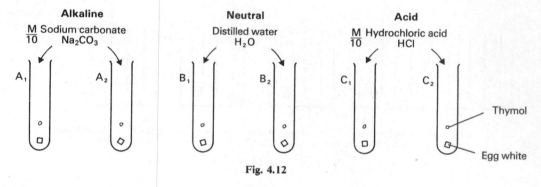

Fig. 4.12

2   Add 2 cm³ pepsin solution to A_1, B_1 and C_1, but not to A_2, B_2 and C_2 (which are controls used to see whether Na_2CO_3, water and HCl alone, digest egg white).

3   Incubate the tubes in a warm place (about 35°C) for 24 hours and then look at the cubes.

Results:

Not digested:
in tubes A_1, A_2, B_2, C_2
Sharp edges

Slightly digested:
in tube B_1
Smaller cube
with fuzzy edges

Totally digested:
in tube C_1
Cube absent

Conclusion: pepsin requires acid conditions to digest cooked albumen.

4.14   MAMMAL TEETH AND JAWS

Only vertebrate group with *differentiated* teeth (4 types with special uses):

1   Incisors – for obtaining mouthfuls
2   Canines – for stabbing, holding prey
3   Pre-molars – for grinding
4   Molars – for grinding

Number of each kind can be expressed in a **dental formula:** top line for number in upper half-jaw, lower line for lower half-jaw, e.g. for man:

First set of teeth are shed ('milk teeth'): $I\frac{2}{2}$ $C\frac{1}{1}$ $Pm\frac{2}{2}$ (no molars)

Adult set includes 'wisdoms' (back molars): $I\frac{2}{2}$ $C\frac{1}{1}$ $Pm\frac{2}{2}$ $M\frac{3}{3}$

Structure of teeth: layers of modified bone nourished from pulp cavity and shaped according to function. (See Fig. 4.13.)

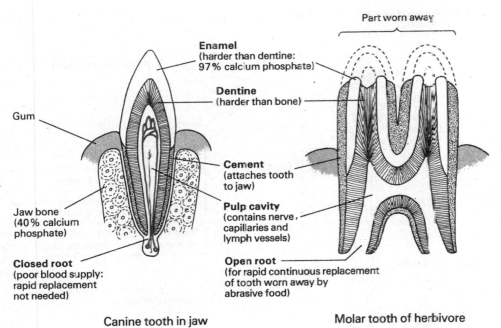

Fig. 4.13 Vertical section through two kinds of teeth

4.15 Mammal alimentary canal

See Fig. 4.15 on the next page for the treatment of food from mouth to anus.

4.16 Herbivores and carnivores: teeth and jaws

See Fig. 4.14 for a comparison of teeth and jaws in herbivores and carnivores.

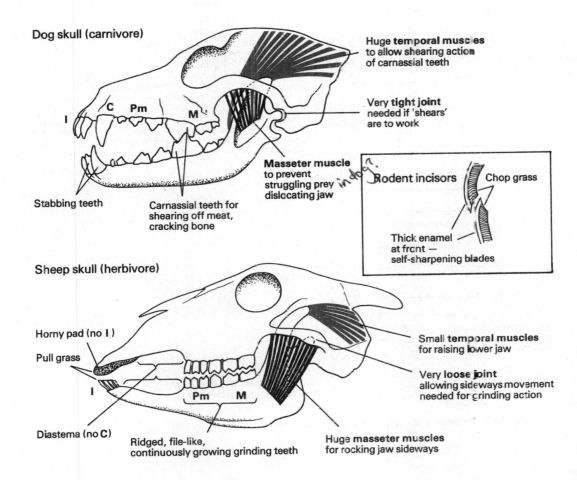

Fig. 4.14 Comparison of herbivore and carnivore jaws and teeth

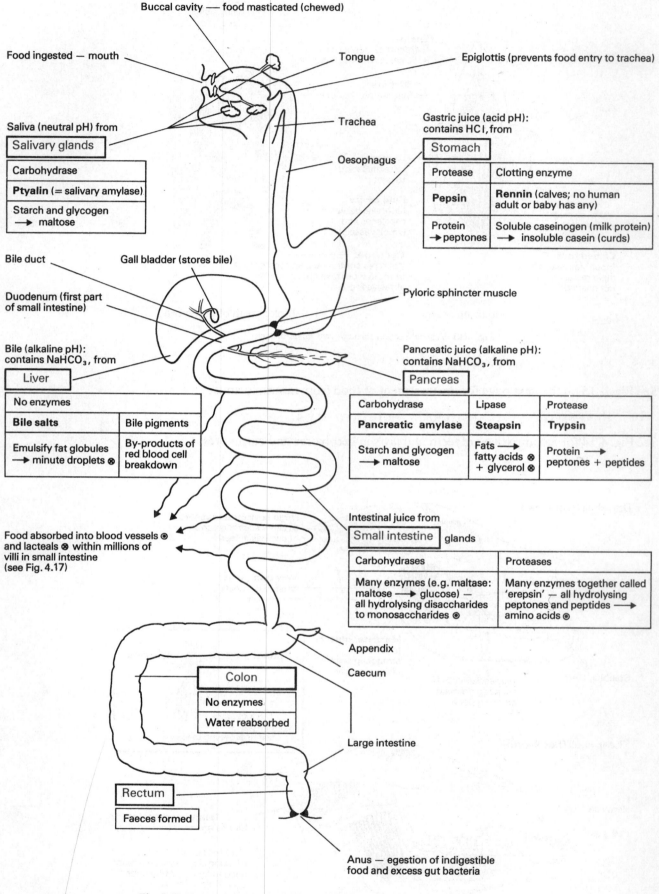

Buccal cavity — food masticated (chewed)

Food ingested — mouth

Tongue

Epiglottis (prevents food entry to trachea)

Saliva (neutral pH) from

Salivary glands

Carbohydrase
Ptyalin (= salivary amylase)
Starch and glycogen → maltose

Trachea

Oesophagus

Gastric juice (acid pH): contains HCl, from

Stomach	
Protease	Clotting enzyme
Pepsin	**Rennin** (calves; no human adult or baby has any)
Protein → peptones	Soluble caseinogen (milk protein) → insoluble casein (curds)

Bile duct

Gall bladder (stores bile)

Duodenum (first part of small intestine)

Pyloric sphincter muscle

Bile (alkaline pH): contains $NaHCO_3$, from

Liver	
No enzymes	
Bile salts	Bile pigments
Emulsify fat globules → minute droplets ⊗	By-products of red blood cell breakdown

Pancreatic juice (alkaline pH): contains $NaHCO_3$, from

Pancreas		
Carbohydrase	Lipase	Protease
Pancreatic amylase	**Steapsin**	**Trypsin**
Starch and glycogen → maltose	Fats → fatty acids ⊗ + glycerol ⊗	Protein → peptones + peptides

Food absorbed into blood vessels ◉ and lacteals ⊗ within millions of villi in small intestine (see Fig. 4.17)

Intestinal juice from

Small intestine	glands
Carbohydrases	Proteases
Many enzymes (e.g. maltase: maltose → glucose) — all hydrolysing disaccharides to monosaccharides ◉	Many enzymes together called 'erepsin' — all hydrolysing peptones and peptides → amino acids ◉

Appendix

Caecum

Colon
No enzymes
Water reabsorbed

Large intestine

Rectum
Faeces formed

Anus — egestion of indigestible food and excess gut bacteria

Fig. 4.15 Treatment of food from mouth to anus in mammals (based on man)

4.17 HERBIVORES AND CARNIVORES: THE GUT

Carnivore: gut *short* – food is largely protein so it is easy to digest.

Herbivore: gut *long* – no mammal has cellulases (cellulose-digesting enzymes). Aid from bacteria which have *cellulases*, living in symbiosis (see Section 15.3) in *rumen* of ruminants, e.g. cows, sheep; or *caecum*, e.g. of horses, rabbits. Rabbits eat their green nutritious faeces from first passage through gut ('refection'), absorbing more food during second passage. Horses do not refect (see Fig. 4.16).

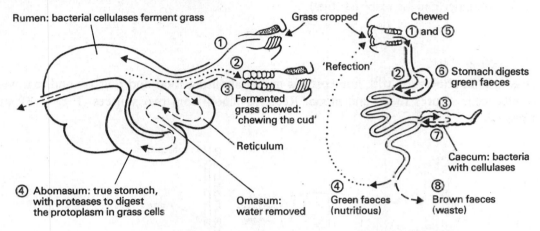

Fig. 4.16 Adaptations to herbivorous diet

4.18 ABSORPTION OF FOOD AT VILLI

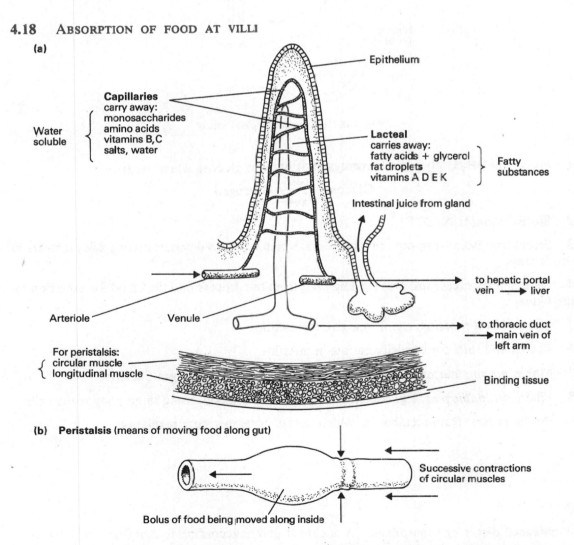

Fig. 4.17 (a) Enlarged longitudinal section of a villus (millions lining the small intestine) (b) Peristalsis

4.19   STORAGE OF FOOD

1   Monosaccharides, e.g. glucose: condensed to glycogen in liver and muscles, excess converted to fats stored under skin.

2   Fatty substances: stored in liver (including vitamins A, D) and under skin.

3   Amino acids: used immediately, *not* stored; excess de-aminated in liver to give two parts:

(*i*) nitrogen-containing part (ammonia) becomes urea – excreted by kidneys
(*ii*) remainder can be respired (fuel).

4.20   THE LIVER

A large organ, concerned with homeostasis by metabolising food and poisons and removing unwanted cells. Stores foods and blood. Receives blood from two sources (Fig. 4.18); discharges bile.

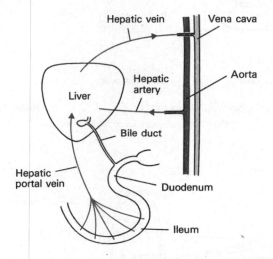

Fig. 4.18 The liver and its blood supply

1   Stores *glucose* as glycogen, hydrolysing it back to glucose when needed:

$$\text{Glucose} \underset{\text{Adrenalin}}{\overset{\text{Insulin}}{\rightleftharpoons}} \text{Glycogen}$$

2   Stores *vitamins* A, D, B_{12}.

3   Stores *iron* from worn-out red blood cells, which it breaks down, excreting *bile pigments* in the process.

4   De-aminates excess proteins sending *urea* from the process into the blood for excretion by the kidneys.

5   Makes *blood proteins*, e.g. fibrinogen, for clotting.

6   Makes *bile salts* for emulsifying fats in intestine.

7   Makes *poisons* harmless, e.g. ethanol drunk, or poisons from gut bacteria.

8   Filters out *pathogens*, e.g. bacteria, protozoa in the blood, using large phagocytic cells.

9   Produces *heat* from metabolism which assists in temperature regulation

4.21   DIET

A **balanced diet** is one that maintains health. It differs according to *age* (baby or adult); *occupation* (manual worker or typist); *climate* (Arctic or tropical); *sex*. A diet must provide:

(*a*) energy (carbohydrates and fats). Manual worker uses 24 000 kJ/day, typist uses 12 000 kJ/day

(*b*) materials for growth and repair (proteins). (See note below)

(*c*) co-factors for enzymes to work (vitamins)

(*d*) salts (to replace those lost in sweat)

(*e*) water (see Section 5.1)

(*f*) roughage (indigestible 'bulk' to help peristalsis)

Note: first class proteins contain the 8 amino acids that man cannot make. Animal protein is rich in them, plant protein usually poor. Without them, *kwashiorkor* results (wasting of limbs, pot-belly full of fluid). Occurs in maize-eating Africans eating only second class protein. Beans are richer in first class protein than maize.

SAPROPHYTIC NUTRITION

4.22   SAPROPHYTES

See examples of fungi (Section 17.5) and bacteria (Section 17.2). Note some similarity with saprozoite method of feeding (see Section 14.11).

5 Water and transport systems

5.1   IMPORTANCE OF WATER

Water makes up two-thirds or more of living active protoplasm:

Solvent:
(*a*) all *reactions* of metabolism occur in solution.
(*b*) foods, hormones, etc. are *transported* in solution (in blood, sap).

Reactant:
(*a*) with CO_2 during *photosynthesis*.
(*b*) in *hydrolysis* reactions, e.g. digestion.

Coolant:
(*a*) *absorbs a lot of heat* without much change in temperature, thus keeping habitats like the sea relatively stable in temperature.
(*b*) *removes a lot of heat* when evaporated, keeping bodies cool, e.g. in sweating, transpiration.

Support:
(*a*) aquatic organisms need less strong skeletons than land organisms because *Archimedes force* makes them 'lighter'.
(*b*) *turgor pressure* in plant cells supports leaves and herbaceous plant stems; without it they wilt.

Lubricant:
E.g. synovial fluid in joints; mucus in guts.

5.2   DIFFUSION, ACTIVE TRANSPORT AND OSMOSIS

Substances move into cells by:

1   **Diffusion** (gases and liquids)
2   **Active transport**
3   **Osmosis** (water)

Table 5.1   Comparison of diffusion and active transport

Diffusion	Active transport
Slow	Rapid
Not selective	Selective (cell only absorbs what it wants)
Substances move only *along* a concentration gradient	Substances move in even *against* a concentration gradient
Living membrane not essential	Living membrane essential
Cell provides no energy	Respiration provides energy for absorption

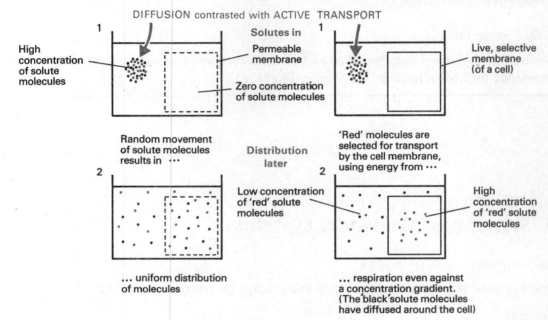

Fig. 5.1 Diffusion contrasted with active transport

Osmosis: the diffusion of water *only*, through a 'semi-permeable' membrane from a weak solution to a strong one (see Fig. 5.2).

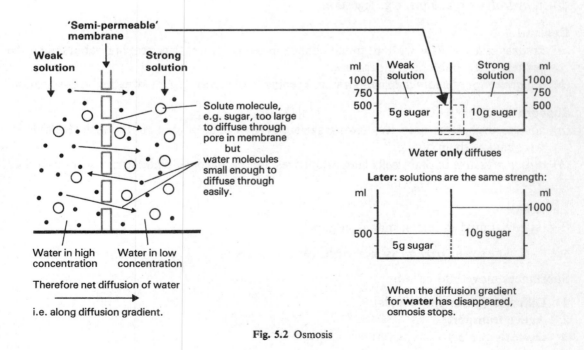

Fig. 5.2 Osmosis

Requires *no* respiration (cf. active uptake of salts in roots).

Requires *live* cell membrane for osmosis to occur in cells, but will happen with suitable non-living membranes.

All solutions have an **osmotic potential** (which can be measured as an **osmotic pressure** using a manometer. See Fig. 5.3).

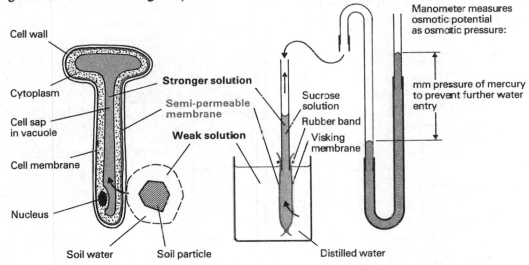

Fig. 5.3 Comparison of osmosis in a living cell (root hair) and a non-living system

Cells prevent continued flow of water into them (which would burst them) by **osmoregulating.**

Angiosperms

5.3   Water uptake and loss in angiosperms

Cells

Cells fluctuate between being flaccid and fully turgid in nature. However plasmolysis is relatively rare (except in experiments) and will result in the cell's death if it is prolonged (see Fig. 5.4).

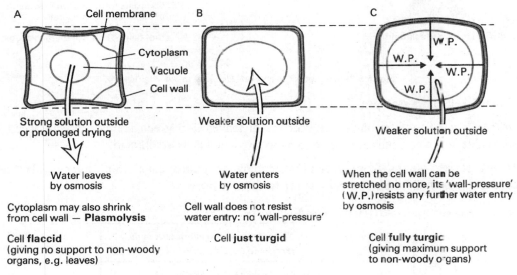

Fig. 5.4 Osmosis in plant cells

Whole plants

1   Leaves and green stems are waterproofed by a waxy *cuticle*, but most keep open *stomata* to get CO_2 for photosynthesis. Through stomata, **transpiration** (the loss of water vapour via the aerial parts of a plant) occurs. This creates a *suction upward* of water from below.

2   Old stems and roots are waterproofed with *cork* (of bark). Their xylem acts as a conduit for water. Some water-loss occurs via *lenticels* (pores in bark).

3 Young roots – particularly *root-hair* region – absorb water by osmosis. This continues owing to suction generated by transpiration.

If soil water supply dries up, leaf cells become flaccid and leaf *wilts*. Only *after* this will guard cells become flaccid, closing stomata, thus conserving water but also stopping photosynthesis (see Section 4.7 and Fig. 5.5).

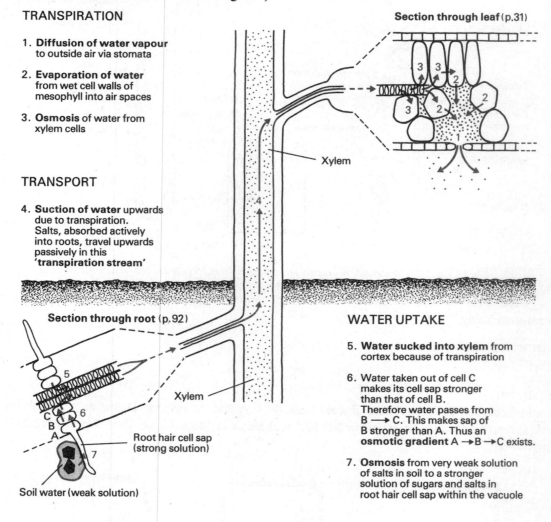

TRANSPIRATION

1. **Diffusion of water vapour** to outside air via stomata

2. **Evaporation of water** from wet cell walls of mesophyll into air spaces

3. **Osmosis** of water from xylem cells

TRANSPORT

4. **Suction of water** upwards due to transpiration. Salts, absorbed actively into roots, travel upwards passively in this **'transpiration stream'**

Section through leaf (p.31)

Xylem

Section through root (p.92)

Xylem

Root hair cell sap (strong solution)

Soil water (weak solution)

WATER UPTAKE

5. **Water sucked into xylem** from cortex because of transpiration

6. Water taken out of cell C makes its cell sap stronger than that of cell B. Therefore water passes from B ⟶ C. This makes sap of B stronger than A. Thus an **osmotic gradient** A →B →C exists.

7. **Osmosis** from very weak solution of salts in soil to a stronger solution of sugars and salts in root hair cell sap within the vacuole

Fig. 5.5 Water uptake, transport and loss in an angiosperm

4 Guard cells and stomata

Guard cells are found in pairs in epidermis of leaves and green stems; pore between them (*stoma*) enlarges when cells are turgid; disappears when cells are flaccid.

Open stoma results from greater stretching of guard cells' thin outer walls than of thickened inner walls, bending cells apart to form a pore.

Table 5.2   Features of guard cells in the turgid and flaccid states

	Stoma open	*Surface view of two guard cells in the turgid and flaccid states*		*Stoma closed*
Osmotic potential of cell sap	High	Turgid cells	Flaccid cells	Low
Turgidity	Turgid			Flaccid
Gas exchange and transpiration	Possible			Impossible
Normal rhythm	Open in day	Open stoma	Closed stoma	Closed at night

5.4   TRANSPIRATION

Loss of water by transpiration occurs:

(*i*) mainly through open stomata
(*ii*) through waxy cuticle (a small amount)

Functions:

(*i*) provides a means of transporting salts upward in xylem
(*ii*) evaporation cools the leaf heated by the sun (cf. sweating).

Factors raising transpiration rate (opposite conditions lower the rate)

1   **High temperature** – provides more energy to evaporate water.

2   **Low humidity** – greater diffusion gradient between air inside leaf spaces and the drier air outside.

3   **Open stomata** – thousands of pores per leaf (usually open in *sunlight*).

4   **Wind** – removes water molecules as fast as they arrive outside stoma, thereby maintaining high diffusion rate. Water vapour 'pumped out' due to bending and unbending of leaf. (Severe buffeting by wind actually closes stomata, reducing transpiration.)

Measurement of transpiration rate
(Temperature, humidity, and wind must be recorded.)

1   **Weighing** – a leaf, or cut shoot, in a test-tube of water covered by oil; or a whole pot plant, the pot and soil sealed off in a polythene bag.

2   **Cobalt chloride** – blue when anhydrous (dry), turns pink when hydrated (moist). Thus dry blue cobalt chloride paper, sellotaped to upper and lower leaf surfaces, green stems and bark-covered stems turns pink with moisture of transpiration. Timing how long it takes compares rates.

3   **Potometer** – measures water uptake (not loss) of a cut shoot (a little of the water is used in photosynthesis). Change *one* condition at a time to determine which factor has greatest effect.

Note: light and dark affect opening and closing of stomata. Light may also have a heating effect.

Allow time for plant to adjust to new conditions before taking new measurement of rate.

Never allow air to get into cut end of shoot (air-locks form in xylem) – cut shoot under water, and keep it wet (see Fig. 5.6).

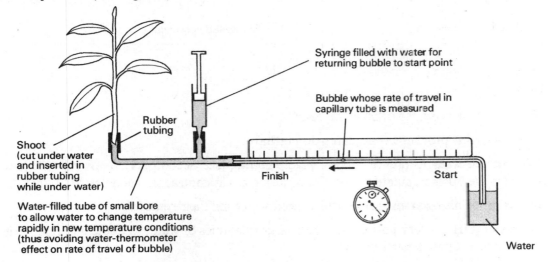

5.5   TRANSPORT OF ORGANIC FOOD

Flows through **phloem** sieve tube cells in bark (see Table 5.3). Flow rate affected by temperature, available oxygen, poisons – suggests a mechanism involving *living* cells. Mechanism not fully understood.

Flows both *upwards and downwards*. Photosynthesised sugars transported as sucrose (see Section 4.4) from leaves up to stem tips (for growth); to fruits and seeds (for storage as starch); down to root tips (for growth); and to or from storage organs, e.g. tubers (see Section 12.2).

Evidence for pathway:

Ring-barking: sugars accumulate where bark ends (due to cutting).

Tracers: radioactive $^{14}CO_2$ supplied to photosynthesising leaf becomes part of sucrose (or other organic molecules), the paths of which can be traced with a Geiger counter.

Table 5.3 Comparison of methods of transport in phloem and xylem

	Phloem (sieve tubes)	*Xylem* (vessels)
Transport	Sugars, amino acids, etc.	Water and salts
Direction	Both *downward* from leaves and *upward* from storage organs, e.g. tubers	Only *upward*
Cells	Cellulose tubes with sieve ends, containing cytoplasm but no nucleus	Woody tubes containing no living matter. Wood is strong and provides support too

Sectioned sieve cell

- Strands of cytoplasm
- Pores in end wall
- Thin cellulose cell wall (not strong)
- Organic food flows upwards and downwards in solution

Sectioned vessel cell

- Thick woody cell wall strengthened further by woody rings — for support of plant
- Space free of protoplasm allowing water and salts to flow unhindered upwards

ANIMALS

5.6   WATER UPTAKE AND LOSS IN ANIMALS

Animals have two problems that plants do not have:

1 **Lack of cell walls** to prevent excess water entering (see Section 2.1). Thus cells liable to burst unless they osmoregulate by ejecting water, e.g. via contractile vacuoles or 'kidneys'.

2 **Excretion of nitrogenous wastes** which need water for their removal:

(*a*) **ammonia** (NH_3) – very poisonous; needs large quantities of water to dilute and remove it. Fresh-water animals particularly.

(*b*) **urea** ($CO(NH_2)_2$) – less poisonous; needs some water to remove it. Many terrestrial animals, e.g. mammals.

(*c*) **uric acid** – not poisonous, since insoluble; can be removed as a paste. Essential for all animals laying eggs on land to avoid poisoning of embryo, e.g. insects, birds. Very little water wasted.

Like plants, animals have three problems: **obtaining** water, **conserving** what has been obtained and **removing excess** water that has entered. These problems and their solutions differ according to the animal and the habitat in which it lives (see Fig. 5.7).

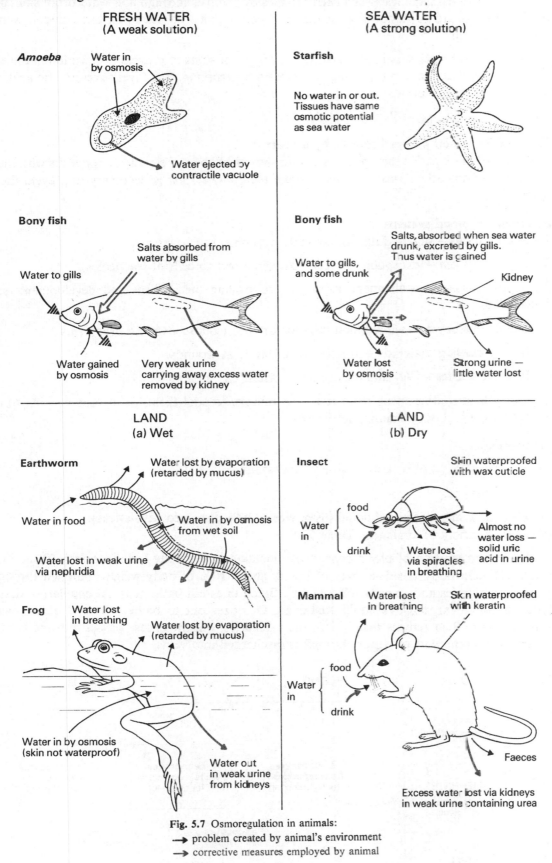

Fig. 5.7 Osmoregulation in animals:
→ problem created by animal's environment
→ corrective measures employed by animal

1 In **fresh-water**, water *enters* by osmosis, tending to flood tissues since they have a higher osmotic potential than their external surroundings.

2 In **sea-water**, the water inside tissues tends to *leave* by osmosis into the sea since its salty water has a higher osmotic potential than tissues in many cases.

3 In **wet-land** habitats, water still *enters* tissues by osmosis through non-waterproof skin, but there is the hazard of desiccation in the air. Such animals do not drink but can gain some water from food.

4 In **dry-land** habitats, animals must have waterproof skins to prevent desiccation in the air, replacing what they lose in breathing and excreta by *drinking*. Egg-layers excrete uric acid, so little water is lost in urine.

5.7   BLOOD SYSTEMS

The need for blood pumped to cells by a heart
Animals are more active than plants and diffusion would be too slow to supply cells with their needs and remove their wastes. A more *rapid transport system* is necessary to prevent them from dying.

Functions of blood systems
1 Supply **foods** – sugars, fats, amino acids, vitamins, salts, water.

2 Supply **oxygen** – (exception: insects – oxygen direct to cells at tracheoles).

3 Supply **hormones** – chemical 'messages' controlling metabolism and development (see Section 9.8).

4 Supply **leucocytes** – white blood cells for defence against invading organisms.

5 Supply **clotting materials** – to stop loss of blood at wounds.

6 Remove **wastes** – CO_2 and nitrogenous wastes, e.g. urea.

7 Carry **heat** – either away from cells, e.g. muscle, to cool them, or to cells needing to be warmed up, e.g. during 'sunning' of lizards.

MAMMALS

5.8   MAMMAL BLOOD AND OTHER BODY FLUIDS

Blood consists of:

(*a*) **plasma,** a straw-coloured liquid (90% water, 10% dissolved substances).
(*b*) **cells,** a variety of kinds (see Table 5.4).

Exact composition of blood depends on location in the body (see Section 5.10) and on health. Human body has 5–6 litres of blood, about 10% of body-weight, pumped through arteries, capillaries and veins (see Table 5.5). Blood does not bathe cells. At capillaries, **tissue fluid** – a colourless nutritive liquid containing O_2 oozes out to bathe cells and carry away wastes. Tissue fluid returns mainly into the capillaries; but the excess passes into the lymph vessels to become part of **lymph.** Lymph is discharged into veins.

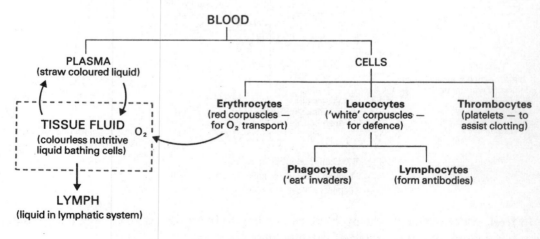

Fig. 5.8 Constituents of blood and their functions

Serum is plasma less fibrinogen (protein needed for clotting). Stored by hospitals for transfusions.

Plasma consists of:

1 Water – (90%) solvent for substances listed below; carrier of heat (for temperature regulation).

2 Blood proteins – (7%) e.g. fibrinogen (for blood clotting); antibodies (for defence against pathogens); and albumen (for osmosis, Fig. 5.14).

3 Soluble foods – (1%) e.g. glucose, oil droplets, amino acids (from digestion).

4 Mineral salts – as ions, e.g. Na^+, Cl^-, Ca^{2+}, HCO_3^- (bicarbonate, the main method of transporting CO_2).

5 Wastes – e.g. CO_2, urea.

6 Hormones – in minute traces, e.g. adrenalin and insulin.

7 Gases – small quantities of, e.g. O_2, N_2.

Table 5.4　Blood cells and their functions

Cell structure		No./mm³	Formation	Destruction	Function of cells
Erythrocyte T.S.	Bi-concave cell with no nucleus. Cytoplasm: mainly red haemoglobin 7.5μm	5 million (more at high altitudes)	In red bone marrow, e.g. of ribs, vertebrae	In liver – by-product: bile pigments　Life: 2–3 months	1 Haemoglobin (Hb) combines with O_2 to form unstable oxyhaemoglobin ($Hb.O_2$) at lungs – Passes **oxygen to tissues** 2 O_2 detaches from Hb at capillaries, diffusing into the tissue fluid going to cells (see Section 6.6) $$Hb + O_2 \underset{Tissues}{\overset{Lungs}{\rightleftharpoons}} Hb.O_2$$
Phagocyte 10μm	Multi-lobed nucleus in granular cytoplasm, engulfs bacteria	7000 (more during infections)	In red bone marrow		Actively seek and **engulf bacteria** – even squeeze through capillary walls to reach infected tissue. Often die loaded with killed bacteria. In boils this is seen as yellow 'pus
Lymphocyte 10μm	Huge nucleus in little cytoplasm	2–3000 (more during infections)	In lymph nodes		React to proteins of invading organisms by making **'antibodies'**, which kill invaders and make their poisons (toxins) harmless (see Section 15.11)
Thrombocyte 2μm	Platelets are fragments of cells	¼ million	In red bone marrow		1 At cut, stick to each other forming **temporary plug.** 2 Liberate enzyme thrombokinase to promote **clotting.** (a) Prothrombin $\xrightarrow{\text{Thrombokinase in presence of Ca}^{2+}}$ Thrombin (inactive enzyme) (active enzyme) (b) Fibrinogen $\xrightarrow{\text{Thrombin}}$ Fibrin (soluble protein) (mesh of fibres) (c) fibrin traps blood cells which seal up the blood leak, prevent entry of harmful organisms, and dry to a protective *scab*, allowing healing of the wound beneath it

Notes:

1   Haemoglobin has a greater affinity for carbon monoxide (CO) than O_2 (230 times greater) forming a stable compound, **carboxy-haemoglobin** (Hb . CO) with it. Thus even at small concentrations in the air, CO (which is odourless) tends to be taken up into the blood, preventing O_2 from being carried. This can kill.

2   Haemophiliacs ('bleeders') continue to bleed – perhaps to death – even after minor wounding, e.g. tooth extraction. They have platelets but lack a certain other clotting factor. Effects in males only, who usually die young (see Section 13.10).

5.9   HEART, BLOOD VESSELS AND CIRCULATORY SYSTEM

Table 5.5   Blood vessels and their functions

Arteries	Capillaries	Veins
Carry blood *away* from heart under *high* pressure	Carry blood from artery to vein, very slowly, giving maximum time for diffusion	Carry blood *towards* heart under *low* pressure
Carry *oxygenated* blood (except pulmonary artery)		Carry *deoxygenated* blood (except pulmonary vein)

[Table 5.5 continues with diagrams]

Arteries — T.S.
Elastic layer; Elastic and muscle layer; Endothelium
(a) Heart refilling; elastic walls squeezing on blood to help it along
(b) Heart pumping; 'pulse' felt as bore expands. Thick walls needed, but no valves
Bore of arteries can be altered by nerve messages to muscle, e.g., more blood to legs and less to guts during exercise.

Capillaries — Endothelium only; Phagocyte emerging between cells of endothelium; 10µm
Tissue fluid leaking out to cells — blood pressure forcing it through

Veins — T.S.   L.S.
(a) free flow   (b) back-pressure
No pulse: pressure is low at capillaries. Wall has 3 layers as in arteries but is thinner
Valve open   Valve closed
Blood returns partly by muscles of body squeezing veins — hence the need for non-return valves

Portal veins have capillaries at either end, i.e. they carry blood from one organ to another (e.g. hepatic portal vein between small intestine and liver).

The heart

Found between the two lungs inside the chest cavity.

Consists of two pumps fused together, each having an *auricle* and a *ventricle*.

The two pumps contract simultaneously according to a heart cycle (Fig. 5.14).

Right one pumps deoxygenated blood to the lungs for oxygenation.

Left one pumps oxygenated blood to the body, which deoxygenates it.

Thus blood passes twice through the heart before going to the body. This ensures high blood pressure for:

(*a*)   speedy supplies to the tissues
(*b*)   squeezing out tissue fluid at capillaries.

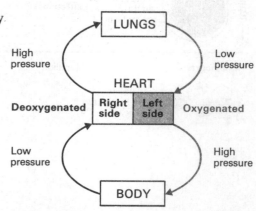

Fig. 5.9 Double circulation of blood through the heart of a mammal

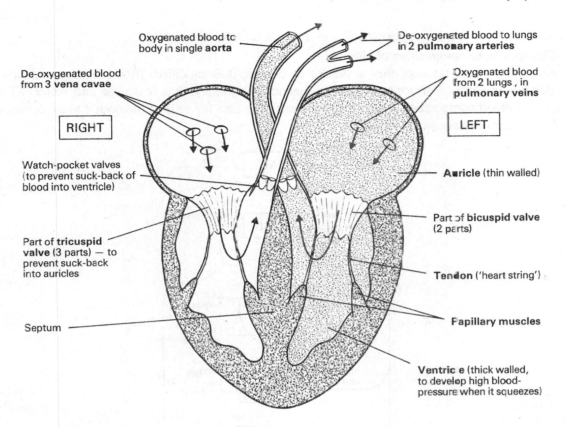

Oxygenated blood to
body in single **aorta**

De-oxygenated blood to lungs
in 2 **pulmonary arteries**

De-oxygenated blood
from 3 **vena cavae**

Oxygenated blood
from 2 lungs, in
pulmonary veins

RIGHT

LEFT

Watch-pocket valves
(to prevent suck-back of
blood into ventricle)

Auricle (thin walled)

Part of **bicuspid valve**
(2 parts)

Part of **tricuspid
valve** (3 parts) — to
prevent suck-back
into auricles

Tendon ('heart string')

Papillary muscles

Septum

Ventricle (thick walled,
to develop high blood-
pressure when it squeezes)

Fig. 5.10 The mammal heart in section: structure and function

Heart seen from the side during the two stages of contraction (systole)

1. Auricular systole (AS)

2. Ventricular systole (VS)

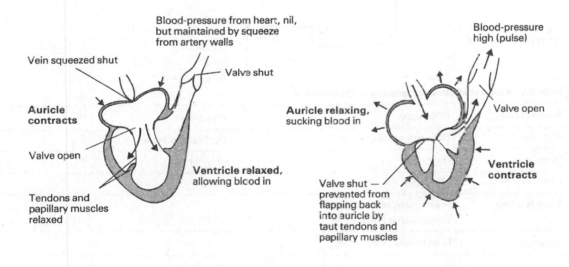

Blood-pressure from heart, nil,
but maintained by squeeze
from artery walls

Blood-pressure
high (pulse)

Vein squeezed shut

Valve shut

**Auricle
contracts**

Auricle relaxing,
sucking blood in

Valve open

Valve open

Tendons and
papillary muscles
relaxed

Ventricle relaxed,
allowing blood in

Valve shut —
prevented from
flapping back
into auricle by
taut tendons and
papillary muscles

**Ventricle
contracts**

3. Diastole

(relaxation of ventricle)
follows before the next
auricular systole

Duration of heart cycle in man

Diastole 0.7 sec 0 0.1 sec Systoles
                    AS
0.6 sec   0.2 sec
                    VS
0.5 sec   0.3 sec
        0.4 sec

Fig. 5.11 The heart cycle of a mammal

5.10   CHANGES IN BLOOD AROUND THE CIRCULATORY SYSTEM

Changes in the composition of blood

As blood passes through the capillaries of organs, it is modified. Blood leaving endocrine glands has gained hormones, while that leaving the kidneys has lost urea and water. Thus *overall* blood composition is kept constant, ensuring that the cells of the body have a constant environment (tissue fluid) to live in.

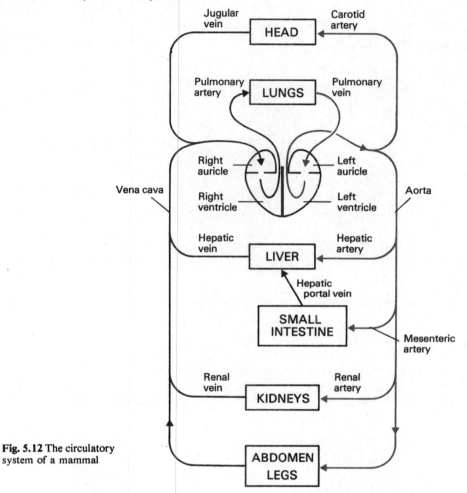

Fig. 5.12 The circulatory system of a mammal

Table 5.6   Changes in blood composition in the human body

Region of body	Blood gains	Blood loses
All tissues	CO_2; nitrogenous wastes	O_2; food; hormones
Lungs	O_2	CO_2; water
Thyroid gland	Thyroxin	Iodine
Small intestine	Food: water, salts, vitamins sugars, amino acids	
Thoracic duct	Fats; lymphocytes; lymph	
Liver	Controlled quantities of glucose and fats; urea	Glucose (for storage as glycogen); excess amino acids; worn out erythrocytes
Kidneys		Urea; water; salts
Spleen	Stored erythrocytes	Worn out erythrocytes
Bones	New erythrocytes and phagocytes	Iron (for haemoglobin) Calcium and phosphate (for bone growth)
Skin	Vitamin D	Heat (by radiation and by evaporation of water in sweat) Salts and urea (in sweat)

5.11 LYMPHATIC SYSTEM

A system of fine tubes ending blindly amongst the tissues, e.g. lacteals in villi of small intestine (see Section 4.18), which join up into ever larger tubes with non-return valves. Along their length are swellings (lymph nodes). The largest tube (thoracic duct) discharges into main vein of left arm.

Functions:

1 Returns tissue fluid to blood as lymph.

2 Adds lymphocytes to blood (for defence).

3 Absorbs fats (into lacteals of villi) to discharge them to blood.

4 Filters out bacteria from lymph by means of phagocytes stationary within lymph nodes (see Fig. 5.13).

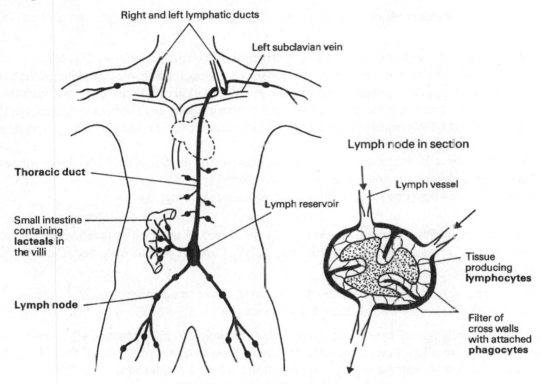

Fig. 5.13 The lymphatic system in man

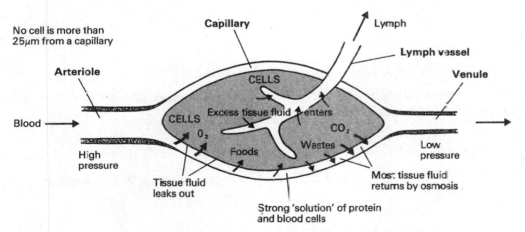

Fig. 5.14 The relationship between blood, tissue fluid, cells and lymph

6 Respiration

6.1   BREATHING, GASEOUS EXCHANGE AND CELLULAR RESPIRATION

Respiration is the sum of processes in organisms that leads to the release of energy from organic molecules, for use in vital functions. *All* organisms respire – plants as well as animals. Thereby they form ATP (see Section 6.9) – energy molecules that power the chemical reactions of metabolism. Depending on the kind of organism, up to *three processes* may be involved:

1   Breathing: *movements*, in animals, that bring a source of O_2 to a surface for gaseous exchange, e.g. chest movements of mammals bring air into lungs; throat movements in fish bring water (containing dissolved O_2) to gills.

2   Gaseous exchange: diffusion, at a moist surface, of O_2 into the organism and of CO_2 outwards.

(*a*) in *single-celled* organisms this exchange surface is the cell membrane (see Fig. 6.8).
(*b*) in *multicellular animals* specialised body parts, e.g. lungs, tracheoles or gills, provide the surface for gaseous exchange. Usually gases are transported rapidly by blood between these surfaces and a second extensive surface area where gaseous exchange occurs between the blood and cells. Only insects pipe air directly to cells and do not use blood for this purpose (see Fig. 6.11).
(*c*) in *multicellular plants* a network of air spaces *between* cells allows for direct gaseous exchange between cells and the air. There is no blood system.
Thus gaseous *exchange* occurs only when organisms respire using oxygen.

3   Cellular respiration (= internal respiration): the chemical reactions occurring within cells that result in the release of energy to form ATP. These reactions can occur under two conditions:

(*a*) anaerobically – no oxygen needed (thus **1** and **2** above unnecessary).
(*b*) aerobically – oxygen needed (thus **2** above essential).

Note: since breathing and gaseous exchange are essentially *physical* processes occurring *outside* cells, they are often lumped together as **external respiration** to distinguish them from the *chemical* processes occurring *within* cells which are **internal respiration**.

Unfortunately the terms above are often used loosely in exams, e.g. since *Amoeba*, the earthworm and the flowering plant do not make *movements* to gain O_2, strictly speaking they do not *breathe* but they do respire.

6.2   INTERNAL RESPIRATION (AEROBIC AND ANAEROBIC)

Glucose is the main substance respired (other foods can be turned into glucose). The results of respiration are different under anaerobic and aerobic conditions:

1   Aerobic
In plants and animals:

$$\text{Glucose} + \text{Oxygen} \xrightarrow{\text{Enzymes in mitochondria}} \text{Carbon dioxide} + \text{Water} + \textbf{A lot of energy}$$
$$C_6H_{12}O_6 + 6O_2 \qquad\qquad\qquad 6CO_2 + 6H_2O$$

2   Anaerobic
(*a*) in plants:

$$\text{Glucose} \xrightarrow[\text{matrix}]{\text{Enzymes in cytoplasmic}} \text{Ethanol} + \text{Carbon dioxide} + \textbf{A little energy}$$
$$C_6H_{12}O_6 \qquad\qquad 2C_2H_5OH + 2CO_2$$

(*b*) in animals:

Glucose $\xrightarrow[\text{matrix}]{\text{Enzymes in cytoplasmic}}$ Lactic acid + **A little energy**

$C_6H_{12}O_6$ $2C_3H_6O_3$

Table 6.1   Comparison of the two stages in respiration

	Anaerobic	*Aerobic*
Oxygen requirement	Nil	Essential
Useful energy from each glucose molecule respired	2 ATP	About 40 ATP
Chemical products	Organic, i.e. still energy-rich, e.g. lactic acid	Inorganic: CO_2 and H_2O, i.e. no energy left
Takes place in	Cytoplasmic matrix (Sec. 2.2)	Mitochondria (Sec. 2.2)

Note: aerobic and anaerobic respiration are *not* alternatives. Anaerobic reactions are the *first few stages* in a much longer set of reactions made possible under aerobic conditions (Fig. 6.1). Since aerobic respiration has the great advantage over anaerobic of providing about twenty times more energy, not surprisingly most organisms respire aerobically. Only certain bacteria cannot. However, some organisms are forced to respire anaerobically in their environment, e.g. tapeworms (see Section 17.11), or yeast in brewing operations. See Fig. 6.1 for a summary of respiration.

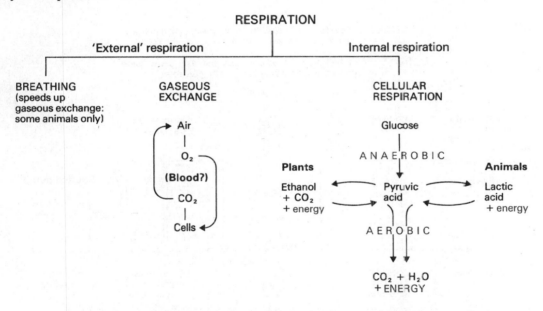

Note: Pyruvic acid (a 3 carbon compound) is common to all three respiration pathways

Fig. 6.1 Respiration: breathing, gaseous exchange and cellular respiration

Examples of anaerobic respiration in aerobic organisms

1 Man

(*a*) at rest, most of the pyruvic acid his cells produce is oxidised to CO_2 and H_2O. The blood contains very little lactic acid.

(*b*) during exercise, blood samples show that the lactic acid level rises at least ten-fold indicating that despite increased breathing and heart rates, oxygen supply to tissues is inadequate. In this relatively anaerobic state man is in **'oxygen debt'**. This debt is 'paid off' by continued rapid aerobic respiration *after* exercise has finished; one fifth of the lactic acid is respired to CO_2 and H_2O. This provides energy to turn the other four-fifths of lactic acid back into glycogen (stored in liver and muscles).

2 Yeast

(*a*) if aerated, the colony grows very rapidly in nourishing sugared water until all the glucose disappears as CO_2 and H_2O (no use to brewers!).

(*b*) without air, in similar conditions, the colony grows more slowly, eventually killing itself in the ethanol it produces. This is the basis for *making wine and beer*. The ethanol can be distilled off (as in making *spirits*, e.g. whisky). This will burn, showing it is energy-rich.

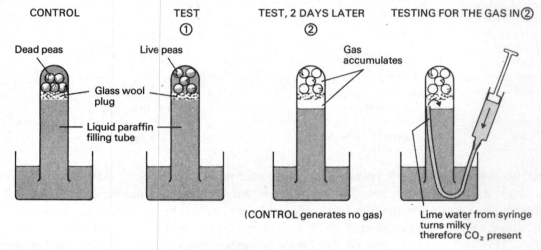

CONTROL   TEST   TEST, 2 DAYS LATER   TESTING FOR THE GAS IN ②
                   ①   ②

Dead peas   Live peas   Gas accumulates

Glass wool plug

Liquid paraffin filling tube

(CONTROL generates no gas)

Lime water from syringe turns milky therefore CO_2 present

Note: Mercury can be used instead of liquid paraffin (both lack dissolved O_2)

Fig. 6.2 Demonstration that germinating peas respire anaerobically

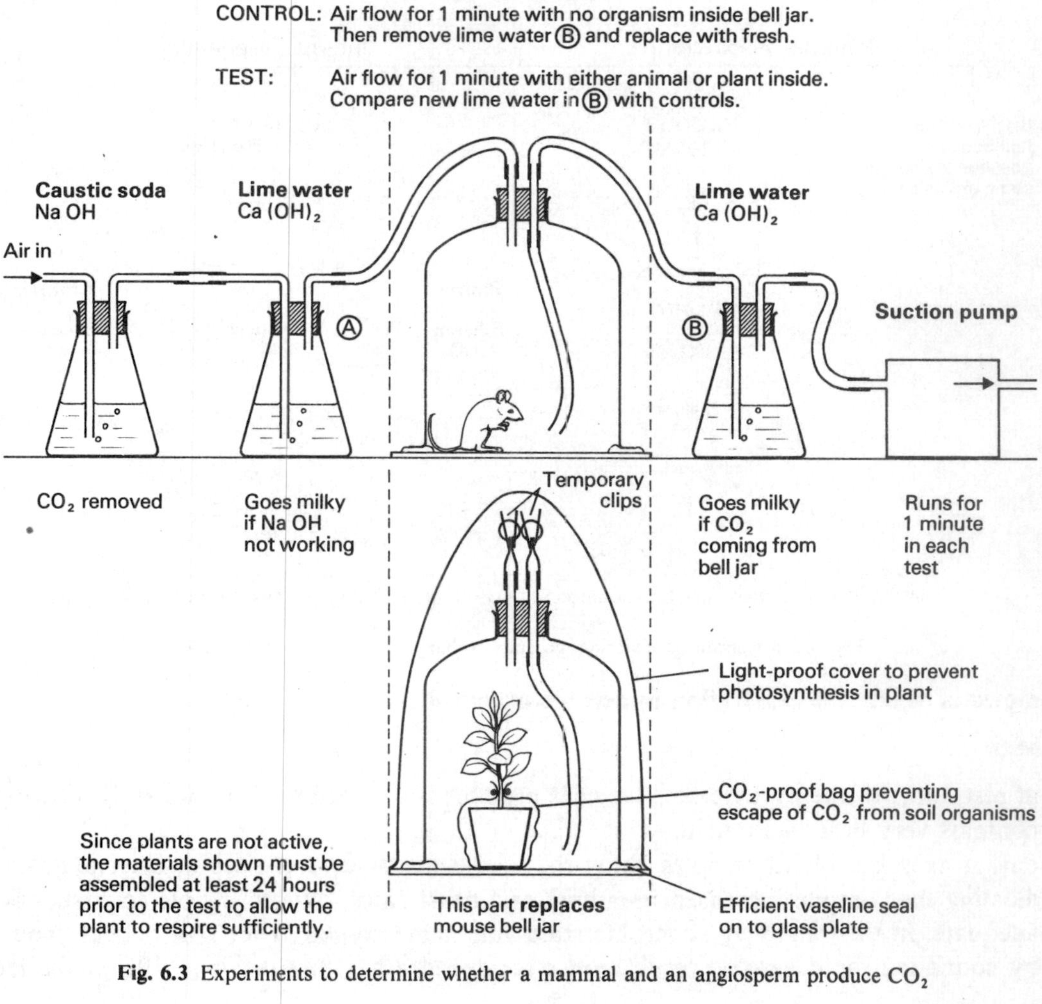

CONTROL: Air flow for 1 minute with no organism inside bell jar. Then remove lime water Ⓑ and replace with fresh.

TEST: Air flow for 1 minute with either animal or plant inside. Compare new lime water in Ⓑ with controls.

Caustic soda
Na OH

Lime water
Ca (OH)$_2$

Lime water
Ca (OH)$_2$

Air in

Ⓐ

Ⓑ

Suction pump

CO_2 removed

Goes milky if Na OH not working

Goes milky if CO_2 coming from bell jar

Runs for 1 minute in each test

Temporary clips

Light-proof cover to prevent photosynthesis in plant

CO_2-proof bag preventing escape of CO_2 from soil organisms

Since plants are not active, the materials shown must be assembled at least 24 hours prior to the test to allow the plant to respire sufficiently.

This part **replaces** mouse bell jar

Efficient vaseline seal on to glass plate

Fig. 6.3 Experiments to determine whether a mammal and an angiosperm produce CO_2

3 Germinating peas

Half a batch of germinating peas is killed by boiling. Live and dead peas are washed in thymol solution to kill bacteria (which would produce CO_2). Both batches are put in boiling tubes in anaerobic conditions (see Fig. 6.2). Two days later the live peas have produced gas in an anaerobic environment.

Three lines of evidence that organisms are respiring aerobically

1 CO_2 evolved (see Fig. 6.3).

2 O_2 absorbed (see Fig. 6.4).

3 **Heat** evolved. The energy in glucose is not totally converted into ATP during respiration. Some (around 40%) is wasted as heat (see Fig. 6.5). In the experiment shown in Fig. 6.5 both the dead peas (killed by boiling and then cooled for half an hour) and the live ones had been washed in thymol solution to exclude the possibility that bacterial respiration could be causing a rise in temperature.

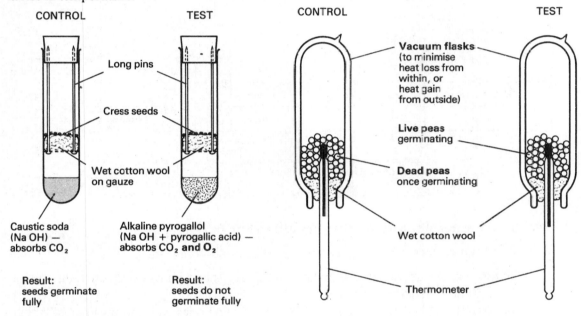

The rate of gaseous exchange (i.e. **1** and **2** above) can be used to determine the **rate of respiration** (Fig. 6.6).

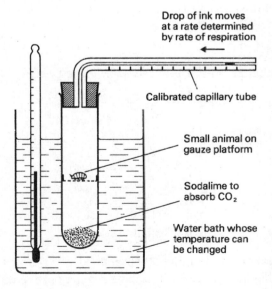

Fig. 6.6 Experiment to determine the rate of respiration, using a respirometer

6.3   EXTERNAL RESPIRATION (GASEOUS EXCHANGE)

Exchange of gases at cells: All cells receive O_2 and lose CO_2 in solution (via water or tissue fluids). Diffusion, a slow process, plays a major part in this (see Section 5.2). Rate of diffusion can be increased by increasing the rate of supply and removal of gases where they are exchanged, e.g. at alveoli and capillaries in man. Hence breathing movements and blood flow.

Gases still have to move (slowly) through the cytoplasm. Thus if a cell were too large (>1 mm diameter), diffusion of O_2 and CO_2 would not be fast enough to sustain life. Hence cell division is necessary to keep the surface area-to-volume ratio high, i.e. keep the cell small (see Fig. 6.7). Thus the volume of *Amoeba*, say 0.1 mm³, is adequately served by its cell membrane area, say 2.5 mm². But man's volume, say 80 litres, could not be served adequately by his skin surface area, say 1.8 m², *if* it were used for gaseous exchange.

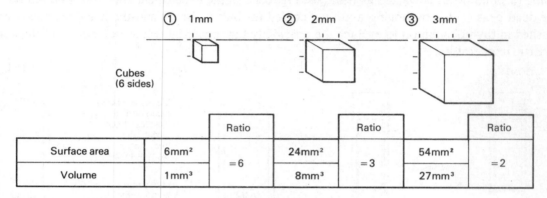

		Ratio		Ratio		Ratio
Surface area	6mm²	= 6	24mm²	= 3	54mm²	= 2
Volume	1mm³		8mm³		27mm³	

i.e. progressively smaller surface area through which diffusion can occur for each mm³ of bulk: 6mm²/mm³ in ①; 2mm²/mm³ in ③.

Fig. 6.7 The relationship between surface area and volume

For efficient external respiration there must therefore be:

(*a*) a large enough **surface area** for gaseous exchange, both

  (*i*) *with air,* e.g. in man about 600 million alveoli in his two lungs provide a total area of about 180 m² (2 tennis courts) and

  (*ii*) *with tissues,* e.g. in man about 95 000 km of capillaries provide an area of about 700 m² of which about 200 m² are in use at one time

(*b*) a high enough **rate of supply** of O_2 and removal of CO_2, e.g in a man exercising: breathing rate goes up 4-fold; volume inhaled per breath, 7-fold; heart rate doubles; volume of blood pumped doubles or trebles (athletes can do better).

6.4   ORGANISMS RESPIRING IN WATER AND AIR

Respiration in water
Water contains $<1\%$ dissolved O_2.

1   **Amoeba:** gaseous exchange over whole *cell membrane* (see Fig. 6.8).

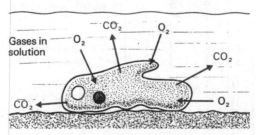

Fig. 6.8 Respiration in *Amoeba*

2   **Bony fish:** gaseous exchange at minutely branched *gill filaments* aided by blood containing erythrocytes flowing in capillaries. Breathing requires use of mouth, pharynx and operculum (see Fig. 6.9).

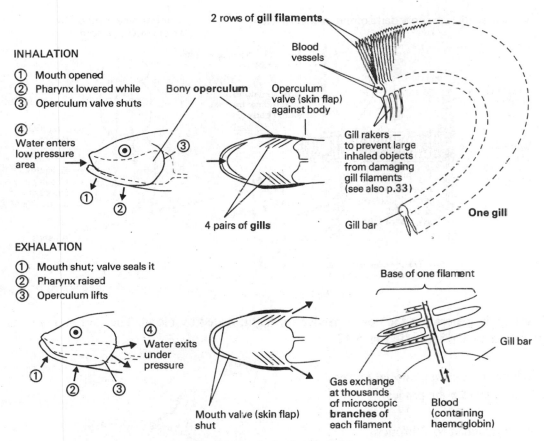

Fig. 6.9 Respiration in a bony fish

Respiration with wet skins – in air or water

1 Earthworm: gaseous exchange over whole mucus-covered skin aided by blood containing haemoglobin in solution flowing in *skin capillaries*. No breathing movements.

2 Frog: gaseous exchange at mucus-covered skin aided by blood containing erythrocytes flowing in *skin capillaries*. Supplemented by breathing movements of buccal floor ventilating *lungs* and *buccal cavity* (see Fig. 6.10).

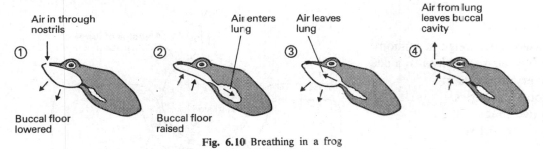

Fig. 6.10 Breathing in a frog

Respiration in air
Air contains almost 21% O_2.

1 Insect: gaseous exchange at *tracheoles*, thin tubes 1 μm in diameter supplying cells with air *direct* – blood not used for this. Much of the time O_2 and CO_2 just diffuse via *spiracles* and *tracheae* to tracheoles (see Fig. 6.11). Active or strong-flying insects, e.g. bees, and locusts, have air sacs. Abdominal *breathing movements* squash and unsquash these, assisting ventilation of tracheae. Locust group have a 'through system' for air (in through anterior spiracles, out through posterior) – *cf.* birds.

6.5 BIRD RESPIRATION

Gaseous exchange at minute *air passages* (like alveoli open at both ends) since air passes *through*. This happens *twice* for each breath, making gaseous exchange highly efficient – great

Vertical section to show parts of the tracheal system

Longitudinal section of strong-flying insect

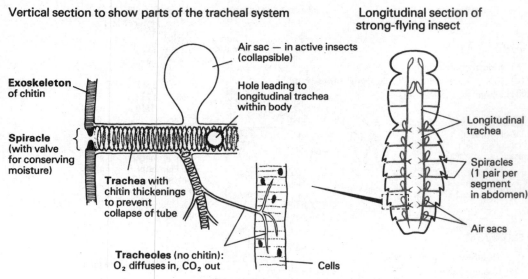

Fig. 6.11 Respiration in an insect

advantage in generating the power needed for flight. Aided by blood. The four stages of bird respiration are illustrated in Fig. 6.12.

Breathing movements, special valves and tubes ensure air passes:

1   in via trachea to 2 bronchi
2   through 2 lungs (gaseous exchange) to 4 posterior air sacs
3   through 2 lungs (gaseous exchange) to 5 anterior air sacs
4   out via bronchi and trachea.

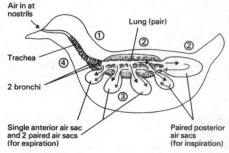

Fig. 6.12 Respiration in a bird

Air sacs are not lungs, simply air reservoirs inflated and deflated by body movements to ensure double flow of air through lungs (e.g. in flight, flight-muscles contract next to air sacs and sternum moves in and out). May assist in cooling bird.

6.6   MAMMAL RESPIRATION

Gaseous exchange at millions of tiny air-sacs (*alveoli*), aided by erythrocytes in blood capillaries, in two lungs (see Fig. 6.13).

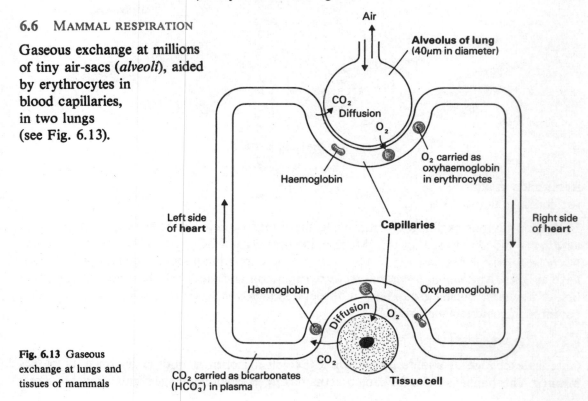

Fig. 6.13 Gaseous exchange at lungs and tissues of mammals

Table 6.2 Breathing movements

	Exhalation	*Inhalation*
Muscles contracted	Internal intercostals, in *forced* breathing only, e.g. exercise	External intercostals
Ribs	Lowered inwards	Raised outwards
Diaphragm	Relaxes to domed position	Contracts and becomes flatter
Pressure in chest cavity	Raised, therefore air leaves lungs	Lowered, therefore air enters lungs
Vertical section		
Cross-section		

Note: exhalation occurs mainly because lung is elastic, collapsing if allowed to, thus deflating alveoli and bronchioles. Lungs may be made functionless by introducing air between pleural membranes, e.g. medically when treating tuberculosis (T.B.), or accidentally in a motor crash. Breathing rate is determined by the CO_2-sensitive part of the brain.

Air breathed

Tidal air: about 0.5 dm³ ($\frac{1}{2}$ litre) – quiet breathing at rest.

Vital capacity: about 3.5 dm³ – volume inhaled or expelled in forced breathing.

Residual air: about 1.5 dm³ – air that cannot be expelled at all (remains in lungs).

Table 6.3 Approximate composition of air inhaled and exhaled (after removal of water vapour)

	Inhaled	*Exhaled*	*Change*
Oxygen	21%	17%	20% decrease
Carbon dioxide	0.04%	4%	10 000% increase
Nitrogen	79%	79%	Nil

Air exhaled is also always saturated with water vapour (6%) – a variable loss of water from the body occurs, depending on how moist the inhaled air was.

Respiratory pathway

Air passes to alveoli via nostrils, nasal cavity, trachea, two bronchi with many branches, and millions of bronchioles (see Fig. 6.14). Dust, including bacteria, is 'filtered out' on sticky *mucus* in the nasal cavity as well as in the trachea where *cilia* of lining cells beat the 'sputum' upwards to be swallowed into the acid-bath in the stomach. Heavy *smoking*, especially when young, inactivates ciliated cells making lung infections and the chance of getting lung cancer more likely.

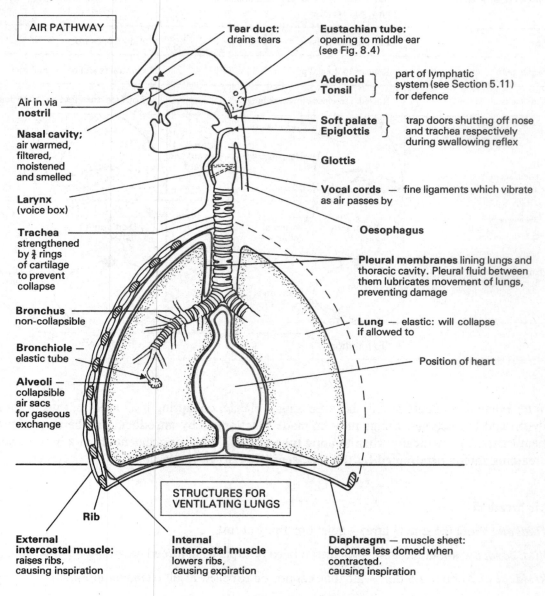

Fig. 6.14 Respiratory pathway in man

6.7   GASEOUS EXCHANGE IN ANGIOSPERMS

Angiosperms are flowering plants. Air diffuses through *stomata* (mostly on leaves; some on green stems) (see Section 4.8) and *lenticels* (on cork-covered roots and stems – see Section 12.3) to *air-spaces* between cells, particularly of cortex and mesophyll (see Section 4.8).

Gaseous exchange: O_2 absorbed and CO_2 released direct from cells to air spaces during **respiration**. However *green* cells in sunlight absorb CO_2 and release O_2 during **photosynthesis** (see Section 4.6) at a rate far greater than the reverse process (due to respiration). In dim light, e.g. dusk or dawn, rates of respiration and photosynthesis can be equal – the **compensation point**. No dead cells, e.g. xylem vessels (the majority in a big tree), respire or photosynthesise.

6.8   USES FOR ENERGY FROM RESPIRATION

Mnemonic: Make tea (**MECH T**).

1   **Mechanical** work, e.g. in contraction of muscles.

2   **Electro-chemical** work, e.g. generating nerve impulses.

3 **Chemical** work, e.g. synthesising large molecules, such as protein, frcm amino acids during growth.

4 **Heating,** e.g. maintaining mammal body temperature.

5 **Transporting,** e.g. 'active transport' of materials across cell membranes (see Section 5.2).

6.9 ATP (ADENOSINE TRI-PHOSPHATE)

ATP is the 'energy molecule' of cells.

When the terminal phosphate is removed, leaving ADP (adenosine di-phosphate), energy is released for use in any vital function, e.g. movement or growth. The phosphate may be added to ADP again, making ATP, during respiration in mitochondria. The energy for this comes from the bond energy in the sugar that is respired:

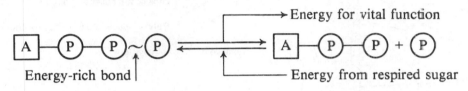

---

7 Excretion, temperature regulation and homeostasis

7.1 WASTES AND MEANS OF EXCRETION

Excretion is the removal of waste products of metabolism. Accumulation of wastes would lead to death. Examples of excretion:

In **animals:**
    (*i*) CO_2 (from respiration).
    (*ii*) ammonia, urea or uric acid (from protein metabolism – see Section 5.6).

In **green plants:**
    (*i*) O_2 (from photosynthesis).
    (*ii*) shedding leaves or bark (contain various wastes).

In **all organisms:**
    Heat energy (from metabolism – especially respiration, see Sections 2.2, 7.4). An important waste only in animals, when they move around. Loss of water unfortunately accompanies most forms of excretion. (See question 10, p. 168.)

Mammal excretory organs
1 **Lungs:** excrete CO_2; lose water vapour.
2 **Kidneys:** excrete urea; eliminate excess water and salts.
3 **Liver:** excretes bile pigments (see Section 4.20).
4 **Skin:** excretes heat, loses water, salts and some urea (in sweat).

7.2 MAMMAL URINARY SYSTEM

Two **kidneys** (see Fig. 7.1) at back of abdominal cavity:

(*a*) **excrete** waste **nitrogen** (from excess protein in diet) as urea.
(*b*) **eliminate** excess **salts** (e.g. NaCl in very salty food).
(*c*) **osmoregulate** to maintain **water** content of blood.

Urine, formed by kidneys, is passed by peristalsis along two **ureters** to bladder (storage); thence via **urethra** to outside (urination) (see Fig. 7.1 Ⓐ).

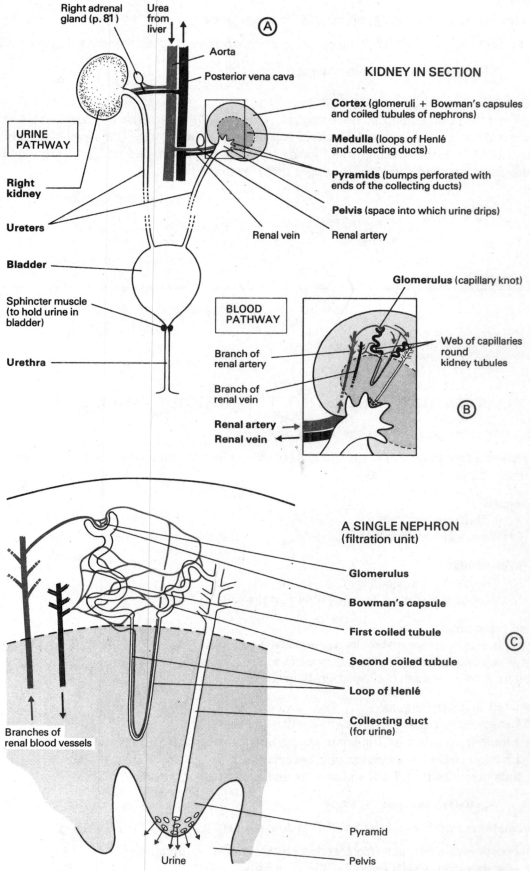

Right adrenal gland (p. 81)

Urea from liver

Ⓐ

Aorta

Posterior vena cava

KIDNEY IN SECTION

Cortex (glomeruli + Bowman's capsules and coiled tubules of nephrons)

Medulla (loops of Henlé and collecting ducts)

Pyramids (bumps perforated with ends of the collecting ducts)

Pelvis (space into which urine drips)

URINE PATHWAY

Right kidney

Ureters

Renal vein

Renal artery

Bladder

Glomerulus (capillary knot)

Sphincter muscle (to hold urine in bladder)

BLOOD PATHWAY

Urethra

Branch of renal artery

Branch of renal vein

Renal artery

Renal vein

Web of capillaries round kidney tubules

Ⓑ

A SINGLE NEPHRON (filtration unit)

Glomerulus

Bowman's capsule

First coiled tubule

Second coiled tubule

Ⓒ

Loop of Henlé

Collecting duct (for urine)

Branches of renal blood vessels

Pyramid

Pelvis

Urine

Fig. 7.1 The mammal urinary system: Ⓐ urine pathway from the kidney; Ⓑ blood pathway in the kidney; Ⓒ a single nephron

Kidney function

1   Blood pathway (see Fig. 7.1 ⓑ)

Blood containing urea (made in the liver) passes into kidney from aorta via renal artery to about one million **glomeruli** (knots of capillaries); thence via further capillary network to renal vein and posterior vena cava.

2   Nephron (see Fig. 7.1 ⓒ)

A nephron is a kidney unit receiving tissue fluid and modifying it into urine. Tissue fluid (a filtrate of blood lacking cells and proteins) leaks out from the glomerulus (because of blood pressure) into the cavity of a **Bowman's capsule**. Along the tubules all food and most other useful substances are reabsorbed from the tissue fluid, leaving urine.

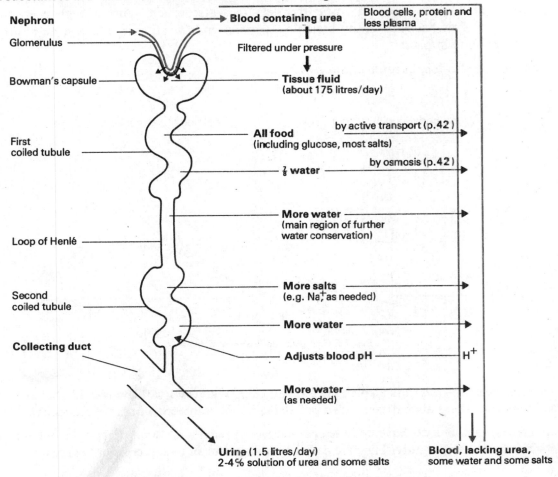

Fig. 7.2 How nephrons make urine in man

Urine in man is a 2–4% solution of urea, some salts, yellow colouring (bile pigments accidentally absorbed in intestine), poisons, drugs and hormones (variously modified). Exact composition varies according to diet, activity and health, e.g. *water loss* exceeds normal 1.5 litres per day if excess water is drunk or extra salts and urea need removing. Level of hormone (ADH) controls this: high levels promote water conservation in kidney – less urine formed.

7.3   ABNORMAL KIDNEY FUNCTION

Faulty excretion: sugar diabetes – glucose appears in urine. Lack of hormone **insulin** allows high glucose level in blood (see Section 9.8). Consequently tissue fluid is too glucose-rich for first coiled tubule to reabsorb it all into the blood. Therefore glucose is drained, little by little, from the body; can cause coma and death. Remedied by regular insulin injections.

Faulty osmoregulation: water diabetes – large quantities of dilute urine, e.g. 20 litres per day. Lack of **ADH** is cause. Leads to dehydration of body unless large volumes of water drunk.

7.4   BODY TEMPERATURE IN ORGANISMS

Skin and temperature control

1   The *body generates heat* by its metabolism (40% of energy from respiration is wasted as heat) e.g. blood leaving contracting muscles or the liver is warmer than when it entered them.

2   At the *skin*, blood either *loses* this heat to cooler surroundings or *gains* even more if the surroundings are warmer.

3   *Gain or loss of heat* can happen in 4 main ways (see Fig. 7.3):

(*a*)   *radiation* (important in air) – man, at rest in shade, loses most this way.

(*b*)   *conduction* (important in water) – e.g. elephants bathing.

(*c*)   *convection* (air circulation; speeds up (*a*) and (*b*)).

(*d*)   *evaporation* (heat *loss* only – heat transfers to water which gains enough energy to vaporise. This happens during breathing, panting and sweating in animals; and during transpiration in plants).

Some heat is also lost in *urine* and *faeces*.

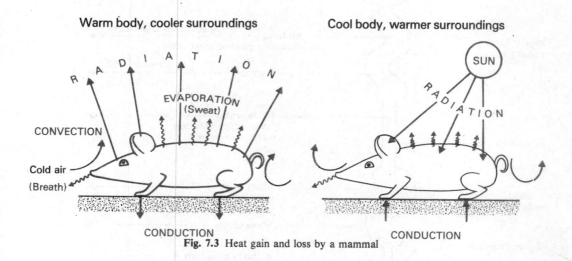

Fig. 7.3 Heat gain and loss by a mammal

4   Thus *most animals* (and all plants) have body **temperatures that fluctuate** with that of their environment. These animals are called poikilotherms or **ectotherms** or 'cold-blooded'.

Birds and mammals have body **temperatures that remain constant** despite the fluctuating environmental temperature. They are called homoiotherms or **endotherms** or 'warm-blooded'.

5   When cold, ectotherms are sluggish (because their enzymes work slowly); they fall easy prey to more active animals. To avoid death they may have to **hibernate** in winter or **aestivate** in summer, e.g. earthworm – inactive ball deep in soil.

Endotherms can be constantly active and thus have an advantage over ectotherms; but they need relatively more food to keep up their temperature.

7.5   MAMMAL TEMPERATURE CONTROL

Mammals have a *thermostat* in the fore-brain (hypothalamus) which monitors blood temperature. Its information causes changes in:

1   Behaviour: e.g. seeking shade or getting wet if it is hot; seeking shelter and huddling into a ball if it is cold (see Fig. 7.4).

2   Skin (physical control):

(*a*)   **hair:** traps air – a good insulator. Amount of insulation can be varied by raising or lowering hair using erector muscles.

(b) **fat:** also a good insulator. Whales (in very cold water) have thick 'blubber' but camels have no fat except in hump. Mammals prepare for winter cold by laying down more fat.

(c) **capillaries and shunts:** skin 'flushes' with blood flowing to surface capillaries which radiate heat (*vaso-dilation*) when mammal is hot. Skin goes pale if cold since blood is diverted from surface capillaries (*vaso-constriction*) often by going through a 'shunt' deeper down.

(d) **sweat glands:** secrete sweat (salty water containing some urea). Water evaporates, removing excess heat.

3 Metabolic control:

(a) **shivering:** involuntary contractions of skin muscles generate heat.

(b) **liver:** metabolises faster owing to increased thyroxin secretion (see Section 4.20).

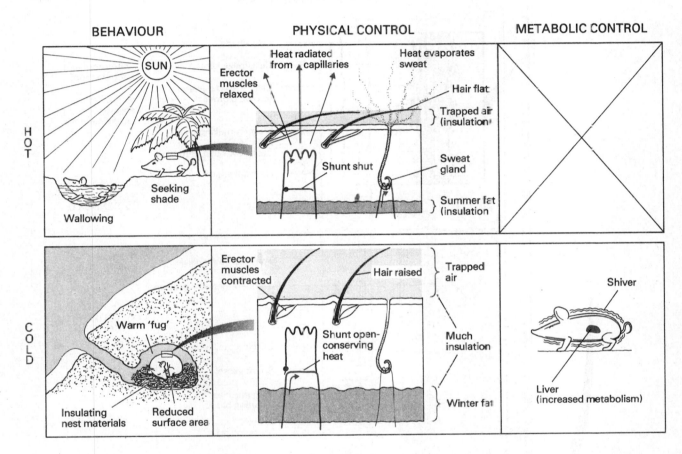

Fig. 7.4 Three ways of maintaining constant body temperature

Temperature control in other organisms

1 **Ectotherms:** attempt to keep a constant temperature by moving to warm or cold places as the situation demands. Do not use skin or metabolic means as mammals do.

2 **Angiosperms:** cannot move; perennate if temperature becomes impossible. If hot they *transpire* more (water evaporation) or *wilt* reducing area of leaves gaining heat from sun.

7.6   HOMEOSTASIS

Homeostasis is the maintenance of a constant environment immediately around cells. For unicellular organisms this is the water they inhabit and their only means of homeostasis is to move (if they can) to a suitable area. The immediate environment of cells in a multicellular animal is the tissue fluid. In mammals the composition of this is kept very constant by a variety of organs, each of which controls particular factors in the blood (the source of tissue fluid).

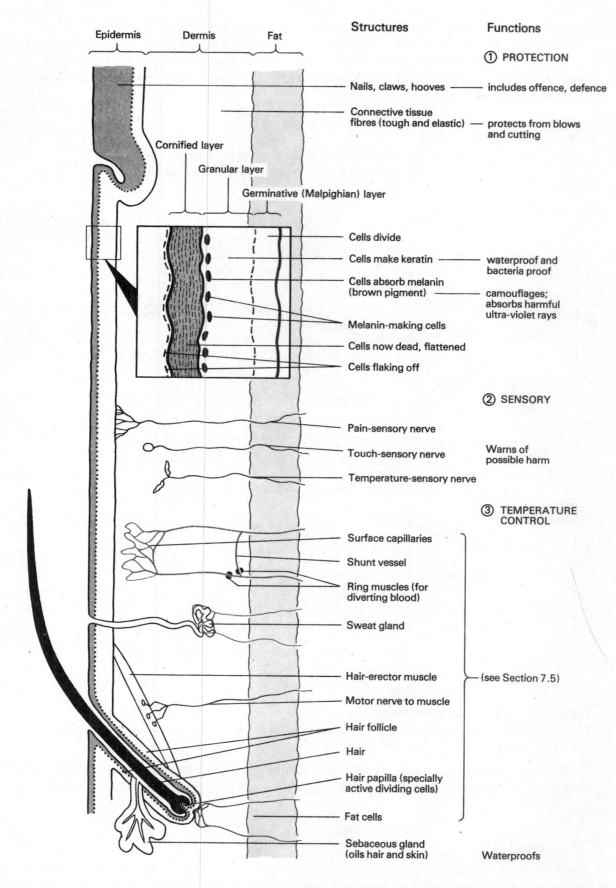

Structures

Functions

① PROTECTION

Nails, claws, hooves — includes offence, defence

Connective tissue
fibres (tough and elastic) — protects from blows
and cutting

Cornified layer

Granular layer

Germinative (Malpighian) layer

Cells divide

Cells make keratin — waterproof and
bacteria proof

Cells absorb melanin
(brown pigment) — camouflages;
absorbs harmful
ultra-violet rays

Melanin-making cells

Cells now dead, flattened

Cells flaking off

② SENSORY

Pain-sensory nerve

Touch-sensory nerve — Warns of
possible harm

Temperature-sensory nerve

③ TEMPERATURE
CONTROL

Surface capillaries

Shunt vessel

Ring muscles (for
diverting blood)

Sweat gland

Hair-erector muscle — (see Section 7.5)

Motor nerve to muscle

Hair follicle

Hair

Hair papilla (specially
active dividing cells)

Fat cells

Sebaceous gland
(oils hair and skin) — Waterproofs

Epidermis   Dermis   Fat

Fig. 7.5 The structure and functions of mammal skin

Table 7.1 Organs concerned with homeostasis in man

Organs concerned	Factors controlled in blood	Healthy blood levels in man
Liver and islet tissue of pancreas (Sec. 4.15)	Glucose	1 g/l
Skin, liver (Fig. 7.4)	Temperature	36.8°C (under tongue)
Kidneys (Sec. 7.2)	Osmoregulation (water) pH (acidity/alkalinity) Urea (nitrogen waste)	90% pH 7.4 0·3 g/l
Lungs (Sec. 6.6)	Carbon dioxide (carbon waste) Oxygen	550 cm³/l (at rest, deoxygenated) 193 cm³/l (at rest, oxygenated)

Note: blood does of course vary in composition according to where it is in the body (see Section 5.10), but overall the levels of factors affecting the vital functions of cells are kept within narrow limits.

7.7 SKIN FUNCTIONS

1 Sensory: sensitive nerve endings give warning of harm – pain, touch, heat or cold.

2 Protection: skin acts as barrier between the internal environment of cells (tissue fluid) and the external environment (anything from climate, air or water to bacteria or predators).
   Skin *resists*:

(*a*) **puncture** – (from slashes, blows or friction) by being tough and hair-padded.

(*b*) **desiccation** – (drying of body) by the waterproof protein keratin, aided by oils.

(*c*) **entry of pathogens** – (viruses, bacteria, etc.).

(*d*) **damage from ultra violet light** – ('sunburn'; skin cancer) by suntanning, i.e. producing more pigment when in sunshine.

   Skin *assists* predators and prey by providing:

(*e*) **weapons** from modified skin – (claws, hooves) for attacking or defending.

(*f*) **camouflage** – by special distribution of pigment in three ways:

   (*i*) *blending:* similar colour to background, e.g. khaki colour of lion.

   (*ii*) *countershading:* pale belly is darkened by shadow; dark back is made paler by sun. Therefore from the side the animal looks 'flat'; difficult to see, e.g. deer.

   (*iii*) *disruptive:* regular outline broken up by stripes or blotches to blend with light and shade amongst vegetation, e.g. leopard.

3 Synthesis: certain oils in the skin are changed to *vitamin D* (see Section 4.5) when subjected to ultra violet light.

4 Excretion: some *urea* is lost in sweat.

5 Temperature control is dealt with in Section 7.5.

8 Sensitivity

8.1 SENSITIVITY IN PLANTS AND ANIMALS

Organisms must be aware of their surroundings and respond to them, where necessary, to keep alive. Plants must seek light; animals, food. Organisms respond to various **stimuli**. Plants respond to light, gravity, touch, water (see Sections 9.12, 9.13) and animals respond to these as well as temperature, chemicals in air (smells) or water (tastes) and sound. Plants and animals show fundamental differences both in the complexity of their sensory areas and in the way they respond to stimuli (see Chapter 9).

Table 8.1 Comparison of sensitivity and response in animals and plants

Multicellular animals	*Multicellular plants*
1 **Special sense cells** or organs (which usually do nothing else – e.g. eyes which only see)	No *special* sense organs, e.g. shoot tips sense light
2 **Nerves** relay messages from sensory areas	No nerves
3 **Brain** (present in most) 'computes a decision', sent to muscles	No brain
4 **Muscles** which can move the whole body towards or away from the stimulus	No muscles: cannot move the whole body

8.2 Mammal sense organs

Sense organs *sense*, but sensations are interpreted (*perceived*) by the brain, e.g. eyes may work perfectly but if the optic nerve or the visual centre of the brain is damaged, the person is blind.

Sense organs sense stimuli in both the external and internal environments:

External

(*a*) *skin* – touch, heat, cold, pressure (extremes of which can cause pain) (see Section 7.7).
(*b*) *nose* – air-borne chemicals (smells – including the 'taste' of food).
(*c*) *tongue* – chemicals causing perception of bitter, sweet, salt and sour tastes.
(*d*) *ear* – sound (high frequency pressure changes); changes of body position.
(*e*) *eye* – light (as light or dark, colour, and the form of objects).

Internal (often concerned with homeostasis, see Section 7.6). Examples:
(*a*) *thermostat* in hypothalamus of brain (see Section 7.5).
(*b*) *breathing centre* (CO_2-sensitive) in medulla oblongata of brain (see Section 6.6).

There are many others, e.g. *spindle organs* (sensing tension) in muscles. These assist muscle co-ordination.

8.3 The eye

1 The **eyeball** is tough (*sclera*) and transparent in front (*cornea*); kept in shape by pressure from tissue fluid (exuded from *ciliary body* capillaries) (see Fig. 8.1).

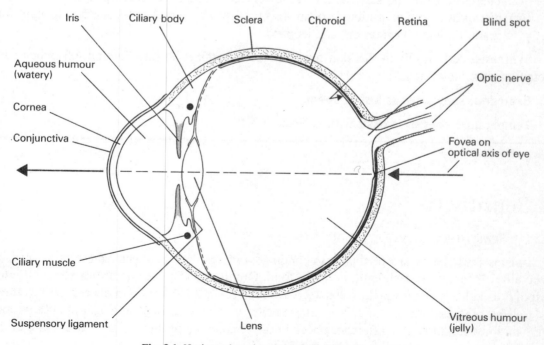

Fig. 8.1 Horizontal section through the left eye of man

2 It is **protected** within a bony socket (*orbit*) and by **three reflexes**:

(*a*) *weep reflex: dust and irritants* sensed by the **conjunctiva** cause an increase in tears and blinking to wash them away.

(*b*) *iris reflex: strong light* on the *retina* causes a narrowing of the pupil to prevent damage to the light-sensitive cells.

(*c*) *blinking reflex:* seen *objects* which may hit the head cause the eyelids to close.

3 The **retina** contains nerve cells linked with two kinds of **light-sensitive** cell:

(*a*) *rods:* see in black and white, in dim light.

(*b*) *cones:* see in colour, in brighter light.

The *fovea* has cones only, very close together: colour vision only and in great detail. Image is only in complete focus at this spot.

The *blind spot* has only nerve cells (gathering into the *optic nerve*): no vision.

4 The **choroid:**

(*a*) black pigment cells prevent internal reflection of light.

(*b*) capillaries nourish the retina with tissue fluid.

Focusing

Cornea responsible for most (at least 70%) of the converging of light rays.

Lens makes the final adjustment, i.e. *accommodates*.

1 **Far-focusing: lens pulled thin** by strain on suspensory ligaments exerted by sclera under pressure from tissue fluid.

2 **Near-focusing:** strain on suspensory ligaments relieved by contraction of ciliary muscle, so **lens collapses fat** due to its elasticity.

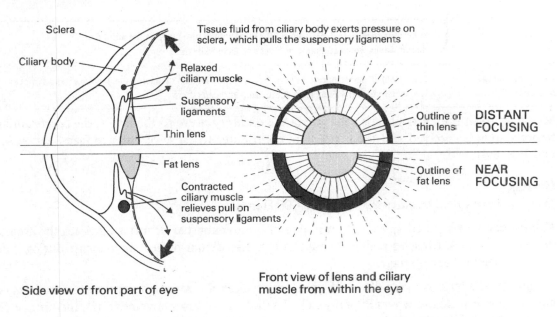

Fig. 8.2 Focusing in the eye

8.4   ABNORMALITIES IN FOCUSING

In normal young human eyes, cornea has a focusing power of 43 dioptres (D); lens has 16D.

1 In old people, *lens becomes less elastic* (collapsible), power falling to 1D. This **presbyopia** is corrected by wearing bifocal lenses or reading glasses (they give extra power).

2 Long sight (**hypermetropia**) ⎫
3 Short sight (**myopia**) ⎭ the problems and solutions are shown in Fig. 8.3.

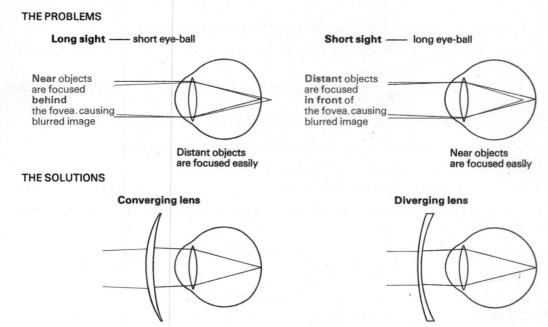

THE PROBLEMS

Long sight —— short eye-ball

Near objects
are focused
behind
the fovea, causing
blurred image

Distant objects
are focused easily

Short sight —— long eye-ball

Distant objects
are focused
in front of
the fovea, causing
blurred image

Near objects
are focused easily

THE SOLUTIONS

Converging lens

Diverging lens

Fig. 8.3 Long sight and short sight and their correction

8.5   THE EAR

Table 8.2   Functions and parts of the ear

Functions	Parts
Hearing	Outer: ear *pinna* and *canal* for sound-gathering
	Middle: *ear-drum* vibrates; *3 ossicles* transmit vibrations; together they amplify the sound at *oval window*
	Inner: (*a*) *cochlea* (a 3-part spiral tube filled with liquid) receives the amplified sound waves which stimulate *hair cells* in the middle tube
Detecting change in position	Inner: (*b*) *3 semicircular canals* (set at right angles to each other) whose liquid moves inside *ampullae* (swellings), so stimulating *hair cells* there

Messages from both sets of hair cells go via the *auditory nerve* to the brain: the *cerebrum* interprets sounds received and the cerebellum contributes to sense of balance (see Section 9.7 and Fig. 8.4).

Hearing

Man can hear sound *frequencies* of 20—20 000 Hertz.

Volume can be amplified up to 22 times; area of tympanum (ear-drum) is 22 times the area of the base of stapes. Muscles acting on ossicles can also diminish their movements during loud noise, preventing ear damage.

Stapes vibrates in sympathy with tympanum; thus air-borne sound waves are changed into water-borne sound waves in perilymph. These waves cause movement of a membrane on which hair-cells sit. Their hairs, embedded in a jelly shelf, are pulled or crushed as the cells rise or fall on the membrane, sending impulses along the auditory nerve. This sound-sensing part of the cochlea is called the organ of Corti (see Fig. 8.5).

Detecting change in position

Inside the ampulla are hair cells capped by a cone of jelly (cupula) which can move like a swing-door. Head movement in the same plane as one of the canals causes the canal to move, but not the endolymph within it; this lags behind due to inertia. The static endolymph thus swings the cupula, distorting hairs of the hair-cells, which send impulses to the brain (see Fig. 8.6). According to which of the 6 semicircular canals (in 2 ears) are stimulated, the brain can 'compute' how to keep balance. Eye information assists in this.

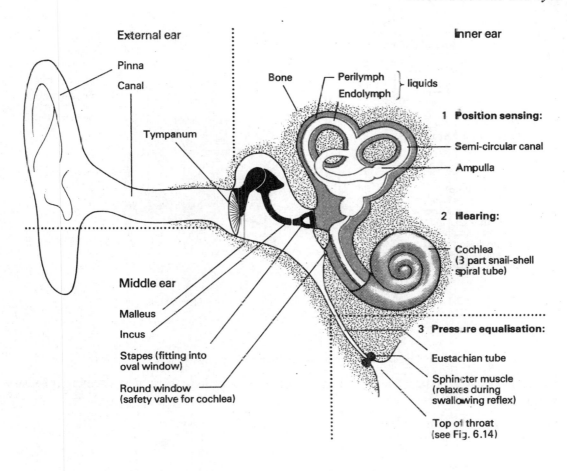

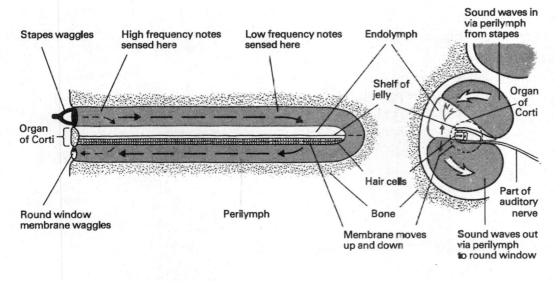

Fig. 8.5 How sounds are sensed in the cochlea

8.6 INSECT ANTENNAE AND EYES

The whole insect exoskeleton has variety of sensory cells (especially touch-bristles).

Antennae (depending on species) may have:

(*a*) touch-bristles (possibly also sensitive to sound).

(*b*) taste or smell (chemical sense) pegs or pits.

Eyes

1 Compound eye: up to thousands of light-sensing units (*ommatidia*) side by side. Ommatidium gathers light from a small angle, focuses it by 2 lenses into a clear rod (*rhabdom*)

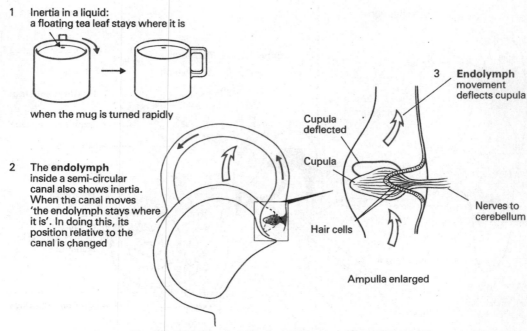

1   Inertia in a liquid:
     a floating tea leaf stays where it is

     when the mug is turned rapidly

2   The **endolymph**
     inside a semi-circular
     canal also shows inertia.
     When the canal moves
     'the endolymph stays where
     it is'. In doing this, its
     position relative to the
     canal is changed

3   **Endolymph**
     movement
     deflects cupula

Cupula
deflected

Cupula

Hair cells

Nerves to
cerebellum

Ampulla enlarged

Fig. 8.6 Detection of change in position by an ampulla

surrounded by 8 light-sensitive cells. Pigment cells on outside prevent light affecting other ommatidia (see Fig. 8.7).

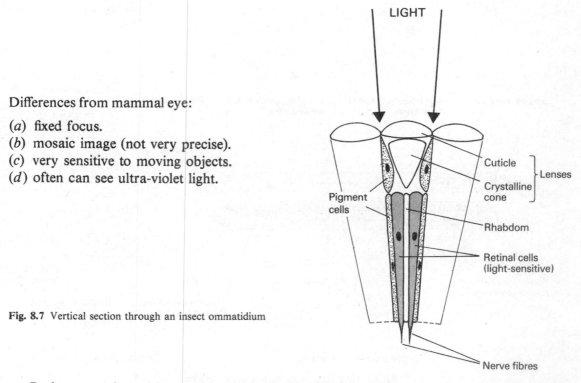

LIGHT

Cuticle ⎫
         ⎬ Lenses
Crystalline ⎭
cone

Pigment
cells

Rhabdom

Retinal cells
(light-sensitive)

Nerve fibres

Differences from mammal eye:

(*a*) fixed focus.
(*b*) mosaic image (not very precise).
(*c*) very sensitive to moving objects.
(*d*) often can see ultra-violet light.

Fig. 8.7 Vertical section through an insect ommatidium

Both mammals and insects have colour-seeing (man and bee) and colour-blind (bull and stick-insect) species.

2   **Simple eye:** an arrangement similar to a single ommatidium.

9 Co-ordination and response

9.1   INFORMATION, MESSAGES AND ACTION

1   **Information** both from an organism's external and its internal environments is received by sensory cells (see Section 8.1). Often this has to be acted upon if the organism is to remain alive.

2 Messages of two types result from the information:

(*a*) *chemical* – hormones, transported in solution, relatively slowly (animals and plants).
(*b*) *electrical* – along nerves, relatively quickly (animals only).

This accounts for the different rates at which plants and animals react.

3 Action resulting from the message:

(*a*) in *plants* is usually by:

    (*i*) *special growth*, e.g. tropisms, flowering, or
    (*ii*) *inhibiting growth*, e.g. dormancy of seed, leaf shedding.

Plants have no muscles or obvious glands like the liver, as have animals.

(*b*) in *animals* action is by:

    (*i*) *movement* (muscles), or
    (*ii*) *secretion* (glands).

Growth, although still controlled by hormones, as in plants, is a response only to the rate at which food can be built up into protoplasm.

Co-ordination of actions

Each response to a stimulus, unless co-ordinated with others, would lead to chaos. Thus feeding on bread includes muscle co-ordination to get the bread into the mouth (and not the ear) and to cause chewing, swallowing and peristalsis, as well as co-ordination of secretion of saliva, mucus and pancreatic juice (at the right times).

9.2 MAMMAL NERVOUS SYSTEM

Composed of *neurons* (nerve cells). Neurons are bundled up into *nerves* in the *peripheral nervous system* (*PNS*). Nerves link sensory cells and action (effector) cells with the *central nervous system* (*CNS*) – the brain and spinal cord (see Figs. 9.1a, 9.1b).

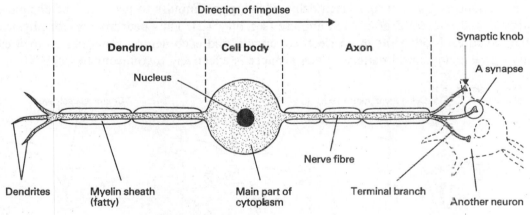

Fig. 9.1a A generalised neuron

As far as function is concerned there are *four types of neuron:*

1 Sensory: may connect with sensory cells, e.g. in retina of eye, or have sensory ends themselves, e.g. touch receptors in skin. Have long dendrons, short axons; carry 'messages' about the environment *to* the CNS.

2 Relay: always act as links between neurons, e.g. sensory neurons and either motor neurons or pyramidal neurons. Thus allow a large number of cross-connections, as in a switch-board.

3 Pyramidal: connect with relay neurons and other pyramidal neurons which have a vast network of cell processes (up to 50 000), each a possible inter-connection. This allows the 'computer' function of the brain.

4   Motor: always link with relay neurons and with muscle or gland cells, to which they carry 'messages' *from* the CNS, calling for action; have short dendrons, long axons.

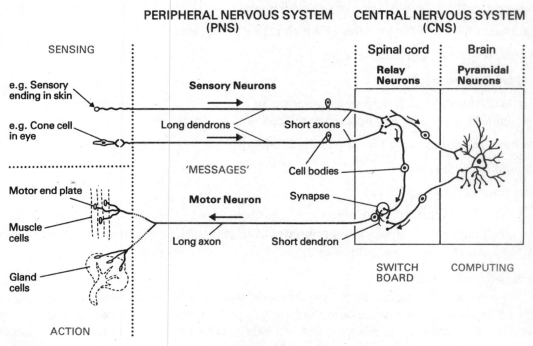

Fig. 9.1b Four different kinds of neuron and their functions in the body

9.3   NERVOUS IMPULSES

Neuron 'messages' (impulses) are *identical* from neuron to neuron. *Electro-chemical* in nature, they require flow of Na^+ ions into neuron and K^+ out, giving about 100 millivolts potential difference at cell membrane only, passing along neuron at up to 120 m/s.

Cause secretion of a chemical substance at a *synaptic knob* which, for less than one millisecond, 'connects' two neurons electrically, allowing the impulse to pass on. The chemical is destroyed and re-created after each impulse (see Fig. 9.2). Thus neurons are not physically connected to each other (as in an electrical circuit) and each neuron generates its own electricity (there is no central battery). Each synapse is effectively a connecting switch.

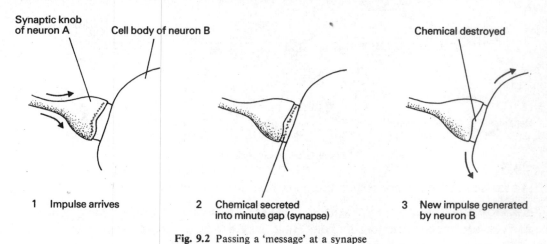

Fig. 9.2 Passing a 'message' at a synapse

9.4   TYPES OF NERVOUS SYSTEM

1   Nerve net (Coelenterates, e.g. *Hydra*). No nerves; each neuron passes its message to a number of others, so the message 'spreads' in all directions (see Section 17.6).

2   Central nervous system (higher animals). Neurons are grouped into nerves both receiving and sending messages and are linked to a nerve cord. Nerve cord acts as:

(*a*) local 'decision-maker' (reflex actions).

(*b*) 'switch-board' for passing messages on to brain for higher decisions (intelligent actions).

Animals with small brains rely mostly on automatic reactions (instinct). Those with larger brains have more scope for working out solutions (intelligence).

9.5   REFLEX, CONDITIONED REFLEX AND INTELLIGENT ACTION

Reflex action: an automatic, rapid *unlearned* response to a stimulus which has a high survival value. It is a reaction to sensory information of an *urgent* nature (e.g. withdrawing hand from flame; righting oneself when overbalancing; swallowing) which could mean the difference between survival and death (see also Section 8.3 – eye).

A maximum of *five* kinds of cell (*reflex arc*) take part in the action (see Fig. 9.3).

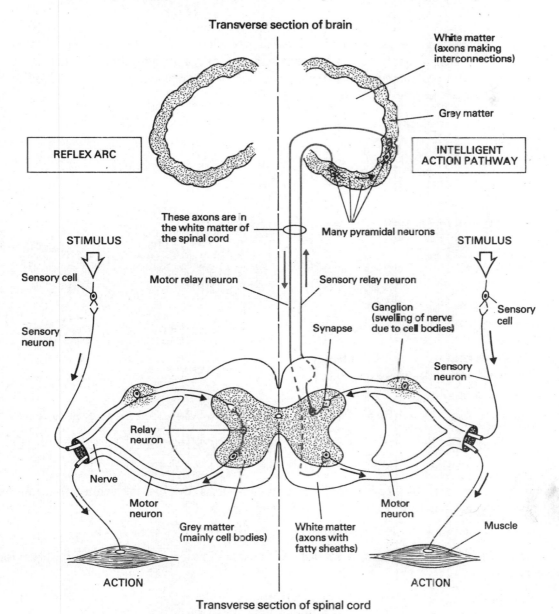

Fig. 9.3 Comparison of reflex and intelligent action pathways

Conditioned reflex action: a *learned* reflex, i.e. the brain is involved. During the training period an inappropriate stimulus is substituted for the appropriate one, as Pavlov discovered with dogs (see Table 9.1).

Conditioned reflexes can be 'unlearned' too, if the reaction is not rewarded. Many skills, e.g. feeding oneself, writing, riding a bicycle, are conditioned reflexes learned by hard practice (training).

Table 9.1   Pavlov's experiment – conditioned reflex in dogs

	Stimulus	*Reaction*
Reflex action	Smell of food	Saliva flows
Training period	Bell rung when food given	Saliva flows
Conditioned reflex	Bell rung (inappropriate)	Saliva still flows

Intelligent action: sensory information goes to the brain before action is taken (see Fig. 9.3). All the little delays in transmission of messages at thousands of synapses in the brain add up to make reaction time slower than in reflex actions.

9.6   INSTINCTIVE BEHAVIOUR

Instinctive behaviour: a series of reflex actions, the completion of one being the signal for starting the next. Often a highly complex 'behaviour pattern', any disruption of which leads to total failure and a recommencement of the sequence of actions, e.g. provision of food for a hunting-wasp's larvae (see Fig. 9.4).

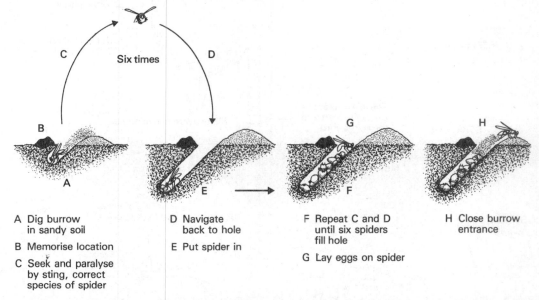

A Dig burrow
  in sandy soil
B Memorise location
C Seek and paralyse
  by sting, correct
  species of spider

D Navigate
  back to hole
E Put spider in

F Repeat C and D
  until six spiders
  fill hole
G Lay eggs on spider

H Close burrow
  entrance

If at stage E, spiders are removed by forceps, wasp continues to bring more spiders, eventually giving up and starting at A again, elsewhere.

Fig. 9.4 Instinctive behaviour of a hunting wasp in providing food for its larvae

9.7   THE BRAIN

Expanded front part of nerve cord; but grey matter is outside the white. In primitive vertebrates, brain has three main parts: fore-, mid- and hind-.

In most mammals, same three parts are easily seen.

In man, fore- part (cerebrum) is so vast that it covers mid-brain and part of hind-brain too (see Fig. 9.5).

1   Fore-brain

(*a*) **olfactory lobes** (in front) – sense of smell.

(*b*) **cerebrum** (upper part) – centre for memory, aesthetic and moral sense, hearing, vision, speech and muscular action, other than in the viscera (guts).

(*c*) **hypothalamus** (lower part) – receptors for control of internal environment (homeostasis), e.g. temperature, water content of blood. An outgrowth of it is the **pituitary** (the 'master' endocrine gland, see Section 9.8).

2   Mid-brain

   Optic lobes (upper part) – simple auditory and visual (pupil) reflexes.

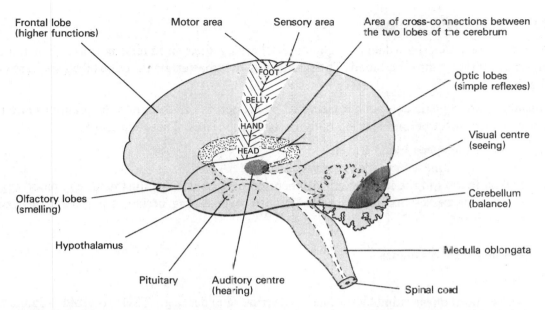

Frontal lobe (higher functions)

Motor area

Sensory area

Area of cross-connections between the two lobes of the cerebrum

FOOT

BELLY

HAND

HEAD

Optic lobes (simple reflexes)

Visual centre (seeing)

Cerebellum (balance)

Olfactory lobes (smelling)

Hypothalamus

Pituitary

Auditory centre (hearing)

Medulla oblongata

Spinal cord

Fig. 9.5 Functional areas of the human brain. (Fore-brain shown overlying mid-brain and hind-brain in section)

3 Hind-brain

(*a*) **cerebellum** (large upper outgrowth) – balance, co-ordination of muscle action.

(*b*) **medulla oblongata** (brain-stem, merging with spinal cord behind) – control of many vital 'automatic' actions, e.g. breathing, heart rate, constriction of arteries to direct blood to specific regions of the body etc.

Summary of brain functions: receives all sensory information and 'processes' it (see Fig. 9.6) either:

(*a*) immediately – reflex action (as in spinal cord), or

(*b*) more slowly – *storing* it as 'memory'
- – using past memory to compare with the new, and *calculating*
- – *co-ordinating* memories from other brain centres
- – reaching a *'decision'*
- – passing out *'orders'* via neurons and hormones (from the pituitary).

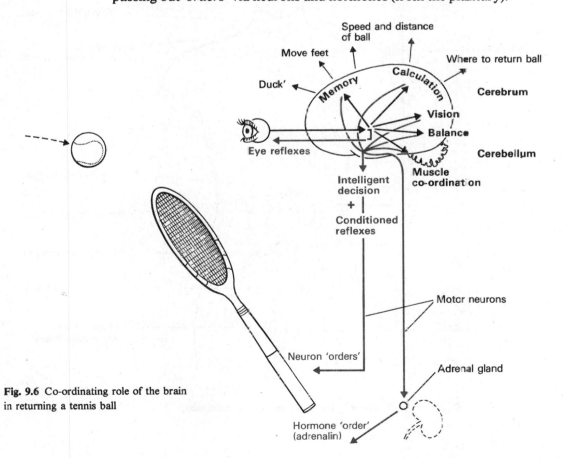

Fig. 9.6 Co-ordinating role of the brain in returning a tennis ball

9.8   ENDOCRINE SYSTEM

A variety of endocrine (ductless) glands discharging their products, hormones, in minute quantities directly into the blood. The pituitary is the 'master gland' controlling the rest (see Fig. 9.7).

Hormones are organic compounds (secreted by endocrine glands in minute quantities into the blood) which affect certain specific body parts or processes. These 'messages':

(*a*) arrive at the speed blood travels
(*b*) have long-lasting effects (hours, days)
(*c*) control factors in the internal environment needing constant adjustment, e.g. blood sugar level; or processes needing integrated control over a long period, e.g. growth or sexual development.

Glands and their hormones

1   Pituitary

(*a*) **tropic hormones:** stimulate other endocrine glands, e.g. TSH (thyroid stimulating hormone).
(*b*) **growth hormone:** promotes growth of muscle, bone (protein synthesis). Deficiency results in a dwarf; excess – a giant.
(*c*) **antidiuretic hormone** (ADH): water conservation in kidney. Deficiency causes *water diabetes* (see Section 7.3).
(*d*) secretes many other hormones, including *oxytocin* (ensures contraction of uterus during birth and milk ejection during suckling) and *prolactin* (milk synthesis).

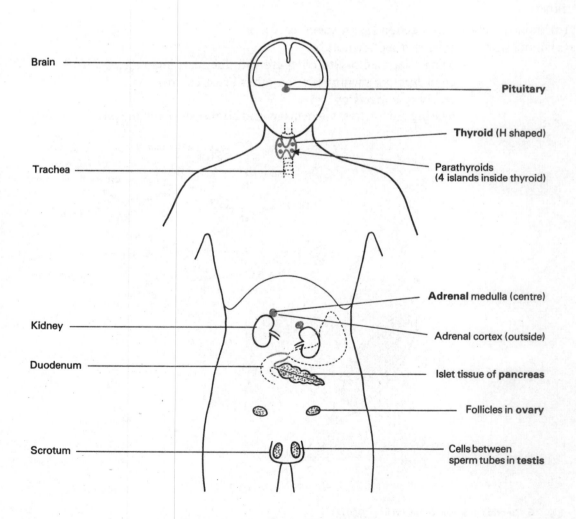

Fig. 9.7 The endocrine system in humans

2 Thyroid

Thyroxin: affects energy release at mitochondria (see Section 2.2) in all cells, raising metabolic rate. Deficiency causes sluggishness, puffy skin; excess produces over-active person with 'pop-eyes'. Deficiency in baby causes *cretinism* – mental and physical retardation (see also mongolism, Section 16.10, and goitre, Section 4.3).

3 Parathyroids

Separate glands embedded in thyroid secreting *parathormone* (promotes Ca^{2+} release from bones to blood).

4 Islet tissue of the pancreas

Insulin: causes absorption of glucose from blood into cells, e.g. by liver and muscles to store it as *glycogen*. Deficiency causes *sugar diabetes* (*diabetes mellitus* – see Section 7.3).

5 Adrenals

Adrenalin (the 'fight or flight hormone'): raises blood glucose level (from glycogen breakdown in liver); increases heart and breathing rates; diverts blood from guts to limb muscles. Adrenalin comes from the adrenal **medulla** which is nerve-stimulated.

The adrenal **cortex** (hormone-stimulated) secretes other hormones including *aldosterone* (Na^+ conservation in kidney) and *cortisol* (promotes protein breakdown).

6 Ovaries and testes

Produce **sex-hormones**, e.g. oestrogen and testosterone respectively, which promote changes in body proportions, development of gametes and hair, and changes in behaviour and voice, at *puberty* (see Fig. 9.8). (For oestrous cycle, see Section 12.18.)

7 Duodenum (HCl-sensitive cells)

Secretin: causes secretion of pancreatic juice when acid contents of stomach reach duodenum.

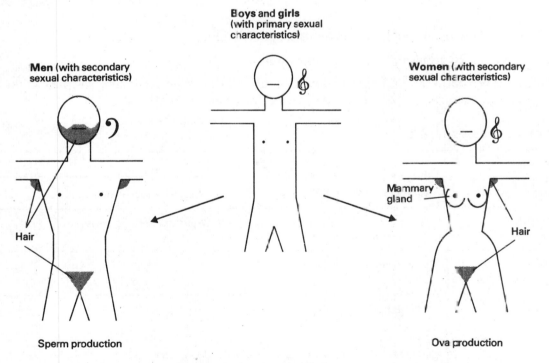

Fig. 9.8 Changes at puberty in humans

9.9 NERVOUS AND HORMONAL SYSTEMS COMPARED

Both achieve co-ordination by *antagonistic action*, e.g. biceps/triceps control of forearm position (see Section 10.4), and insulin/adrenalin control of blood sugar (see Section 4.20).

Table 9.2   Comparison of nervous and endocrine systems

	Nervous system	Endocrine system
Speed of 'message'	Fast	Slow
Duration of effect	Short	Long
Precision of 'message'	To a very precise area	A more general effect
Reaction required	Immediate	Long-term

Both systems are *linked to each other*, e.g. hypothalamus (nervous) stimulates pituitary (hormonal); nerves stimulate adrenal medulla; adrenalin stimulates the heart, just as certain nerves do.

9.10   FEED-BACK

Feed-back is the means by which a hormone adjusts its own output by affecting the endocrine glands that cause its secretion. Very important in oestrus cycle (see Section 12.18). If faulty, can cause metabolic disease, e.g. goitre (see summary diagram).

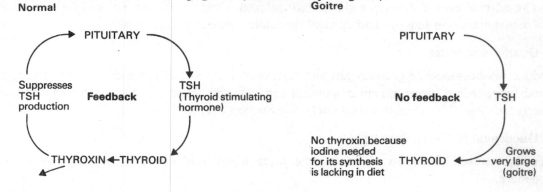

9.11   TAXIS

There are three main simple responses to simple stimuli:

1 taxis,   **2** tropism,   **3** photoperiodism.

Taxis: movement of an organism bodily towards or away from a stimulus. Applies to many invertebrate animals, unicells and even sperm. For examples see Table 9.3.

Table 9.3   Examples of taxes

Stimulus (and response prefix)	*Responses*	
	Positive (+ = towards stimulus)	*Negative* (− = away from stimulus)
Light (photo-)	Fly, having escaped swatting, flies towards window	Woodlouse seeks darkness
Water (hydro-)	Woodlouse seeks humid area	
Gravity (geo-)	Fly maggots burrow to pupate	
Chemicals (chemo-)	*Amoeba* follows chemicals diffusing from prey	Earthworms rise from soil dosed with formalin
Contact (thigmo-)	Woodlice huddle together	

Thus woodlice can be described as negatively phototaxic and positively hydrotaxic.

9.12 TROPISMS

Tropism: growth-movement of a plant towards or away from a stimulus. Usually controlled by hormones. For examples see Table 9.4.

Mechanism: auxin (hormone) is made at root and shoot tips (which are sensitive). It diffuses back to region of cell elongation (Fig. 9.9) and here it affects the rate at which cells swell by osmosis (vacuolate). Under normal conditions, equal distribution of auxin gives even growth. With a one-sided stimulus, distribution becomes unequal giving unequal growth. Roots and shoots behave differently to an increase in auxin concentration (see Fig. 9.9). Thus the auxin

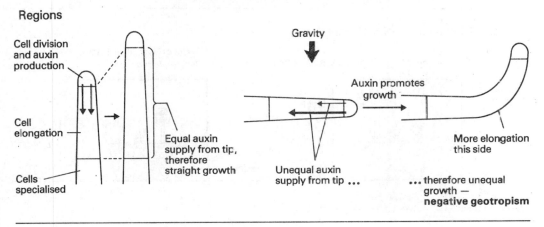

Shoot in dark — response to gravity

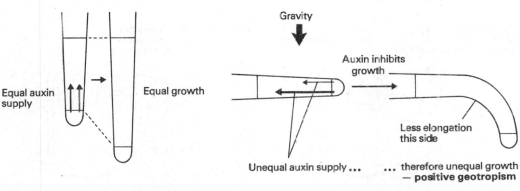

Root in dark — response to gravity

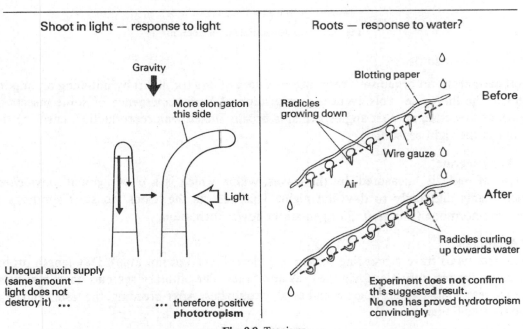

Fig. 9.9 Tropisms

theory explains geotropism and phototropism and is backed by evidence (see Fig. 9.10). No satisfactory evidence for hydrotropism and its mechanism exists.

Table 9.4   Examples of tropisms

Stimulus	Main shoot response	Main root response	Notes
Light	+ Phototropic	Neutral usually	(Lateral roots and shoots do not behave in this way)
Gravity	− Geotropic	+ Geotropic	
Water	Neutral	? + Hydrotropic	Mechanism unknown

1   Oat coleoptiles are positively phototropic:

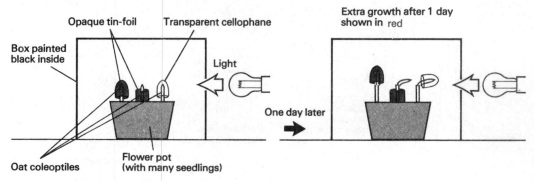

2   A bean tap-root is positively geotropic:

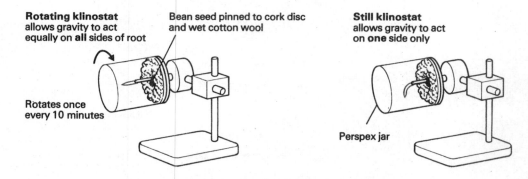

Resulting growth after 1 day shown in red

Fig. 9.10 Two demonstrations of tropisms

9.13   PHOTOPERIODISM

Photoperiodism: an organism's response to *length of day* (or night) by initiating an important event in the life cycle. This event (e.g. migration of birds, emergence of some insects from pupae, or flowering in most angiosperms) is usually linked with reproduction, ensuring that it occurs in the right season.

1   Angiosperms
Length of night is 'measured' by the leaves, within which is a blue pigment, *phytochrome*, which reacts differently to day and night. This acts as the 'clock' to start synthesis of a flowering-hormone (*florigen*). Florigen starts flower formation.

2   Mammals
Many *mammals* have a breeding season, e.g. deer, lions (but not man). Day-length probably influences the pituitary gland via the eyes and brain. The pituitary secretes hormones influencing the testes and ovaries to grow and produce gametes. After breeding, the testes and ovaries become small again.

10 Support and locomotion

10.1   PRINCIPLES OF SUPPORT

Organisms are supported ultimately by their environment (water, land or air).

Plants transmit their weight to it via *cell walls*, e.g. in angiosperms, *turgor pressure* (on cellulose cell walls) (see Section 5.3) and *xylem* (strength of wood-substance) (see Section 5.5) keep the plant in shape by providing mutual *support*.

Animals, since they lack cell walls, have cells specially designed to secrete substances, e.g. chitin, chalk, bone minerals and protein fibres, to provide a *skeleton*. Since most animals move, skeleton is used both for *support and locomotion*.

10.2   SKELETONS USED IN WATER, LAND AND AIR

The environment has a strong influence on **skeleton design** (see below).

Aquatic	*Terrestrial*	*Aerial*
(*a*) *Great support* from water (organism 'made lighter' by mass of water it displaces)	*Negligible support* from air (since volume of air displaced has small mass)	
(*b*) Therefore *weaker skeleton* (sharks manage on cartilage) and massive animals (e.g. whales and giant squids) possible	Therefore *strong skeleton* essential because full weight of body acts through the small areas where limbs are attached to body. Also prevents internal organs crushing each other as they sag downwards	
(*c*) *Streamlining* and *buoyancy* important in saving energy when moving through water (dense medium)	*Foot design* important for efficient movement on, e.g. sand, rock, trees	*Streamlining* and *wing design* important for sufficient lift and speed

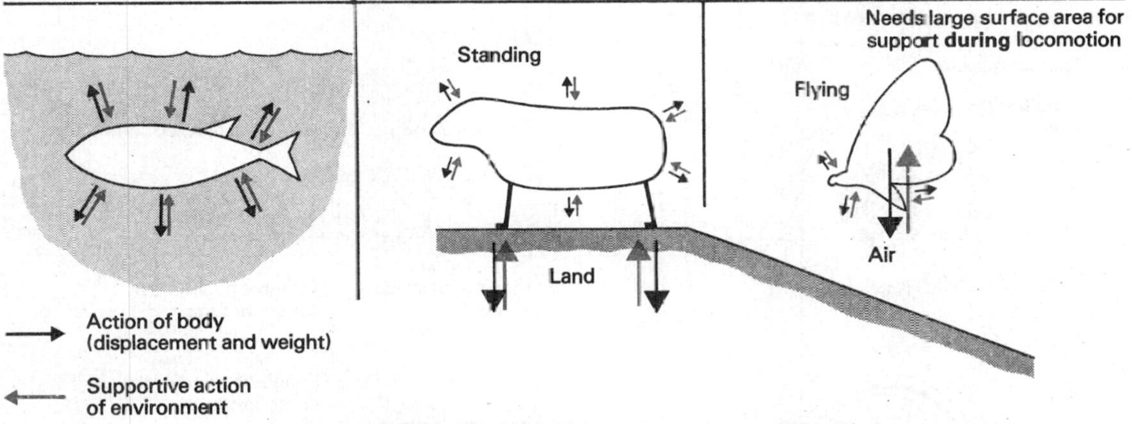

Fig. 10.1 The influence of environment on skeleton design

Various types of vertebrate locomotion
Fish: swimming (see Section 17.20).
Frog: crawling, leaping (see Section 17.22).
Bird: flying (see Section 17.23).

10.3   EXO-, ENDO- AND HYDROSTATIC SKELETONS

1   Exoskeleton (on outside): used by all arthropods (see Section 10.6); made of chitin, with protein or chalk to make it harder; has to be shed (ecdysis) from time to time to allow growth of body within a new one before it hardens. Acts as skin also.

2   Endoskeleton (inside): used by all vertebrates (see Section 10.7); made of bone and cartilage linked up with connective tissue; grows with the rest of the body.

3   Hydrostatic (water inside a cavity): used by annelids (see Section 10.5); its fluid nature allows animal to change shape easily, e.g. in burrowing (see Fig. 10.2), withdrawing into shells, etc. (Liquid food acts as 'skeleton' for muscles of peristalsis (see Section 4.18) in intestine of mammals in a similar way.)

10.4   PRINCIPLES OF MOVEMENT

1 Muscle can only *contract* (pull) – cannot push. To be lengthened again it must (*a*) relax, (*b*) be pulled back into shape – by another muscle, its antagonist, e.g. biceps and triceps (see Fig. 10.3). Thus muscles work in *antagonistic pairs*.

2 Nerve impulses are essential to make muscles *contract* (except heart). The antagonistic muscles are kept *relaxed* by impulses too (reflex inhibition).

3 Skeleton transmits the contraction force of muscle to the environment e.g. water, land, air (or food in gut).

4 Load-bearing surface in contact with the environment must get purchase on it if locomotion is to result, e.g. fish tail on water, bird wing on air, hooves on ground or claws on trees.

10.5   HYDROSTATIC SKELETON AND EARTHWORM MOVEMENT

Earthworm is adapted to moving in *tunnels* and spaces in the soil (mucus lubricates) (see Fig. 10.2). Solid skeleton is a disadvantage for this. Watery 'skeleton' within a segmented body-cavity (coelome) is incompressible, but can be forced hydraulically into different shapes by muscle action:

(*a*) when **circular muscles** contract, coelomic fluid is forced into long thin shape which *extends* the segments, and relaxes the longitudinal muscles.

(*b*) when **longitudinal muscles** contract, fluid is forced into short fat shape which *shortens* segments, and relaxes the circular muscles. Purchase on soil is obtained by pushing out pegs (**chaetae** – 8 per segment) where segments are short and fat.

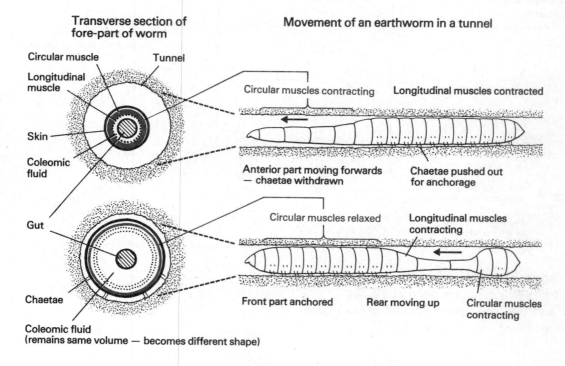

Fig. 10.2 Movement of an earthworm in a tunnel

10.6   EXOSKELETON AND INSECT MOVEMENT

(*a*) **Walking** (see Fig. 10.3)

A system of tubular levers (of hard chitin).

Antagonistic muscles are inside these tubes.

Levers pivot at peg-in-socket joints, sealed by flexible chitin.

Claws or foot-pads provide adhesion to surfaces.

(*b*) **Flight** (see Fig. 10.4)

Wing is a thin plate of chitin, strengthened by veins.

On down-stroke it is horizontal (for maximum lift) (see Section 17.23).

On up-stroke, special muscles rotate it vertically (for minimum air-resistance).

Flight muscles are either:

(*i*) *direct* (large wings, slow beat), e.g. butterfly, or

(*ii*) *indirect* (small wings, fast beat), e.g. fly.

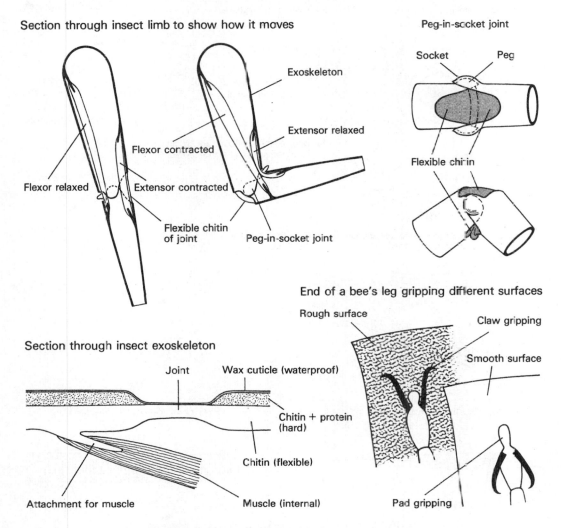

Fig. 10.3 Insect exoskeleton showing parts used for walking

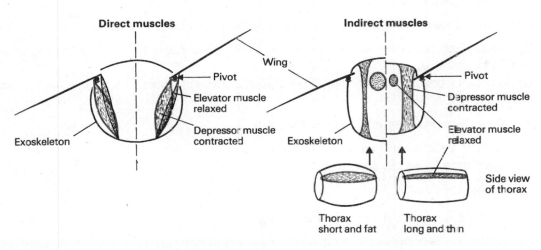

Fig. 10.4 Cross section of insect thorax showing action of flight muscles

10.7   ENDOSKELETON AND MAMMAL MOVEMENT (TISSUES)

Mammal skeletal and muscle tissues:

1   Bone: hard spicules of calcium phosphate, secreted in layers by bone cells, and inelastic protein fibres (see Fig. 10.5).

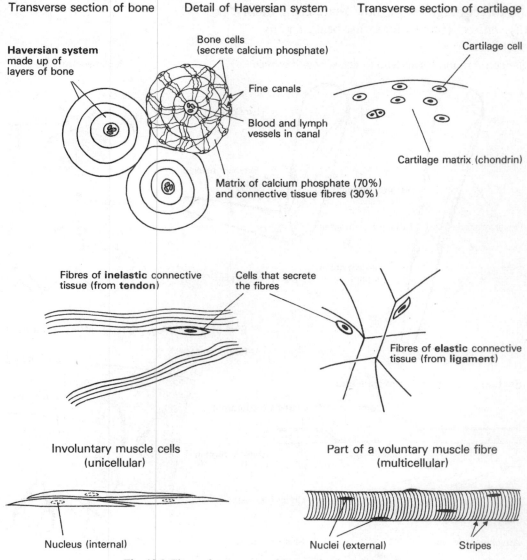

Fibres of **inelastic** connective tissue (from **tendon**)

Cells that secrete the fibres

Fibres of **elastic** connective tissue (from **ligament**)

Involuntary muscle cells (unicellular)

Part of a voluntary muscle fibre (multicellular)

Nucleus (internal)

Nuclei (external)   Stripes

Fig. 10.5 Tissues for support and locomotion in a mammal

2   Cartilage: rubbery protein (chondrin) secreted by cells. Cushions the ends of long bones and vertebrae (shock-absorber).

3   Connective tissue: protein fibres secreted by cells to join bone and muscle.

(*a*) **ligaments** (join bone to bone) – mainly *elastic* branched fibres (elastin) taking the strain from all directions.

(*b*) **tendons** (join bone to muscle) – mainly *inelastic* straight fibres (collagen) taking strain along one line of pull.

4   Muscle: cells containing protein that contracts

(*a*) involuntary muscle, e.g. in gut.

(*b*) voluntary muscle, e.g. in arm.

10.8   JOINTS

Joints are where bones are linked (see Fig. 10.6).

1   Immovable joints (sutures): wavy interlocking edges of bone are held together by collagen, e.g. bones of cranium.

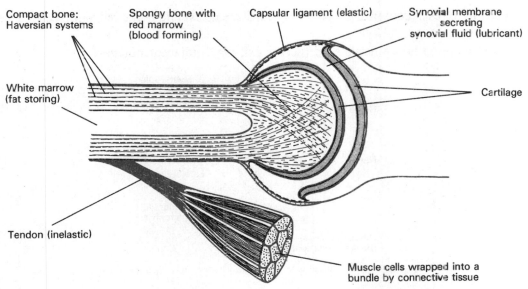

Fig. 10.6 Section through mammal synovial joint

2 Movable joints (synovial joints): bones have cartilage ends; these move on each other, lubricated by synovial fluid secreted by synovial membrane within joint capsule. Types:

(*a*) *ball-and-socket*, e.g. at shoulder, hip – rotation in 2 planes of space.

(*b*) *hinge*, e.g. at elbow (see Fig. 10.7) and knee – movement in one plane only (like door).

(*c*) *slipping*, e.g. at wrist and ankle – limited rocking movement.

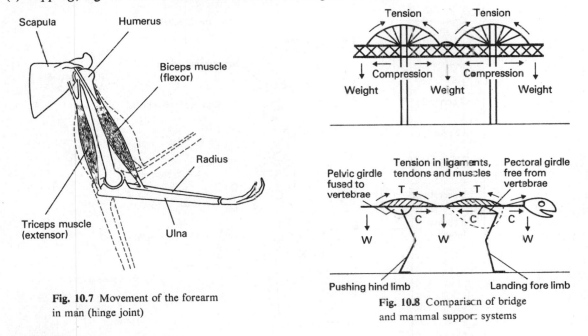

Fig. 10.7 Movement of the forearm in man (hinge joint)

Fig. 10.8 Comparison of bridge and mammal support systems

10.9 MAMMAL SKELETON

1 Skull: cranium protects brain; houses all major sense organs; jaws for chewing.

2 Vertebral column: protects nerve cord; acts as anchorage for 4 limbs via limb girdles and for ribs. Also a flexible, segmented rod from which internal organs are slung.

Overall, acts as a double cantilever bridge in a quadruped, e.g. dog (see Fig. 10.8).

However, limbs are not static, so *pushing* hind limbs need *firm* attachment via pelvic girdle to vertebrae; but *shock-absorbing* front limbs require an *elastically* attached pectoral girdle.

Typical vertebra (see Fig. 10.9) has:

(*a*) **neural spine** and *lateral processes* for ligament and muscle attachment.

(*b*) **zygapophyses** (anterior one fits into posterior one of next vertebra) to prevent vertebrae twisting apart.

(c) **centrum** to resist compression (aided by cartilage discs) and make red blood cells (in its red bone marrow).

(d) **neural canal** to house nerve cord (nerves exit via 2 adjacent notches).

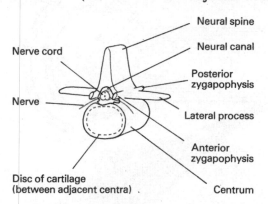

Fig. 10.9 A generalised vertebra and nearby structures (shown in red)

Specialisation of vertebrae

The five types of vertebrae (see Fig. 10.10) have special functions, e.g. thoracic ones have ribs, caudal ones aid balancing (not in man – fused and functionless: the coccyx).

Atlas is first cervical vertebra; supports cranium, allowing nodding i.e. 'yes' movement.

Axis is second; has peg fitting inside atlas which allows swivelling, i.e. 'no' movement.

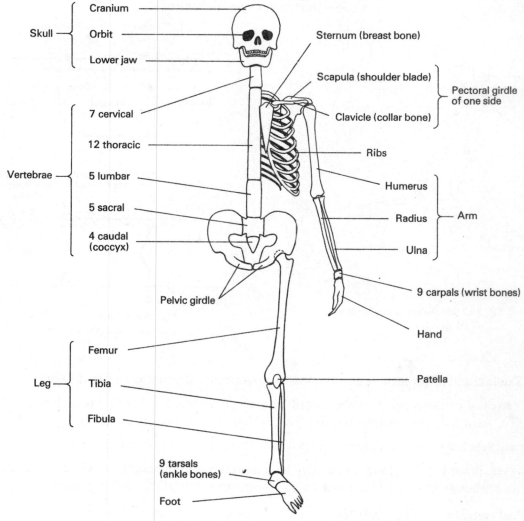

Fig. 10.10 Main parts of the human skeleton

3   Limbs: built on exactly the same plan (see Fig. 10.11) – one upper bone, two lower, and same number of bones in wrist and hand as in ankle and foot (not so in all mammals).

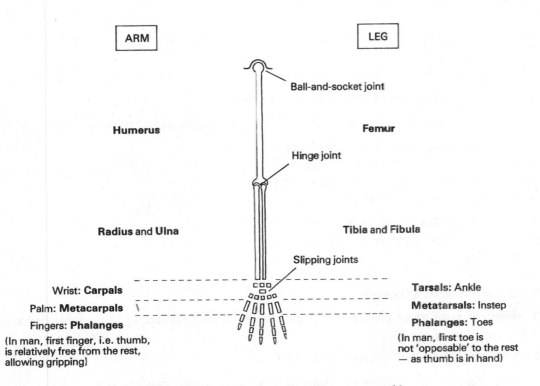

Fig. 10.11 Comparison of bones and joints of human arm and leg

4   Limb-girdles:

(*a*) **pectoral girdle** attached loosely to vertebral column to allow shock of landing to be absorbed (muscles link *scapula* to thoracic vertebrae: *clavicle* links to vertebrae via sternum and ribs).

(*b*) **pelvic girdle** fused very firmly to sacral vertebrae to allow thrust of back legs to be transmitted efficiently up the vertebral column. Made of 3 fused bones on each side, welded into a hoop.

10.10   INSECT AND MAMMAL SKELETONS COMPARED

Functions of mammal skeletons

1   Support: of body off ground; of internal organs, preventing crushing.

2   Shape: important adaptations, e.g. man's hand, bat's wing, porpoise's streamline and flippers.

3   Locomotion: system of levers.

4   Protection: cranium protects brain; ribs protect heart and lungs.

5   Breathing: role of ribs (see Section 6.6).

6   Making blood cells: in red bone marrow, e.g. of ribs, vertebrae (see Fig. 10.6).

7   Sound conduction: 3 ossicles in middle ear (see Section 8.5)

Functions of insect skeletons

1–5 above (but with different examples). *Note:* the tracheal system is chitin and is continuous with the exoskeleton.

6   Skin function, e.g. providing camouflage, barrier to bacteria.

11 Growth

11.1 GROWTH IN PLANTS AND ANIMALS

Growth: increase in size or weight of an organism.

Plants and animals grow differently, resulting in shapes suited to their type of nutrition:

1 Green plants grow at their tips giving a branching shape with a large surface area for absorption of nutrients (necessary when anchored), and of sunlight energy.

2 Animals bodies grow into a compact shape, except for their limbs (needed for food-seeking).

Processes involved in growth

1 Formation of more protoplasm (especially proteins – formed at ribosomes: see Sections 2.2, 2.3).

2 Cell division (mitosis – see Section 13.12).

3 Vacuolation – in plants only; absorption of much water, swelling cell.

4 Differentiation – cells become different for special purposes (see Fig. 11.1).

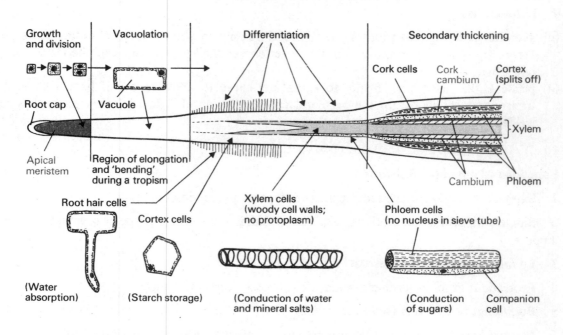

Fig. 11.1 Longitudinal section through a root showing regions of cell division (in red) and subsequent stages in growth

In a similar way, animal cells divide (but do not form vacuoles) and differentiate into cheek cells, muscle cells, neurons and blood cells etc.

All four processes are controlled by hormones (see Sections 9.8: pituitary, 9.12: auxin).

11.2. GROWTH IN ANGIOSPERMS (PRIMARY)

Primary growth: growth mainly in length (see Fig. 11.1) occurring during first season. Results from cell division at root and shoot tips (apical meristems).

11.3 SECONDARY THICKENING

Secondary growth: growth mainly in thickness (see Fig. 11.2) occurring during second and subsequent seasons. Results from cell division of the cambium and cork cambium (forming new vascular tissue and cork respectively) in both roots and shoots.

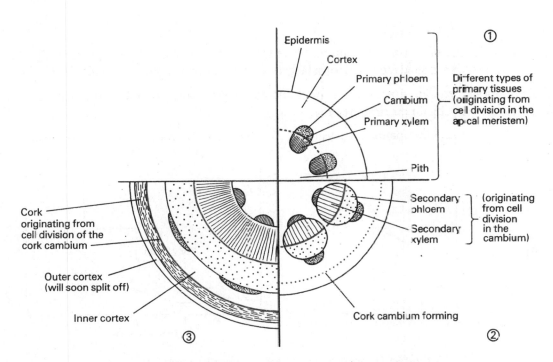

Epidermis

Cortex

Primary phloem

Cambium

Primary xylem

① Different types of primary tissues (originating from cell division in the apical meristem)

Pith

Cork originating from cell division of the cork cambium

Secondary phloem

Secondary xylem

(originating from cell division in the cambium)

Outer cortex (will soon split off)

Inner cortex

③

Cork cambium forming

②

Fig. 11.2 Three stages in secondary thickening – stem shown in cross section

1 In spring the *cambium* grows into a complete ring and begins to divide.

2 The new cells differentiate into *secondary xylem* (wood) *and phloem*. Cork cambium forms in the cortex.

3 *Cork cambium* divides to form cork cells. These waterproof the expanding stem except at **lenticels** (pores for gaseous exchange, formed of loose cells).

4 In autumn, cell division slows down and denser wood with smaller cells is formed. In spring and summer rapid division resumes forming less dense wood. The successive rings of dense and less dense wood are '**annual rings**'. Phloem lacks these rings – older cells are crushed and only the newly formed ones function.

11.4 FACTORS AFFECTING GROWTH

A Plants

1 Genes: responsible for tall and dwarf varieties of pea plants, the different shapes of runner bean, gooseberry bush and beetroot, and the faster growth of pine trees compared with oak. These factors are *inherited*.

2 Climate: *warmth* promotes respiration (source of energy for growth); *sunlight* promotes photosynthesis (source of materials for growth).

3 Nutrients: good supply of mineral salts (e.g. from fertilisers) promotes growth; adequate water essential.

4 Hormones: auxin (and others) promote vacuolation and cell division; tropisms (see Section 9.12).

B Animals

1 Genes: inherited factors – as important as in plants.

2 Climate: temperature affects ectotherms (see Section 7.4) but not endotherms (e.g. mammals) – warmth speeds growth.

3 Nutrients: quantity and quality (a balanced diet, see Section 4.21) of food.

4 Hormones: affect feeding and moulting behaviour in insects; rate of growth in mammals, e.g. growth hormone (see Section 9.8).

11.5   ANIMAL GROWTH PATTERNS

1   Discontinuous: e.g. in insects, animal increases in mass within an *exoskeleton* until it no longer fits, then this is shed (ecdysis) for a larger one formed beneath the old one.

2   Continuous: e.g. in mammals, animal increases gradually in both mass and size, its *endoskeleton* growing all the time (see Fig. 11.3).

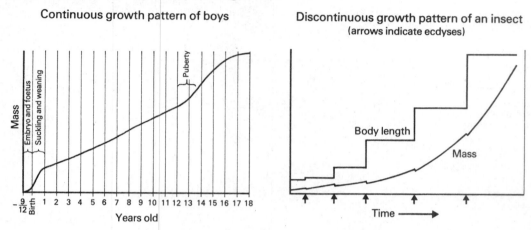

Fig. 11.3 Graphs of continuous and discontinuous growth

11.6   SEEDS (STRUCTURE AND GERMINATION)

Seeds are embryo plants enclosed by the testa (seed coat); found only in *gymnosperms* and *angiosperms*; developed from the ovule (see Section 12.11) after fertilisation. When dormant are dehydrated (about 10% water).

Factors needed for germination (see Fig. 11.4)

1   Water: to hydrate protoplasm, mobilise enzymes, hydrolyse stored food (e.g. starch to sugars).

2   Warmth: to enable enzymes to work.

3   Oxygen: for aerobic respiration to supply energy for growth.

Some seeds require *light*, others dark, for germination; most are indifferent.

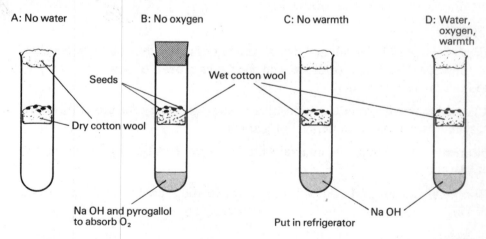

Fig. 11.4 Experiment to determine the conditions necessary for seed germination

Seed structure

All seeds have an embryo consisting of *radicle* (root) and *plumule* (shoot) joined to one or more *cotyledons* (first seed leaves) within the testa. Cotyledons may either not absorb the endosperm (food store) until germination (**endospermic** seeds, e.g. maize (monocot), castor oil (dicot)), or they may be fat with endosperm which has been totally absorbed before the seed was shed (**non-endospermic** seeds, e.g. pea, beans, see Section 12.11). *Testa* (seed coat) bears a hilum (attachment scar where seed linked with the fruit) and a micropyle (pore for water entry during germination) (see Fig. 11.5).

① **Pea** — non-endospermic, dicotyledon

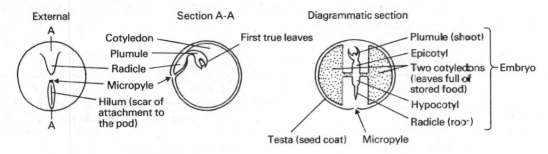

② **Maize** — endospermic, monocotyledon

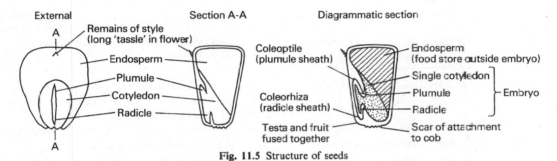

Fig. 11.5 Structure of seeds

Types of germination

1   Hypogeal: cotyledons remain *below ground* (because epicotyl grows rapidly).

2   Epigeal: cotyledons are pushed *above ground* and photosynthesise (because hypocotyl grows rapidly) (see Fig. 11.6).

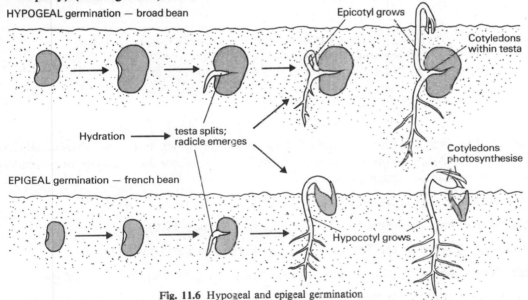

Fig. 11.6 Hypogeal and epigeal germination

11.7   GROWTH MEASUREMENT AND ITS DIFFICULTIES

1   Length or height – all organisms. A crude method: volume would be better.

2   Live mass – terrestrial animals. Difficult for:
(*a*) plants: roots are broken off, or soil remains attached to them.
(*b*) aquatic organisms: how much does one dry them before weighing?

3   Dry mass – all organisms, but they have to be killed (and dried in an oven at 110°C). Avoids errors of hydration, e.g. Did the animal drink or urinate before it was weighed? Were the plant cells fully turgid on weighing?

12 Reproduction

12.1 ASEXUAL AND SEXUAL REPRODUCTION COMPARED

No individual organism is immortal; reproduction avoids extinction. Most organisms reproduce sexually, many asexually as well.

Table 12.1   Comparison of asexual and sexual reproduction

	Asexual	*Sexual*
Parents	One	Two (unless parent is hermaphrodite)
Method	Mitosis forms either: (*a*) reproductive bodies, e.g. spores, tubers, or (*b*) replicas of adult by outgrowth, e.g. runners	Meiosis forms gametes (sperm and ova) which fuse to form zygotes (fertilisation) Zygote grows by mitosis into new organism
Offspring	Genetically identical to parent	Not identical – half its genes are maternal, half paternal
Advantage	Maintains a good strain exactly	Produces new varieties which, if 'better', enable survival and in the long-term, evolution (see Section 14.4)
Disadvantage	Species liable to be wiped out, e.g. by disease, if no resistant varieties	Excellent individuals, e.g. prize milk-cow, cannot give identical offspring
Other points	Only one arrival needed to colonise a new area Often more rapid than sexual methods Always increases population	Both sexes needed Not rapid Need not increase population (two parents may produce only one offspring, then die)
Occurrence	Very common amongst plants and *simple* animals, e.g. *Amoeba, Hydra*	Almost all plants and animals

12.2 ASEXUAL METHODS OF REPRODUCTION

All the offspring from one asexually-reproducing parent are known as a *clone* (a genetically identical population). Many of the following methods of asexual reproduction achieve **perennation** (survival over winter in a dormant state).

1 **Binary fission,** e.g. bacteria (see Section 17.2), *Amoeba* (see Section 17.4).

2 **Spores,** e.g. fungi (see Section 17.5), mosses (see Section 17.8).

3 **Budding,** e.g. *Hydra* (see Section 17.6), tapeworm (see Section 17.11).

4 **Identical twinning,** e.g. in humans, a single zygote may develop into two babies.

5 **Parthenogenesis** ('virgin birth'), e.g. aphids (greenfly) do not have to mate to produce young; drone bees (see Section 17.18) are also produced in this way.

6 **Vegetative propagation** by outgrowths of new plantlets usually from *stems* (see Fig. 12.1) but sometimes from *leaves*, e.g. *Bryophyllum*.

Bulb: a disc-shaped stem bearing roots and:

(*a*) *buds* – for new growth in spring, surrounded by
(*b*) *fleshy leaf-bases* of last year's foliage – swollen with food for buds when they grow, and
(*c*) *brown, papery leaf-bases* – last year's leaf-bases, now totally exhausted of food.

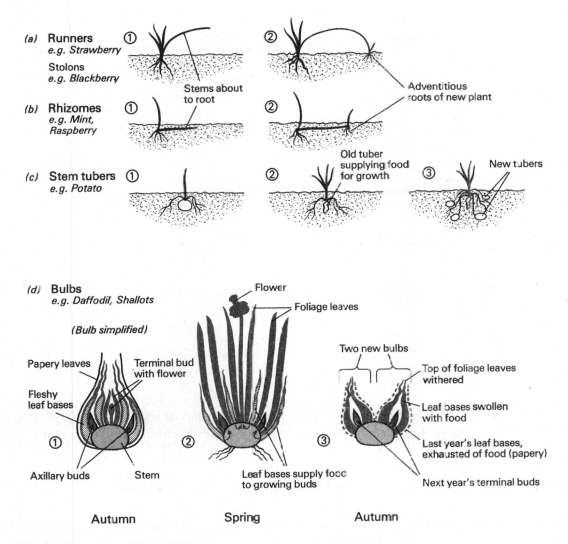

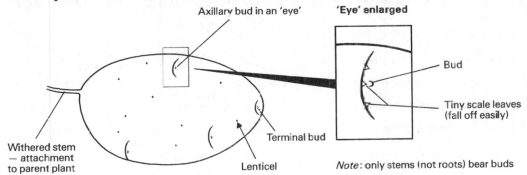

Fig. 12.1 Asexual reproduction: vegetative propagation

In the daffodil, the terminal bud usually flowers and dies. The lateral (axillary) buds form new bulbs, thus *reproducing asexually*. They also *perennate*, dying in their second season i.e. after flowering.

Potato tuber: an underground *stem*-tip swollen with food (especially starch) received from the parent plant, which dies down. Each tuber is a potential new plant (thus *asexual reproduction*) and allows *perennation*. New shoots and adventitious roots arise from 'eyes' (see Fig. 12.2).

Fig. 12.2 A potato tuber

12.3   WINTER TWIG

Many trees also perennate by shedding leaves in autumn, protecting new late summer growth inside *buds* ('compressed stems') (see Fig. 12.3). These consist of protective scale leaves (leathery) around unexpanded foliage leaves spaced at very short internodes. If they also contain flower buds, growth ends there after flowering, leaving a *scar* where the *inflorescence* withered and fell off. Otherwise *terminal* and *lateral* buds continue growth, unless they are dormant. *Dormant* buds lie in reserve, only growing if other buds die.

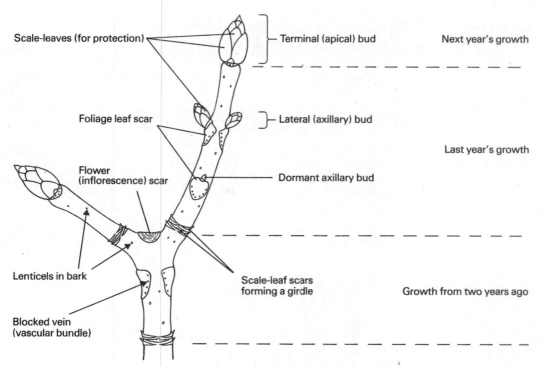

Scale-leaves (for protection)

Terminal (apical) bud

Next year's growth

Foliage leaf scar

Lateral (axillary) bud

Last year's growth

Flower (inflorescence) scar

Dormant axillary bud

Lenticels in bark

Scale-leaf scars forming a girdle

Growth from two years ago

Blocked vein (vascular bundle)

Fig. 12.3 A winter twig

In spring, all buds which burst leave *girdle scars* where rings of scale leaves fall off. These mark the beginning of a new year's growth. *Leaf scars* form in autumn (see Fig. 12.4).

1 Leaf dying	2 Stem sealed off from petiole	3 Leaf-fall
Useful substances passed into stem. Wastes, e.g. tannins received by leaf for excretion. New layer of dividing cells (abscission layer) arises.	Veins blocked, therefore leaf dries up. Abscission layer forms cork cells on stem-side; loosely packed cells (line of weakness) on leaf-side.	Wind or frost tears leaf off at abscission layer leaving leaf scar.

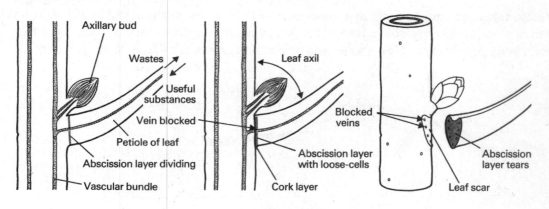

Axillary bud

Wastes

Useful substances

Vein blocked

Petiole of leaf

Abscission layer dividing

Vascular bundle

Leaf axil

Blocked veins

Abscission layer with loose-cells

Cork layer

Abscission layer tears

Leaf scar

Fig. 12.4 Leaf-fall (abcission)

12.4   PERENNIAL, BIENNIAL AND ANNUAL SEED-PLANTS

Perennials: live for a number of years, perennating other than exclusively as seed.

(*a*) *deciduous perennials:* shed leaves all at once usually when water supply becomes short, e.g. in winter. Advantages:

    (*i*) avoids transpiration losses which might kill (plants cannot absorb frozen water).

    (*ii*) avoids uprooting in autumn gales (leaves offer great wind-resistance).

(b) *evergreen perennials:* shed leaves little by little throughout the year:

    (*i*) either leaves are designed to reduce transpiration (see Section 5.4), e.g. by thick cuticles, woody leaves and fewer (often sunken) stomata, e.g. holly, pine, or

    (*ii*) most of the leaves die down, thus reducing transpiration, e.g. iris, grasses.

Biennials: live for two years, dying down to perennating organs at end of year 1 and flowering in year 2 to perennate as seed, e.g. carrot, onion (most root-crops and bulbs) (see Fig. 12.5).

Annuals: complete their life cycle in one year, perennating as seed only, e.g. pea, poppy.

Ephemerals: complete their life cycle in less than one season, thus allowing a number of generations in one year, e.g. groundsel, and desert species causing 'flowering of the desert' – plants germinate, grow and form new seed all in the few weeks of a rare wet spell.

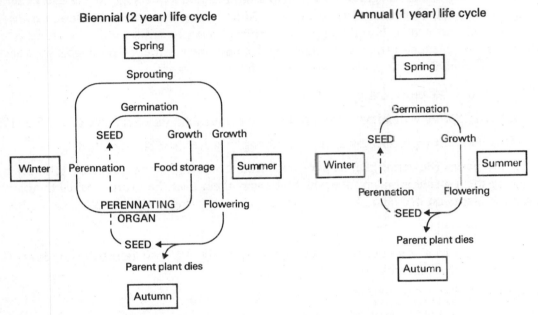

Fig. 12.5 Life cycles of biennials and annuals

12.5 GRAFTING AND CUTTING

(Artificial methods of vegetative propagation)

Grafting: growth together of a vigorous root (**stock**) with a stem (**scion**) bearing large fruit or flowers to give the benefits of both (see Fig. 12.6).

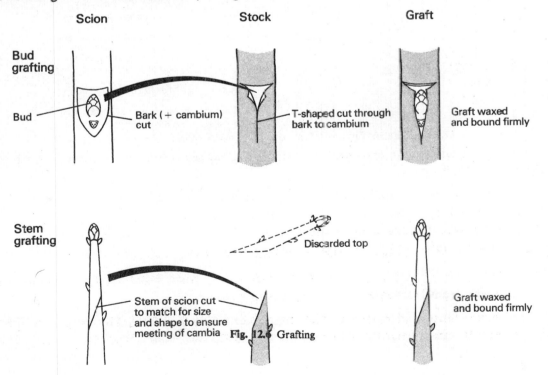

Fig. 12.6 Grafting

Grafting method requires:

(*a*) that cambiums (see Section 11.3) of stock and scion must meet (to grow together).
(*b*) firm binding at junction (to prevent joining tissue tearing).
(*c*) autumn grafting (to minimise death from excessive transpiration).
(*d*) waterproofing wound with tape or wax (minimises infection and desiccation).
(*e*) compatible species (lemon will not graft onto an apple).

Note: Neither stock nor scion are altered *genetically* by grafting, e.g. *'suckers'* from the garden rose 'Masquerade' are stems arising from the *stock*; they will only give wild briar roses, not 'Masquerade', if allowed to flower.

Grafting is used extensively in producing apples, pears, citrus fruit and roses.

Cutting: cutting a short length of young stem at a node and immersing the cut end in aerated damp soil (e.g. sandy peat mix) to form roots. Most leaves are detached to lessen transpiration. Dipping cut end in hormone powder (artificial auxin) assists rooting. Cutting is used extensively to produce ornamental plants and unique new varieties produced by selective breeding. Essential for propagating seedless oranges and grapes.

12.6   SEXUAL REPRODUCTION IN PLANTS

1   Bacteria, *Spirogyra* and *Mucor* reproduce by conjugation (see Sections 17.2, 17.3, 17.5).

2   Moss and fern reproduce by sperm swimming in water (see Section 17.8).

3   Angiosperms (flowering plants) avoid the need for water for male gametes to swim in by enclosing them inside a pollen tube which liberates them near the ovum – hence they are the dominant plants on dry land.

12.7   FLOWERS

The organ of sexual reproduction is the **flower** (see Fig. 12.7). It is usually bi-sexual (hermaphrodite) but sometimes unisexual, e.g. holly.

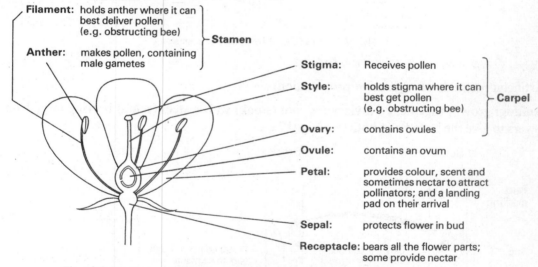

Fig. 12.7 Structure and functions of the parts of a generalised insect-pollinated flower

A flower consists of an expanded stem-tip, the **receptacle,** on which is borne four whorls (rings) of modified leaves:

(*i*) *sepals* – almost leaf-like but protective forming the **calyx.**
(*ii*) *petals* – often coloured and attractive: the **corolla.**
(*iii*) *stamens* – male parts: the **androecium.**
(*iv*) *carpels* – female parts: the **gynoecium.**

There are **two main stages in sexual reproduction**:

1   Pollination: transfer of pollen from stamens to stigmas.

2   Fertilisation: fusion of male with female gametes inside the ovule. This results from the growth of pollen tubes from the pollen on the stigmas to the ovules.

12.8   WIND AND INSECT POLLINATION

Table 12.2   Comparison of flowers adapted for wind or insect pollination

	Wind pollination	*Insect pollination*
1 *Petals*	**Not attractive:** usually green, unscented; no nectar **Small:** leaving stamens and carpels exposed	**Attractive:** coloured, scented, often with nectaries **Large:** protect stamens and carpels inside
2 *Stamens*	Long filaments and large mobile anthers **exposed to wind**	Stiff filaments and anthers **obstruct visiting insects**
3 *Pollen*	**Large quantities** (enormous chances against it all reaching stigmas) Small, dry, light (easily wind-borne)	**Small quantities** (more certain 'delivery service') Rougher, sometimes sticky (to catch on insect 'hairs')
4 *Stigmas*	**Large, exposed** to wind (to catch passing pollen)	**Small, unexposed,** sticky with stiff style (to obstruct insects)
Examples	Plantain, grasses, hazel, oak	Buttercup, dead-nettle, horse-chestnut, cherry

Variations: certain flowers, which appear to be designed for insect pollination, in fact use other methods. For example:

(*a*) *peas* **self-pollinate** when still in the bud stage.
(*b*) *dandelions* develop seed from ovules without fertilisation, i.e. asexually.

12.9   SELF- AND CROSS-POLLINATION

Self-pollination: transfer of pollen from any stamen to any stigma on the same *plant* (not necessarily the same flower). Results in fewer varieties of offspring than cross-pollination. Frequent in cereal crops, grasses.

Cross-pollination: transfer of pollen of one plant to the stigmas of another plant of the same *species*. Thus rose pollen landing on an apple stigma will not germinate there. Results in a great variety of offspring. Since this is biologically desirable many plants have developed means of improving the chances of cross-pollination.

12.10   ADAPTATIONS FOR CROSS-POLLINATION

1   Protandry: stamens ripen first (i.e. androecium), so little pollen is left when the stigma becomes receptive to pollen, e.g. deadnettle (see Fig. 12.8Ⓐ).

2   Protogyny: carpels ripen first (i.e. gynaecium), so pollination and fertilisation by other plants is achieved before the stamens shed their pollen, e.g. plantain (see Fig. 12.8Ⓑ).

Note: comparable mechanisms to ensure cross-fertilisation occur in hermaphrodite animals, e.g. *Hydra* (see Section 17.6), earthworm (see Section 17.7).

3   Incompatibility: chemicals in the stigma prevent germination of the plant's own pollen (same mechanism as that which prevents other species' pollen germinating), e.g. *Primula*.

4   Unisexual plants: impossible to self-pollinate, e.g. holly.

Note: unisexual *flowers*, both on the same plant, *can* allow self-pollination, e.g. hazel, oak.

12.11   FERTILISATION AND ITS CONSEQUENCES

1   Compatible pollen on the stigma germinates, forming a pollen tube containing 3 nuclei; the *pollen tube nucleus* directs growth to the micropyle of the ovule, liberating the *2 male nuclei* into it (see Fig. 12.9).

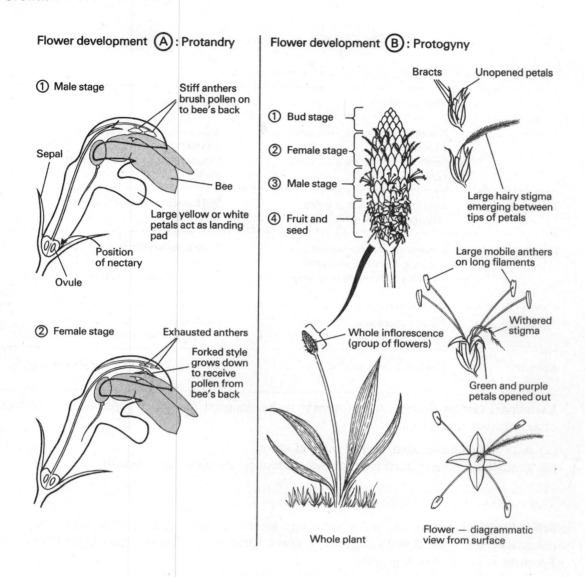

Flower development (A) : Protandry

① Male stage

Sepal

Stiff anthers brush pollen on to bee's back

Bee

Large yellow or white petals act as landing pad

Position of nectary

Ovule

② Female stage

Exhausted anthers

Forked style grows down to receive pollen from bee's back

Flower development (B) : Protogyny

Bracts

Unopened petals

① Bud stage

② Female stage

③ Male stage

④ Fruit and seed

Large hairy stigma emerging between tips of petals

Large mobile anthers on long filaments

Withered stigma

Green and purple petals opened out

Whole inflorescence (group of flowers)

Whole plant

Flower — diagrammatic view from surface

Fig. 12.8 Ⓐ Features of an insect-pollinated flower illustrated by the deadnettle (seen in section) Ⓑ Features of a wind-pollinated flower illustrated by the narrow-leaved plantain

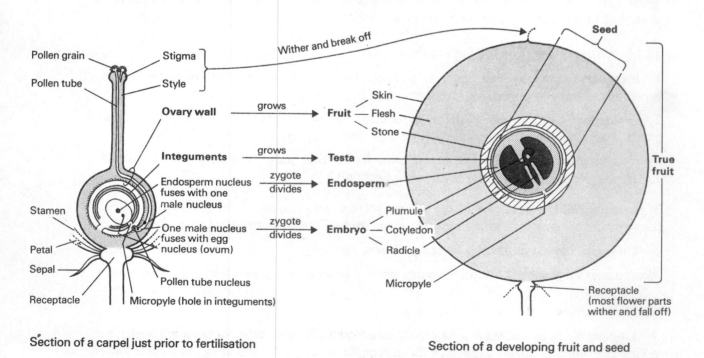

Pollen grain

Pollen tube

Stigma

Style

Wither and break off

Seed

Ovary wall — grows → **Fruit** — Skin / Flesh / Stone

Integuments — grows → **Testa**

Endosperm nucleus fuses with one male nucleus — zygote divides → **Endosperm**

One male nucleus fuses with egg nucleus (ovum) — zygote divides → **Embryo** — Plumule / Cotyledon / Radicle

Stamen

Petal

Sepal

Receptacle

Pollen tube nucleus

Micropyle (hole in integuments)

Micropyle

True fruit

Receptacle (most flower parts wither and fall off)

Section of a carpel just prior to fertilisation

Section of a developing fruit and seed

Fig. 12.9 Fertilisation and its results (based on the cherry)

2 Angiosperms are unique in having a *double fertilisation*:

(*a*) one male nucleus + ovum → *embryo zygote*

This grows into the embryo: plumule (shoot), radicle (root) and one or two cotyledons (seed leaves for absorbing food for embryo).

(*b*) one male nucleus + endosperm nucleus → *endosperm zygote*.

This grows into the *endosperm* (food-store for the embryo) by absorbing food from the parent plant.

If cotyledons absorb endosperm *after* germination an endospermic seed results, e.g. maize; if *before* germination, a non-endospermic one, e.g. pea, bean (see Section 11.6).

3 The integuments grow and harden into the *testa* (seed coat) still with its micropyle (for water entry at germination).

4 The ovary wall grows into the *fruit* (for dispersal of seed).

5 Most of the other flower parts drop off, i.e. sepals, petals, stamens, stigma and style.

12.12 FRUITS

Functions

1 Protects developing seed; in stone-fruits, e.g. peach, protects seed from being eaten by animal.

2 Disperses seed (see below).

Classification of fruits

True fruits: derived mainly from the ovary (i.e. as described in Section 12.11).
False fruits: derived mainly from the *receptacle* which grows fleshy.
Succulent fruits: juicy, often coloured to attract animals.
Dry fruits: non-juicy. To disperse their seed they are either:

(*a*) *dehiscent:* split open.
(*b*) *indehiscent:* do not split, therefore must rot or be broken open:

Succulent			Dry		
			Dehiscent		Indehiscent
Drupe (stone)	Berry (no stone)	False fruits (swollen receptacle)	Legume (pod)	Capsule ('pepper pot')	Nut
e.g. cherry plum	e.g. tomato gooseberry	e.g. strawberry rose-hip	e.g. pea lupin	e.g. poppy	e.g. acorn, hazelnut

For illustrations see Fig. 12.10.

12.13 DISPERSAL OF SEEDS BY FRUITS (see Fig. 12.10)

1 By animals: hooks may cling to mammals' fur, e.g. burr of cleavers.
Succulent fruits may be passed through the gut, depositing seeds, in a dose of manure (faeces), e.g. tomato, or stone is discarded with seed inside, e.g. plum.

2 By wind: fruits have a large surface area to catch wind. Sycamore has a **'wing'** to allow a slow descent away from the tree; dandelion has a **'parachute'** of hairs to allow blowing far away.

3 By 'explosion': as dry fruits dry, strains building up are suddenly released as the fruits split, scattering seeds, e.g. lupin.

4 By water: air or oils make fruits buoyant, e.g. water lilies, coconuts and mangroves.

Dispersal of seed *avoids overcrowding* (a hazard of some methods of asexual reproduction, e.g. by runners); *aids colonisation* of new areas.

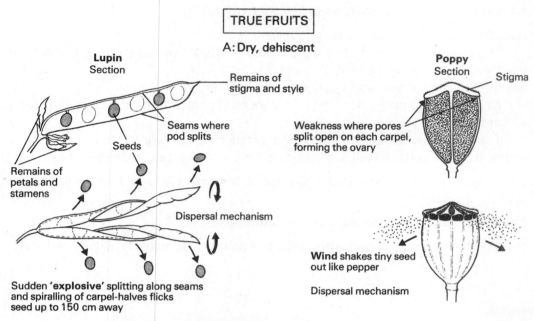

TRUE FRUITS

A: Dry, dehiscent

Lupin
Section

Remains of stigma and style

Seams where pod splits

Seeds

Remains of petals and stamens

Dispersal mechanism

Sudden **'explosive'** splitting along seams and spiralling of carpel-halves flicks seed up to 150 cm away

A succulent true fruit (cherry) dispersed by **animals** is shown in Fig. 12.9

Poppy
Section

Stigma

Weakness where pores split open on each carpel, forming the ovary

Wind shakes tiny seed out like pepper

Dispersal mechanism

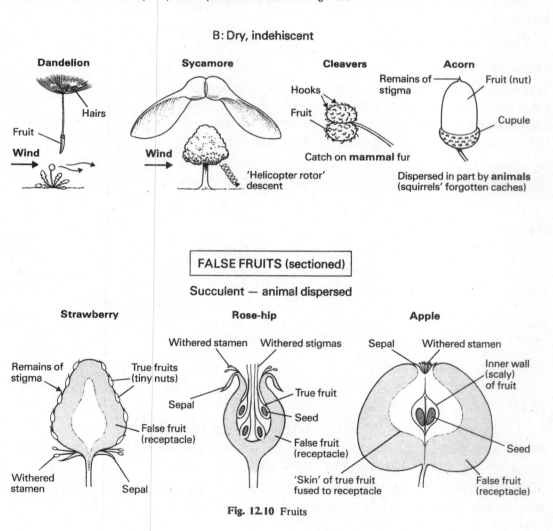

B: Dry, indehiscent

Dandelion

Hairs

Fruit

Wind

Sycamore

Wind

'Helicopter rotor' descent

Cleavers

Hooks

Fruit

Catch on **mammal** fur

Acorn

Remains of stigma

Fruit (nut)

Cupule

Dispersed in part by **animals** (squirrels' forgotten caches)

FALSE FRUITS (sectioned)

Succulent — animal dispersed

Strawberry

Remains of stigma

True fruits (tiny nuts)

False fruit (receptacle)

Withered stamen

Sepal

Rose-hip

Withered stamen   Withered stigmas

Sepal

True fruit

Seed

False fruit (receptacle)

'Skin' of true fruit fused to receptacle

Apple

Sepal   Withered stamen

Inner wall (scaly) of fruit

Seed

False fruit (receptacle)

Fig. 12.10 Fruits

12.14 SEXUAL REPRODUCTION IN MAMMALS

The sexual organs of man and woman are shown in Fig. 12.11.

Sequence of events in the sexual process in man

1   Development of secondary sexual characteristics at **puberty** (12–14 years old) (see Section 9.8) making reproduction possible.

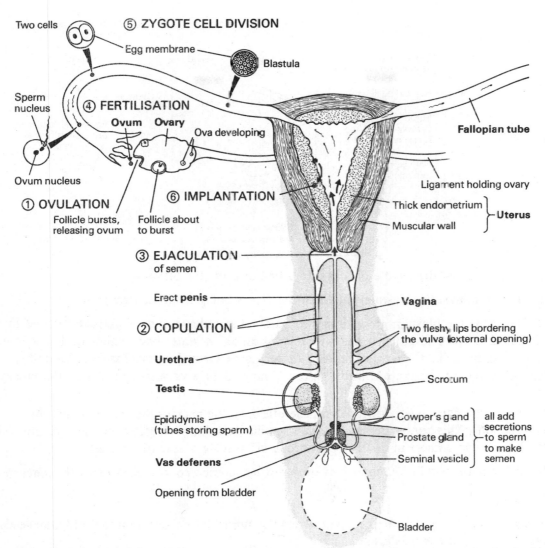

Fig. 12.11 Human male and female sex organs at copulation and the events leading to implantation (see Section 12.14)

2 Gamete production

Table 12.3 Comparison of gamete production in humans

	Male	*Female*
Gonads	Two **testes**, kept outside the body in a sac (scrotum), produce sperm	Two **ovaries**, kept within the body cavity attached to a ligament, produce ova
Gametes	Many millions of **sperm** formed continuously throughout life after puberty (see Fig. 12.12)	Many thousands of potential **ova** formed before birth, but only about 400 will be shed between puberty and menopause (about 45 years old: end of reproduction)
Gamete release	About **200 million** sperm are ejaculated into female by *reflex action* of the penis during copulation. They pass via vas deferens and urethra, picking up nutritive secretions from glands to form *semen*.	Usually only **one** ovum is shed *automatically* per month (Sec. 12.18) from the ovary and wafted into the oviduct (Fallopian tube), the only place where it can be fertilised. Once in the uterus the ovum is lost.

3 Copulation: the erect penis transfers sperm during ejaculation from the testes of the male to the end of the vagina of the female.

4 Fertilisation: any sperm that manages to swim into an oviduct containing an ovum has a chance of fertilising it. One sperm only enters the ovum and the two nuclei fuse, forming the zygote cell.

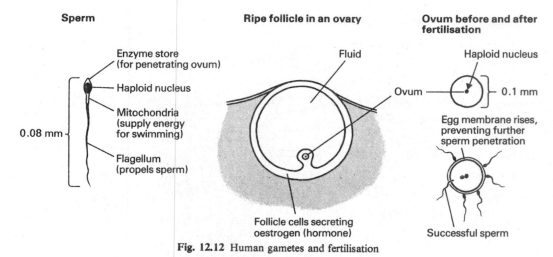

Fig. 12.12 Human gametes and fertilisation

5   Cell division: the zygote divides into a ball of cells (the blastula).

6   Implantation: the blastula sinks into the uterus lining (endometrium).

7   Growth: the blastula grows into two parts – the **embryo** and its **placenta**, joined by the umbilical cord. The embryo lies within an **amnion**, a water-bag, which cushions it from damaging blows and prevents it sticking to the uterus. Growth lasts 38 weeks (9 months) – the **gestation** period. Premature birth, before 7 months (*miscarriage*), results in the embryo's death.

8   Birth: the *baby*, head down, is propelled through the neck of the uterus by uterine muscle contractions. This bursts the amnion. The umbilical cord is severed by the midwife, and when the baby's end withers in 5–10 days it drops off, leaving a scar (the navel).

9   After-birth: within 30 minutes of birth, further uterine contractions expel the *placenta*.

12.15   PLACENTA

The placenta: the temporary organ grown in the uterus during gestation to supply the needs of the embryo. These needs are:

Supply of:

(*a*) *food* – soluble nutrients, e.g. amino acids, glucose.
(*b*) *oxygen* – for respiration.

Removal of:

(*a*) *carbon dioxide*.
(*b*) *urea* and other wastes.

Transfer of these substances occurs at the end of the umbilical cord, at capillaries within villi. These villi lie in small spaces containing maternal blood (see Fig. 12.13). The embryo's blood does *not* mix with its mother's blood.

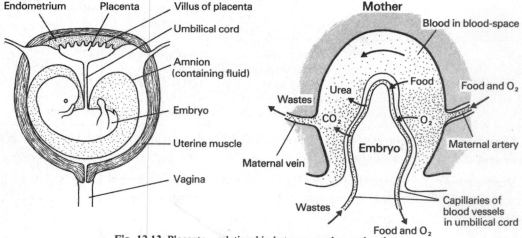

Fig. 12.13 Placenta – relationship between mother and embryo

12.16 PARENTAL CARE

1 Suckling: baby mammals are toothless and need easily digestible food. Milk supplies all the water, sugar (lactose), protein (caseinogen), fats, salts and vitamins for growth (except possibly vitamins A and D in humans).

2 Protection: often in the nest or 'home'; by mother's aggressive behaviour and by her body warmth (many young are hairless).

3 Education: young learn by parents' example, particularly carnivores – hunting techniques.

12.17 BREEDING SUCCESS IN VERTEBRATES COMPARED

Breeding success is measured as the number of adults developed from the number of eggs originally shed. Success improves with internal fertilisation, parental care of eggs and young and adoption of a nest. Table 12.4 excludes exceptions to the rule, e.g. stickleback amongst fish (see Section 17.21):

Table 12.4 Comparison of breeding success of mammals and other vertebrates

	Fish	*Amphibia*	*Reptiles*	*Birds*	*Mammals*
Fertilisation	External	External	Internal	Internal	Internal
Number of eggs laid (*oviparous*)	Very many (thousands)	Many (hundreds)	Few (on land)	Few (in nest)	Do not lay eggs (i.e. are viviparous)
Development	In water	In water	In eggs with chalky shells		In uterus
Food from	Little yolk	Some yolk	Much yolk	Much yolk	Placenta
Parental care	Rare	Rare	Of eggs in some groups	Of eggs and young	Highly developed

12.18 MENSTRUAL CYCLE

Menstrual cycles: periods of approximately 28 days during which a reproductive woman alternately ovulates and menstruates.

Ovulation: shedding of an ovum when a follicle in the ovary bursts (see Fig. 12.11). Copulation within 3 days of ovulation could lead to fertilisation, so the uterus lining (endometrium) is prepared for implantation (see Fig. 12.14).

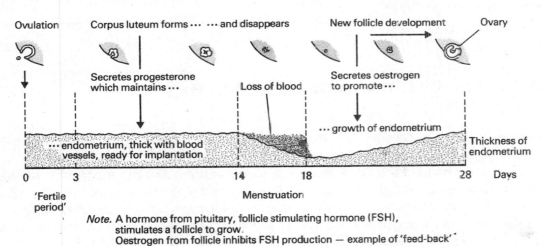

Fig. 12.14 The menstrual cycle

Menstruation: shedding of most of the endometrium 14 days after ovulation, when fertilisation or implantation are unsuccessful. This occurs over 4 days as a loss of up to 500 ml of blood and tissue through the vagina.

(For other mammal breeding cycles see Section 9.13.)

12.19   CONTRACEPTION

Contraception: the prevention of fertilisation and implantation.

1 Restricting copulation to the *'safe period'*, i.e. outside the 'fertile period', is **unreliable**. Ovulation is sometimes irregular; sperm may survive 48 hours in woman.

2   Reliable methods (see Fig. 12.15) include:

(*a*) *temporary* methods allowing sensible spacing of a family.

(*b*) *permanent* methods, when desired family size has been reached. Removal of testes (castration) or ovaries achieves the same result but is undesirable since a person's 'nature' is changed owing to lack of sex hormones from the gonads.

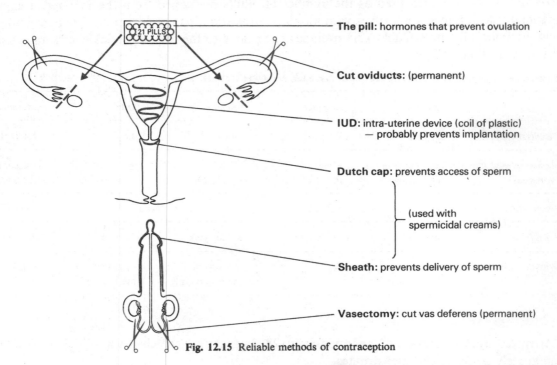

The pill: hormones that prevent ovulation

Cut oviducts: (permanent)

IUD: intra-uterine device (coil of plastic) — probably prevents implantation

Dutch cap: prevents access of sperm

(used with spermicidal creams)

Sheath: prevents delivery of sperm

Vasectomy: cut vas deferens (permanent)

Fig. 12.15 Reliable methods of contraception

Practice of contraception world-wide is essential if humans are to avoid destruction of their environment by pollution (see Section 16.6), erosion, and social problems. A stable or falling birth-rate has been achieved in a number of industrialised nations already; developing nations lag behind in effective contraception.

13 Genes, chromosomes and heredity

13.1   THE NUCLEUS, CHROMOSOMES AND GENES

The **nucleus** normally contains long threads of DNA (see Section 2.3) which are not visible under the light microscope.

Before cell division each DNA thread spiralises, with protein, into a compact 'sausage' called a **chromosome** which, when stained, is visible under the microscope (see Fig. 13.1). Chromosomes are present in **homologous pairs,** both members being of identical length (and gene number). One chromosome of the pair came from the male parent, the other from the female parent, when their gametes fused together to form a zygote. Sections of the DNA strands are **genes,** each determining the synthesis of an enzyme (see Section 2.4).

13.2   GENES AND CHARACTERISTICS

Groups of enzymes from different *genes* co-operate in determining **characteristics**. The *environment* also helps to determine characteristics, e.g. a well-fed youngster is more likely to develop into a larger adult than his starved identical twin; some alpine plants

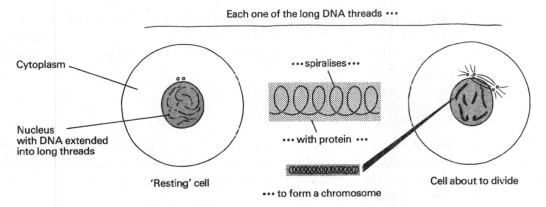

Fig. 13.1 Chromosome formation within the nucleus of a cell

grown in exposed, windy situations develop much hairier leaves than if they grow in sheltered crevices. The gene make-up of an organism is called its **genotype.** The interaction of its genotype with its particular environmental circumstances results in its **phenotype,** i.e. its observable or measurable characteristics. Examples of these are black curly hair, blood group, and hairiness of leaves.

To simplify the above, consider an unfastened pearl necklace. The pearls are genes; the necklace a chromosome. A similar necklace would be its homologous partner (see Fig. 13.2). Genes at an identical position (locus) on two homologous chromosomes, between them determine a characteristic.

Diagram of chromosomes	a B Pair 1 OOO●OOOOOOOOOOOOOOOOOOOOOO●OOOO OOO●OOOOOOOOOOOOOOOOOOOOOO●OOOO a b	C_1 Pair 2 OOOOO●OOOOOOOO OOOOO●OOOOOOOO C_2
Genotype	aa Homozygous	Bb Heterozygous	C_1C_2 Heterozygous
Status of these genes	Recessive	B : dominant b : recessive	C_1 and C_2 are co-dominant
Phenotype	a	B	C_1/C_2 (both)

Fig. 13.2 Genetical terms illustrated with reference to two homologous pairs of chromosomes

Dominant genes (symbolised by capital letters) always express themselves as a characteristic.

Recessive genes (symbolised by small letters) only express themselves when the partner is also recessive.

Thus genotype **AA** or **Aa** will be expressed as an **A** phenotype and genotype **aa** is the only way of producing the **a** phenotype. Organisms with two identical genes at a locus (**AA** or **aa** genotypes) are said to be **homozygous**; those with alternative genes at the locus (**Aa**) are called **heterozygous.**

The alternative genes (**A** and **a**) are called **alleles.**

13.3   HUMAN BLOOD GROUPS: CO-DOMINANCE

Unfortunately things are not always as simple as this. Certain alleles are **co-dominant**: both alleles express themselves, e.g. in the determination of human blood groups (Table 13.1).

Table 13.1   Genetics of blood groups A, B and O in humans

Gene status	Blood Groups (i.e. phenotypes)	Genotypes
O^a (dominant)	A	$O^a O^a$ or $O^a o$
O^b (dominant)	B	$O^b O^b$ or $O^b o$
o (recessive)	O	oo
O^a and O^b are **co-dominant**	AB	$O^a O^b$

In **blood transfusion** a person should only receive blood of his *own* blood group to avoid the possibility of 'foreign' blood cells forming clots in his body. Clots result from the person's antibodies (in the plasma) reacting with the antigens on the 'foreign' blood cells, causing them to clump together (see Section 16.11).

13.4   MENDEL'S EXPERIMENTS

Genetics (the study of heredity) was only put on a firm basis in 1865 thanks to *Gregor Mendel*, an Austrian abbot, who published his research on inheritance in peas. Despite his total lack of knowledge of the nucleus and its chromosomes and the ways in which they divide, his conclusions remain valid today.

His materials: *Pisum sativum*, the garden pea. This:

(*a*) normally *self-pollinates* (and self-fertilises) when the flower is still unopened. To *cross-pollinate* plants, Mendel had to remove the unripe anthers of strain **A** flowers and dust their stigmas with pollen from strain **B** using an artist's paint-brush. Interference by insects was avoided by enclosing the flowers in muslin bags.

(*b*) has *strongly contrasting phenotypes*, e.g. pea plants are either tall (180–150 cm) or dwarf (20–45 cm); the seeds are either round or wrinkled.

His methods: As parents (P_1, or first parental generation) he chose two contrasting 'pure lines' which 'bred true', i.e. were homozygous. These he mated by cross-pollination. The offspring (F_1, or first filial generation) were allowed to self-pollinate. This gave the F_2, or second filial generation.

Results from one such experiment:

P_1 Tall × Dwarf

F_1 All Tall

Conclusion 1: factor for Tall is dominant to factor for Dwarf.

F_2 Ratio of 3 Tall: Dwarf

Conclusion 2: factor for Dwarf was not lost (as it seemed to have been in the F_1). This suggested that 'factors' were particles of hereditary material which remained unaltered as they were handed on at each generation.

We now know that 'factors' are genes, and that the material is DNA in chromosomes.

Mendel had to make five assumptions about gametes before coming to further conclusions, all of which happen to be true. Put in modern terms these were:

1   Gametes carry genes.

2   They carry only *one* gene of the two determining a characteristic.

3   The two members of a gene pair separate and go into different gametes when these are being formed (see **2**); and the two possible types of gamete are formed in *equal numbers*.

4   Each kind of male gamete, e.g. ⌒⌒(A) and ⌒⌒(a) from an adult of **Aa** genotype has an *equal chance* of fusing with each of the female kinds of gamete e.g.(A) and (a). Thus resultant combinations **AA, Aa, aA** and **aa** are all as likely as each other (see Table 13.2).

5   Male and female gametes contribute *equally* to the genotype of the offspring.

Although these assumptions fitted in with Mendel's experimental results some could only be finally proved when the details of e.g. meiosis and fertilisation had been studied (see Section 13.14).

Table 13.2 Summary of a Mendelian experiment using modern genetical terms

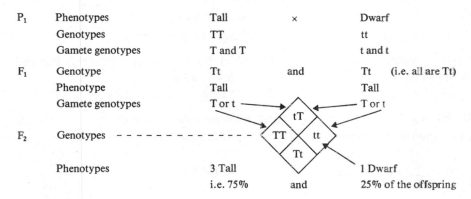

P₁	Phenotypes	Tall	×	Dwarf
	Genotypes	TT		tt
	Gamete genotypes	T and T		t and t
F₁	Genotype	Tt	and	Tt (i.e. all are Tt)
	Phenotype	Tall		Tall
	Gamete genotypes	T or t		T or t
F₂	Genotypes			
	Phenotypes	3 Tall		1 Dwarf
		i.e. 75%	and	25% of the offspring

13.5 HINTS ON TACKLING GENETIC PROBLEMS

When numerical problems are set as questions in genetics it is essential that the eight lines of terms relating to the P_1, F_1, and F_2 on the left of Table 13.2 be set out first before the data in the question is inserted in the appropriate places. By reasoning, the rest of the 'form' you have thus created can be filled in. It is vital to remember that gametes are **haploid** (have *one* set of genes) and organisms are **diploid** (have *two* sets of genes). The diamond checker-board giving the F_2 genotypes is called a Punnett square (after a great geneticist).

13.6 BACK-CROSS TEST

Back-cross test: distinguishes between organisms of dominant phenotype but different genotype.

In Table 13.2, the F_2 shows that both **TT** (homozygous dominant) offspring and **Tt** (heterozygous) offspring have the Tall phenotype. If both kinds are crossed with a homozygous recessive **tt** they can readily be distinguished; only the heterozygous organisms will give recessive phenotype offspring (50%) (see Table 13.3).

Table 13.3

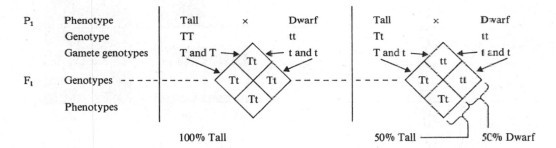

P₁	Phenotype	Tall	×	Dwarf		Tall	×	Dwarf
	Genotype	TT		tt		Tt		tt
	Gamete genotypes	T and T		t and t		T and t		t and t
F₁	Genotypes							
	Phenotypes							
		100% Tall				50% Tall		50% Dwarf

13.7 RATIOS OF PHENOTYPES

Tables 13.2 and 13.3 state certain ratios of offspring: 75:25 and 50:50. These are only *expected* ratios relying on Mendel's assumptions 3–5 in Section 13.4. The ratios *obtained* in a breeding experiment are rarely identical with those expected. Thus Mendel obtained 787 Tall:277 Dwarf in the F_2 of the experiment explained in Table 13.2, a ratio of 2.84:1. Likewise a coin tossed 1000 times is *expected* to give 500 'heads' and 500 'tails' – but rarely does so. Scientists apply a 'test of significance' to ratios obtained to see whether they are near enough to the expected ratios to be regarded as the same. For example, is 26:24 near enough to 25:25 to be regarded as 50% of each?

Note: You are not expected to know the 'test of significance'. But if you were given a ratio of, say, 505:499 offspring in a numerical example, you must first *explain why* you assume this is a 50:50 ratio before proceeding.

13.8   VARIATION IN POPULATIONS

Continuous variation

E.g. human height and intelligence

1 A complete *range* of types, e.g. from giants to dwarfs in humans.

2 Phenotype controlled by

(*a*) *many pairs* of allelles
(*b*) environment (may play a major part).

Discontinuous variation

E.g. height of pea plants

1 Sharply *contrasting* types, e.g. tall and dwarf pea plants.

2 Phenotype controlled by

(*a*) a *single pair* of alleles
(*b*) environment (plays little part).

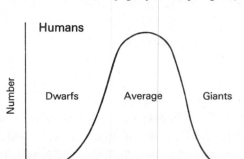

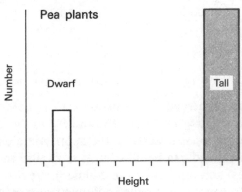

Fig. 13.3 Continuous and discontinuous variation in **populations**

Examples: factors contributing to the variation in human height include those in Table 13.4. For simplicity, imagine these to be the *only* six factors influencing height. Imagine that each can contribute ten units towards height. Stature could then be accounted for by adding together all the contributions from all six sources – as shown for the dwarf and the giant on the right. (This is *one* hypothesis accounting for continuous variation.)

Variation is *inheritable* only if it is due to genes. Effects caused by the environment are *not inheritable* (see Section 14.3, 'Notes on the above' no. **4**).

Table 13.4

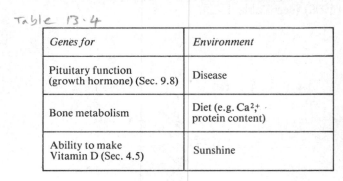

Genes for	Environment
Pituitary function (growth hormone) (Sec. 9.8)	Disease
Bone metabolism	Diet (e.g. Ca²⁺ protein content)
Ability to make Vitamin D (Sec. 4.5)	Sunshine

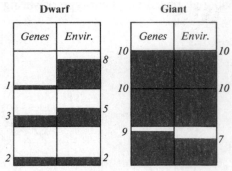

13.9   SEX DETERMINATION IN MAMMALS

Males possess two unlike sex chromosomes called **X** and **Y** after the sex-determining genes they contain. The **Y** (male) is dominant to **X**.

Females possess two similar sex chromosomes, *both* **X**. By this means (see Fig. 13.4) males 'determine' the sex of offspring.

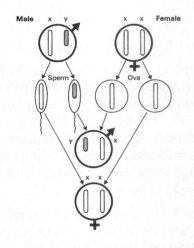

Fig. 13.4 Sex determination

13.10 SEX LINKAGE

Sex linkage: the appearance of certain characteristics in one sex and not the other (in mammals appear in the male).

The **Y** chromosome, being shorter than the **X**, lacks a number of genes present on the longer chromosome. In a male (**XY**) therefore, these genes are present singly and not in pairs, as in the female (**XX**). All these 'single' genes are derived from the mother (on the **X**) and express themselves, even if recessive. Examples: red/green colour blindness, haemophilia (blood fails to clot; so trivial cuts and tooth extractions can be lethal through bleeding).

Possible types   H = normal, is dominant to h = haemophiliac

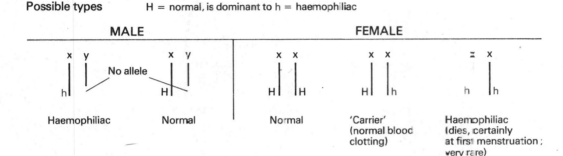

Possible origins

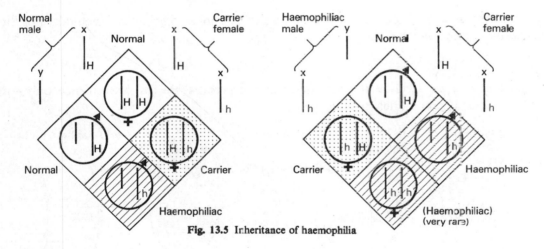

Fig. 13.5 Inheritance of haemophilia

13.11 MUTATION

Mutation: an inheritable change in a cell e.g. the alteration of a gene to a new one (**M → m**).

Cause: cosmic, ultra violet and x-rays and certain chemicals, e.g. LSD or mustard gas are mutagenic agents (induce mutations).

Effect: These change DNA, resulting in the manufacture of 'new' proteins in the cell (see Section 2.3) which may be useless to it. Thus most mutations are harmful to the cell (usually lethal).

Cells surviving mutation have little effect on the *organism* unless they divide frequently (e.g. causing leukaemia, skin cancers).

Mutations in cells that produce gametes can affect *evolution* (see Section 14.3).

13.12 MITOSIS AND MEIOSIS IN THE LIFE CYCLE

1   Most organisms start from a *zygote* cell containing chromosomes in pairs, i.e. the double or *diploid* number (2n).

2   The zygote divides by *mitosis* to form new cells during *growth*.

3   These cells, in a multicellular organism *differentiate* (see Section 11.2) into cells as different as neurons and phagocytes. This happens because although all the cells possess identical genes (see Section 13.14), they use different combinations of them according to their location in the body. For example, muscle cells do not use their hair-colour genes.

4 Certain cells in sex organs divide by *meiosis* to form *gametes*. These contain the single-set or *haploid* (monoploid) number of chromosomes (n).

5 At *fertilisation*, gametes fuse to form a zygote (n + n → 2n). Meiosis thus ensures that the chromosome number does not double at each new generation (which it would if gametes were 2n, i.e. 2n + 2n → 4n).

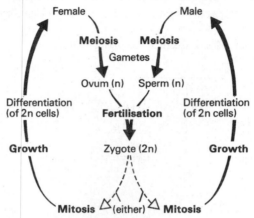

Fig. 13.6 Mitosis and meiosis in a life cycle

Both mitosis and meiosis achieve their results by similar *mechanical* methods, but their *chromosome behaviour* is different.

13.13 Mechanism for separating chromosomes (similarity)

The names used to describe the six stages in the process are for convenience only – the process is actually continuous (see Fig. 13.7).

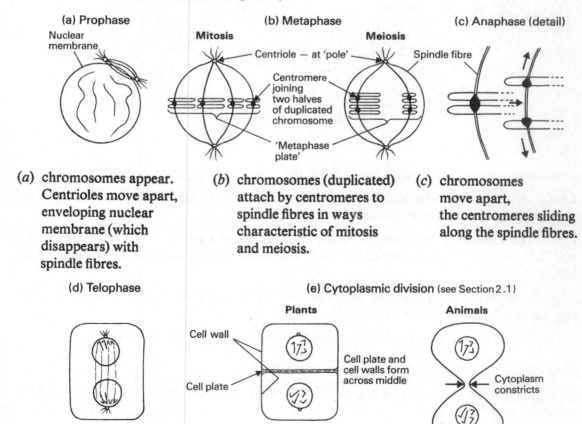

(*a*) chromosomes appear. Centrioles move apart, enveloping nuclear membrane (which disappears) with spindle fibres.

(*b*) chromosomes (duplicated) attach by centromeres to spindle fibres in ways characteristic of mitosis and meiosis.

(*c*) chromosomes move apart, the centromeres sliding along the spindle fibres.

(*d*) a nuclear membrane reappears around each group of chromosomes (which have reached the poles).

Fig. 13.7 Separating chromosomes

(*e*) cytoplasmic division

(*f*) *interphase* ('resting stage').

Chromatids disappear as DNA threads uncoil; these:

(*i*) synthesise proteins (see Section 2.3) for growth, and

(*ii*) duplicate themselves just prior to the next cell division.

13.14 CHROMOSOME BEHAVIOUR (DIFFERENCES)

Table 13.5 Summary comparison of mitosis and meiosis

	Mitosis	*Meiosis*
Number of cell divisions	1	2
Resulting cells are	Diploid, identical	Haploid, not identical
Purpose	Growth, replacement (e.g. of skin, blood cells)	Gamete formation
Occurrence in	Growth areas (Sec. 11.1)	Gonads e.g. testes, ovaries; anthers, ovules (Secs. 12.7, 12.14)

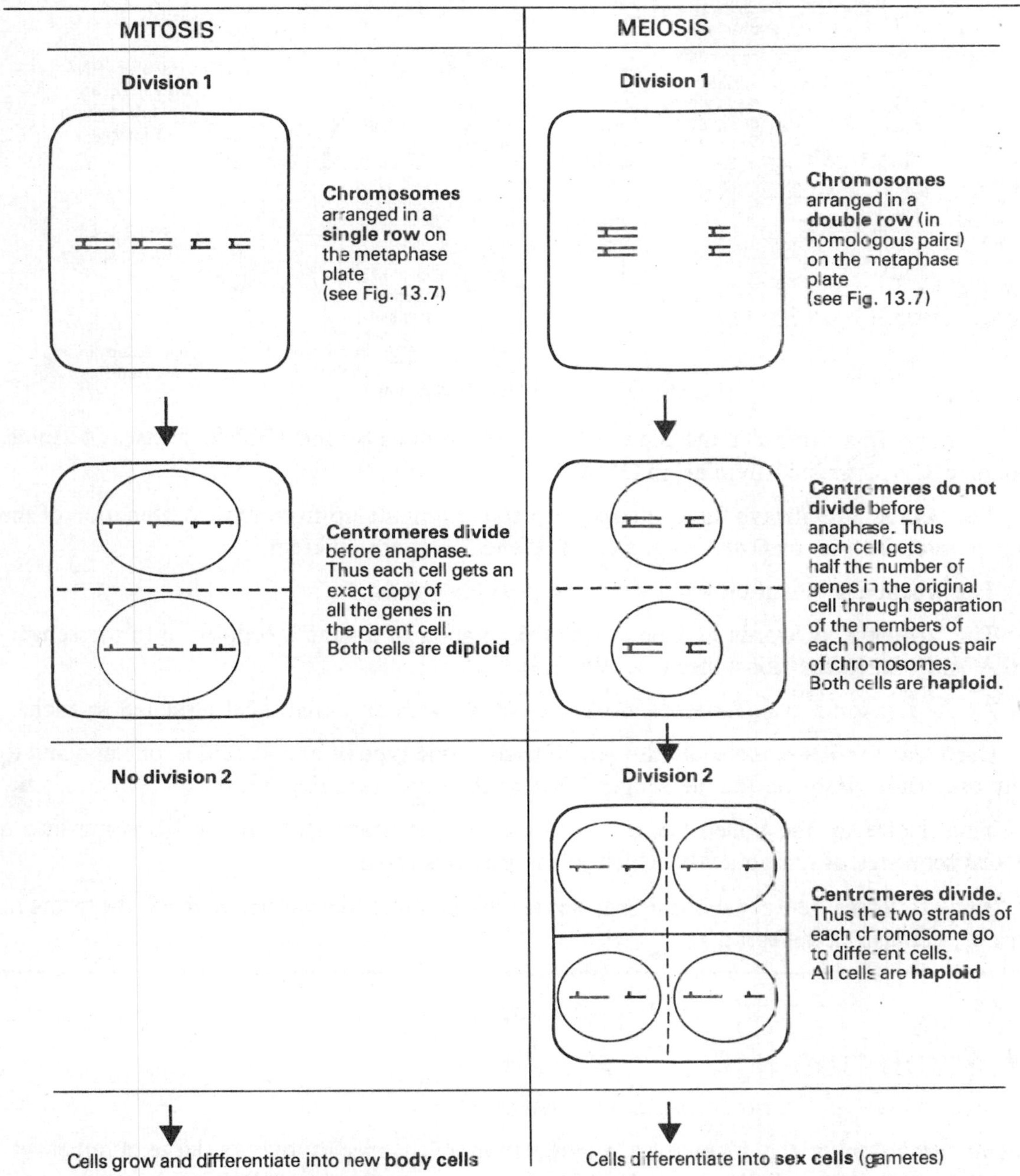

Fig. 13.8 Behaviour of chromosomes in mitosis and meiosis

13.15 Nucleic acids and the genetic code

Nucleic acids

Elements: C, H, O, N, P.

Examples: **RNA** (Ribose nucleic acid).

   DNA (deoxy-ribose nucleic acid).

Units: 4 organic bases + sugar + phosphate.

Functions: DNA carries genetic information from generation to generation in chromosomes (see Section 2.2).

   RNA is involved in protein formation in the cell at ribosomes (see Section 2.3).

The 'genetic code' – and translation of its 'message' (see Fig. 13.9):

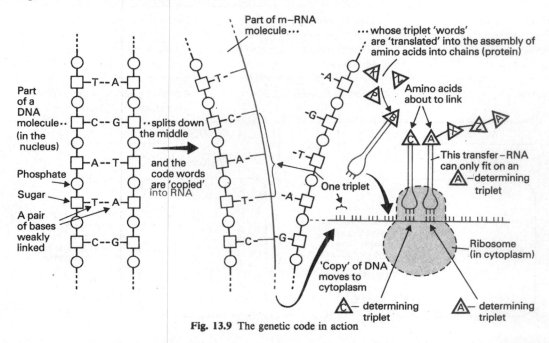

Fig. 13.9 The genetic code in action

1   There are **four 'letters'** in the 'alphabet', each determined by one of the four bases (Adenine, Guanine, Cytosine and Thymine) in DNA.

2   The **'words'** are always three-lettered (triplets) and made up from any combination of the four possible letters, read *one* way, e.g. **AGT** and **TGA** are different.

3   The **'vocabulary'** is thus 4 × 4 × 4 = 64 possible words.

4   The **'sentence'** of words making up the information of a gene is 'copied' into messenger-RNA and sent to the ribosomes (see Fig. 2.3).

5   At the ribosome, transfer-RNA molecules arrive with an amino acid attached to each.

6   Each transfer-RNA molecule can attach to only one type of amino acid at one end and to only one triplet word on the messenger-RNA at the other (see Fig. 13.9).

7   Thus indirectly the coded 'sentence' of the gene is 'translated' at the ribosome into a special sequence of amino acids, which joins up into a protein.

8   Since different genes have different sequences of the code words, each of the proteins formed will also be different.

14 Evolution

14.1 Organic evolution – different theories

Organic evolution is the change in a population of a species over a large number of generations that results in the formation of new species (see Section 3.1). The change implies 'advance' (improvement), i.e. better adaptation to the environment.

Three main views of this idea exist:

1 Neo-Darwinian: species are modified by inheritance of small changes in the *genotype* (see Section 3.2) which have passed the test of *natural selection*.

2 Larmarckian: species are modified by inheritance of changes in the *phenotype* acquired by *'use or disuse'* of body parts (see Section 14.5).

3 Biblical: species do not change ('immutability of the species'). They were created once and for all, as described in *Genesis* (see Section 14.5).

14.2 CHARLES DARWIN (1809–82)

As naturalist on *HMS Beagle* (1831–36), Darwin collected much evidence around the world of 'modification of species by descent' (which challenged biblical views).

In 1839 Darwin read *An essay on population* by Reverend Malthus which suggested that though the human population was growing exponentially (see Section 16.5), the food supply for it was not and starvation would result. This provided Darwin with the idea that in similar circumstances in nature the fittest organisms would survive.

Darwin failed to understand the mechanism of inheritance through ignorance of Mendel's work, published in 1865 (see Section 13.4) and despite his own genetical experiments. **Neo-Darwinians** (evolutionists who understand modern genetics) have added strength to Darwin's theory by pointing to:

(*i*) the 'particulate' (and not 'blending') nature of inheritance in accounting for the variety of types in a species.

(*ii*) the ultimate origin of these new types from mutations.

14.3 SUMMARY OF THE NEO-DARWINIAN THEORY

Observation 1 All organisms could, theoretically, increase in numbers exponentially, i.e. **organisms produce more offspring than could possibly survive.**

Observation 2 Populations of organisms, in fact, remain reasonably constant.

Deduction 1 Organisms must have to **struggle for survival** against factors that check their increase in numbers.

Observation 3 In any population there is a variety of types. Much of this variation is inherited by future generations.

Deduction 2 Those best adapted to their environment will survive, i.e. **survival of the fittest**.

Observation 4 Some species have more than one distinct variety.

Observation 5 Anything hindering the interbreeding of two varieties will tend to accentuate their differences because each variety will accumulate mutations, many of which will be different between the two varieties.

Deduction 3 New species arise when **divergence of the two varieties** is sufficiently extreme to prevent interbreeding between them.

Notes on the above

1 If the mating of one pair of mosquitoes resulted in 200 eggs (and a further 100 breeding pairs breeding at the same rate), the number of mosquitoes in each generation would be:

$1 \rightarrow 100 \rightarrow 10\ 000 \rightarrow 1\ 000\ 000$ pairs. This is exponential growth. Darwin calculated that one pair of elephants (a slow-breeding species) could originate 19 million elephants in 750 years.

2 Neither mosquitoes nor elephants achieve their breeding potential. Mosquitoes in the tropics can achieve their life cycle in less than a week; fossil elephants 25 million years old have been found.

3 The 'factors that check increase in numbers' are the biotic and abiotic factors of the environment (see Section 15.1) e.g. predation, disease and competition (especially for food); or

inclement weather. There is no literal 'struggle' (except in some animals competing for mates). Organisms simply undergo the survival tests set by their environment (**natural selection**) and large numbers perish.

4   *Variety* in a population arises by:

(*a*) *recombination* of genes (mother and father are different).

(*b*) *meiosis* (the way chromosomes end up in the gametes shuffles the genes).

(*c*) *mutation* (the origin of 'new' genes, see Section 13.11).

(*d*) *environmental* influences other than mutagenic agents.

Only (*a*)–(*c*) are inheritable and can have any effect on evolution.

5   An *adaptation* is a solution to a biological problem. The great majority of adaptations are *inherited*. Only mammals (and particularly man) have much scope for altering the destiny laid down in their genes, by reasoning out a solution instead of having the solution ready-made.

Chameleons adapt themselves to different backgrounds by changing colour because they have *inherited* the capacity to do so. Pale peppered moths (see Section 14.4) cannot camouflage themselves on black bark because they have not inherited that ability. Man has inherited intelligence enough to reason out ways of camouflaging soldiers. Those that pass the environment's tests of survival are the 'fittest' and can breed to pass on their genes; those 'unfit' die sooner and their genes are not so well represented in the next generation.

6   The herring gull and lesser black-backed gull (see Fig. 14.1) illustrate this. Something similar occurs with great tits and certain frogs. These species all have varieties that in certain places cannot breed (i.e. are *two* species), yet elsewhere they can and thus are *one* species.

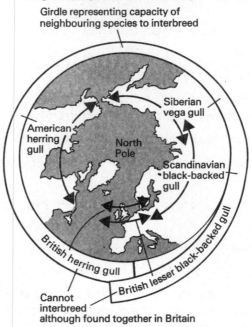

Fig. 14.1 Gulls: two species or one?

7   Darwin studied the **finches of the Galapagos Islands** (1000 kilometres west of South America). They had similar plumage to mainland species and were poor fliers. Those on the various islands, miles apart, were special to each one. On certain islands there were more than one species, each with a different beak shape adapted to a different diet (seeds, insects, cactus flowers etc.). Darwin speculated that these finches, blown perhaps by storm from the mainland, had from a few species evolved into many. The sea around each island had isolated the various populations, and each had accumulated its own inheritable variations to meet the special challenges of its own island.

Factors hindering interbreeding may be:

(*a*) **spatial** – the sea surrounding New Zealand for 1600 kilometres in every direction very effectively isolates her varieties of organisms.

(*b*) **temporal** – varieties of the same species in northern and southern hemispheres tend to be in a breeding condition at different times.

(c) **physical** – dogs are all one species but dachshunds and great danes have problems in mating.

(d) **genetical** – a male donkey mated to a mare can give a mule. Mules are sterile because horse and donkey chromosomes will not pair up properly at meiosis, so they produce ineffective gametes.

8 Darwin recognised that evolution is a *branching* process. Modern types of ape, e.g. gorillas, did *not* give rise to man, but both man and gorillas are likely to have had common ancestors in the distant past (see Fig. 14.2).

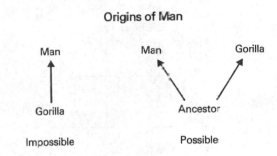

Origins of Man

Man — Gorilla

Impossible

Man — Gorilla — Ancestor

Possible

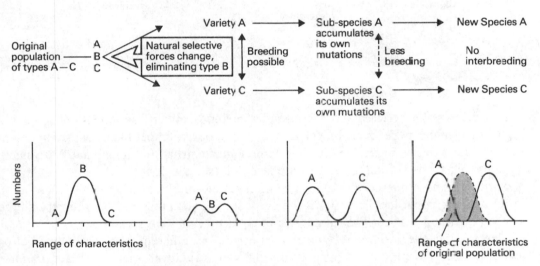

Fig. 14.3 Summary of the processes of evolution

14.4 EVIDENCE FOR EVOLUTION

1 Fossils: organisms from the distant past whose hard parts and sometimes impressions of soft parts are preserved in sedimentary rocks. Are rarely found since dead organisms usually disintegrate by decaying. Oldest fossils known are blue-green algae (similar to bacteria) from 1600 million years ago. The fossil record (see Fig. 14.4) clearly indicates that:

(a) the variety of life today did *not* arise all at once.

(b) first life was aquatic. Terrestrial groups came later (fern-like plants, insects and amphibia arose about 400 million years ago).

(c) groups with improved adaptations increase in importance while those less efficient decline (or even become extinct). Particularly true of improvements in methods of reproduction. Thus ferns, dependent on water for fertilisation (see Section 17.8), gave way to conifers whose gametes are enclosed in a pollen tube and thus need no water to swim in. Similarly, amphibia gave way to reptiles as the dominant land group (see Section 12.17). Fossils of pollinating insects and of insect-pollinated flowers are of approximately the same age. These 'coincidences' can be explained in evolutionary terms.

2 Comparative anatomy

(a) *'link organisms'*, so intermediate in structure between recognised groups that they are hard to place in either, suggest a means of transition. Examples: *Archaeopteryx*, a fossil, was lizard-like but feathered, suggesting a reptile to bird transition. Modern cycads (primitive gymnosperms) have *swimming* gametes inside their pollen tubes, suggesting the

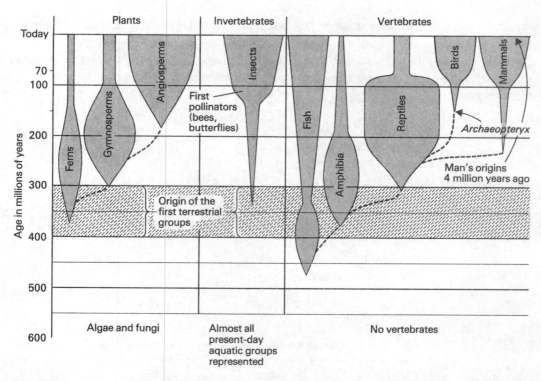

Fig. 14.4 Selected features of the fossil record. Width of areas representing groups named above relates to increase or decrease in abundance.

intermediate stage between fern and conifer methods of fertilisation. Molluscs are unsegmented; annelids segmented. Yet *Neopilina* a modern limpet-like mollusc, apparently very similar to very ancient fossils, has some annelid structures segmentally arranged in its body. This suggests an annelid to mollusc link (see **3** below).

(b) *pentadactyl limb* of vertebrates has a common structure: five fingers, wrist bones and two lower and one upper long bones. Yet the purposes to which they are put are very different in bats, men and whales. Their limbs are thought by evolutionists to have been 'modified by descent', i.e. they are *homologous*: same origin, but different purposes. Wings of bats and butterflies have the same purpose but different structural origins and are *analogous* (see Fig. 14.5).

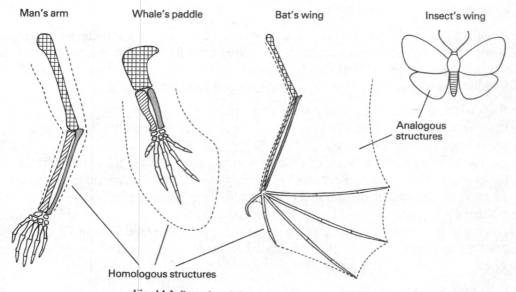

Fig. 14.5 Pentadactyl limbs: homology and analogy

3 Embryos and larvae

(a) despite very different adult forms, early embryos of *all* vertebrates are very similar, e.g. with gill pouches in the neck region.

(*b*) larvae of marine annelids and molluscs are very similar.

Evolutionists claim that, up to a point, each individual organism's development follows its embryonic evolutionary history, and so points to groups from which it has been derived.

4 Classification

Taxonomists (see Section 3.1) often have great difficulty in deciding where one species ends and another begins. This is explicable if one accepts that species are continuously changing into new species. Even Linnaeus believed that species were 'not immutable'.

5 Geographical distribution

Fossil marsupials are found world-wide but decline in numbers soon after fossil placental mammals appeared. Australia, with its abundant marsupials, separated from mainland Asia before placentals appeared. Evolutionists suggest that such a wide range of types of marsupial exists in Australia alone because they were able to evolve in the absence of the more efficient placentals (which had their origin outside Australia).

6 Direct evidence of change in species

(*a*) *resistance:* bacteria become drug-resistant (e.g. to penicillin); insects become insecticide-resistant (e.g. to DDT); and rats resistant to rodenticides (e.g. Warfarin).
(*b*) *selective breeding* has produced radically new strains of plants e.g. rice and maize, and of animals, e.g. dogs and horses (see Section 14.6). What man can do, so can nature.
(*c*) *industrial melanism* in the peppered moth, *Biston betularia*. Paleness results from the genotype **pp**. A mutation to **P** causes blackness (melanism). Black moths survive predation from birds better than pale ones on sooty, lichen-free tree trunks. Pale ones survive better than black on lichen-covered (unpolluted) trunks. From 1850–1900 the proportion of blacks rose to up to 98% in polluted woods to the north-east of our main industrial towns.

Evolutionists argue that the accumulation of many such useful mutations over much longer periods of time lead to evolution of new species.

14.5 OTHER THEORIES OF EVOLUTION

1 Lamarck suggested that ancestors of giraffes (with short necks) achieved longer necks by striving to reach up to foliage of trees. This change, he said, was passed on to offspring. Conversely humans achieved their vestigial tail (coccyx) by failing to use it enough. Weissmann prevented mice from using their tails for one hundred generations by cutting their tails off at birth but the one-hundred-and-first generation had tails as long as the first.

The theory of use and disuse is *wrong*: organisms inherit genotypes not phenotypes.

2 Biblical views (added to by theologians)

(*a*) the variety of organisms was specially created, all at once – Bishop Usher in Victorian times put the date at 4004 BC. Fossil evidence disproves this.
(*b*) man was regarded as the supreme creation, quite separate from and 'lord' over all animals. Now, even the Roman Catholic Encyclical of 1951 recognises the animal origin of man.
(*c*) the 'Creation' was regarded as the product of a grand 'Design' by a 'Designer'. Science emphasises that *chance* events largely shape biological progress. Mutations and meiosis; the first meeting of your parents, and which two of their gametes fused to form your first cell – all events with a strong element of chance in them – these have shaped your destiny.

If the biblical view of design of organisms for special purposes is correct, it is indeed surprising that the 'Designer' should have made so many mistakes (extinction) or created half-way houses such as *Archaeopteryx*.

Very few christians ('fundamentalists') today believe the account of the origin of species exactly as it appears in the book of *Genesis* in the bible. However, the neo-Darwinian theory is still only a theory and requires further evidence to convince some people.

14.6 ARTIFICIAL SELECTION

(Selective breeding by man)

(*a*) **Plants**: by cross-breeding strains with desirable characteristics, increasing the mutation rate in stamens using radioactive materials, and by vegetative propagation of new strains thus obtained, man has produced:

  (*i*) disease-resistant crops, e.g. strawberries resistant to viruses.
  (*ii*) high-yielding crops, e.g. rice plants that do not blow over in wind, so spoiling the rice grains; they also grow fast enough to allow two or three crops per year instead of one.
  (*iii*) nutritious crops, e.g. maize strains containing all the essential amino acids, so helping to fight kwashiorkor (see Section 4.21).

(*b*) **Animals**: by cross-breeding strains and breeding from interesting mutants, man has produced:

  (*i*) dogs as different as bull-dogs, dachshunds, St Bernards and Afghan hounds.
  (*ii*) horses such as Shetlands, shires, race-horses and mules.
  (*iii*) cattle for milk (Jerseys), for beef (Herefords) and resistant to trypanosome diseases in Africa (Xebu × Brahmin).

15 Ecology

15.1 THE BIOSPHERE – (ITS LIMITS AND ORGANISATION)

Ecology is the study of organisms in their environment.

Environment: the influences acting upon organisms. Two kinds:

(*a*) **biotic:** other organisms such as predators, competitors, parasites.
(*b*) **abiotic:** non-living influences, such as climate, soil and water currents.

Habitat: the particular type of locality in an environment in which an organism lives, e.g. amongst weeds in a pond (stickleback) or at low tide mark on exposed rocky shores (mussels).

Usually every species of organism exists as a **population** in its environment and not just as a single individual. Together, all the populations of all the species interact to form a **community** within their ecosystem.

Ecosystem: any area in which organisms interact both with each other *and* with their abiotic environment, to form a self-sustaining unit (see Fig. 15.1).

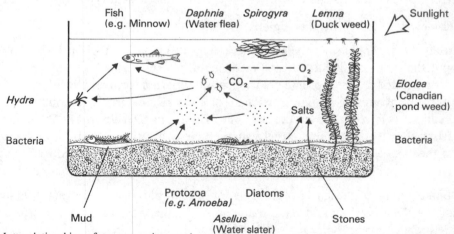

Fig. 15.1 Interrelationships of representative pond organisms in an aquarium ecosystem (arrows represent feeding)

Examples: ponds, jungle, ocean or even a puddle. Ecosystems are not actually distinct, they interact with others. Thus dragonfly nymphs in a pond emerge as flying predators which catch their insect prey over both pond and meadow, so linking both these ecosystems. Even ecosystems in the U.K. and Africa are linked – by the same swallows feeding on insects in both areas according to the time of year.

Biosphere: (the earth's surface that harbours life) a very thin layer of soil and the oceans, lakes, rivers and air (see Fig. 15.2). The biosphere is the sum of all the world's ecosystems and is isolated from any others that may exist in space. However, other celestial bodies influence it:

(*a*) life depends on solar energy (from the sun).
(*b*) other radiations from various sources cause mutations.
(*c*) gravitational fields of sun and moon cause tides.
(*d*) at least 200 tonnes of cosmic dust arrive on earth daily.

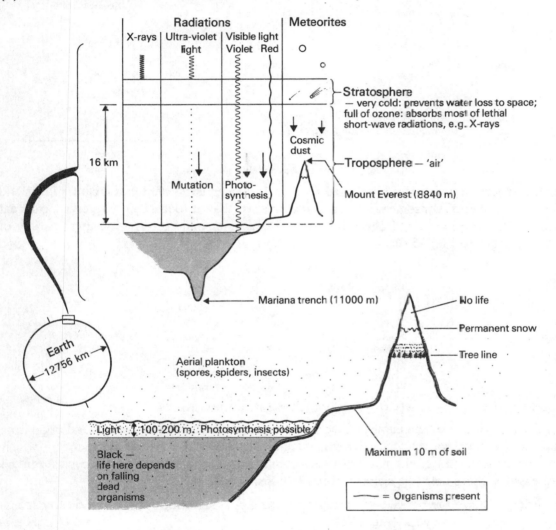

Fig. 15.2 The biosphere in relation to the earth

15.2 FOOD CHAINS, FOOD WEBS AND FOOD CYCLES

Food chains, webs and cycles are units composing an ecosystem.

1 Food chain: a minimum of three organisms, the first always a green plant, the second an animal feeding on the plant, and the third feeding on the second (see Fig. 15.3).

At each transfer of food up the chain there is a great loss in mass (**biomass**) – anything up to 90 per cent. This is because a lot of food consumed by animals is lost due to respiration, excretion and indigestibility (faeces), and never reaches the next member of the chain. Thus food chains can be expressed quantitatively as **pyramids of numbers** or, more usefully to farmers and game-wardens, as **pyramids of biomass** (see Fig. 15.3). Such considerations of quantity (of organisms) explain why:

(*a*) the number of species in a food chain rarely exceeds 5.

(*b*) the biomass of each species is limited by the capacity of producers (green plants) to produce food.

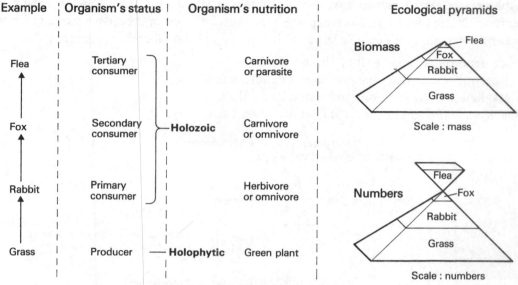

Fig. 15.3 Food chains and their properties

2   Food web: a number of interlinked food chains. In an ecosystem that includes foxes and rabbits, the diet of consumers is usually more varied than a food chain suggests. Foxes eat beetles, voles, chickens and pheasants as well as rabbits, and rabbits eat a great variety of green plants (see Fig. 15.4).

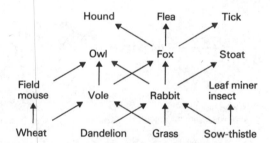

Fig. 15.4 Food web: a number of interrelated food chains

3   Food cycles: food chains with decomposers added. Decomposers decay dead organisms and excreta (organic matter), releasing mineral salts and CO_2 (inorganic matter) – which producers need and could not otherwise obtain (see Section 16.2). Food cycles can be expressed in more detail as element cycles (see Sections 15.6, 15.7).

4   Energy chain: the passage of energy from the sun along a food chain and on to decomposers. Energy is *not* cycled (Fig. 15.5).

The units making up the biosphere may be summarised as in Fig. 15.6.

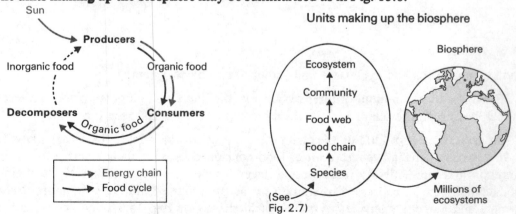

Fig. 15.5 The energy chain in a food cycle   Fig. 15.6 Units making up the biosphere

15.3 FEEDING RELATIONSHIPS BETWEEN SPECIES

1 Predation: a *predator* is usually larger than its *prey*, an organism it kills for food, e.g. fox kills rabbit; seal kills penguin. *Note:* both organisms are animals, never plants.

2 Parasitism: a *parasite* is an organism living on or in another organism called its *host*, from which it derives its food usually without killing it.

Examples: mosquito, green-fly (ecto-parasites); tapeworm (see Section 17.11), trypanosome (endo-parasites).

3 Symbiosis: a *symbiont* and its partner (also a *symbiont*) live in close association mutually assisting each other, e.g. nitrogen-fixing bacteria supply nitrates they have made to legumes, which supply carbohydrates in return (see Section 16.3); or bees gain nectar and pollen from plants which in return get pollinated (see Section 17.18).

4 Competition: occurs between two organisms (*competitors*) both attempting to obtain a commodity which is in short supply in the environment.

Examples: plants compete for light, birds for nesting sites, stags for hinds, foxes and owls for voles.

Table 15.1 Summary comparison of feeding relationships between organisms (+ = benefits, − = harmed)

| | Organisms | | Size relationship |
	A	B	
Predation	Predator +	Prey −	A > B
Parasitism	Parasite +	Host −	A < B
Symbiosis	Symbiont +	Symbiont +	Any
Competition	Competitor −	Competitor −	Any

15.4 STABLE AND UNSTABLE ECOSYSTEMS

Stable ecosystem: the numbers of organisms fluctuate about a mean, e.g. due to winter and summer. Has main (dominant) plant species which cannot be out-competed in its environment, e.g. oaks in mature oakwood.

Unstable ecosystem: large changes in numbers of most species due to a changing environment. Examples:

(*a*) *succession* – one dominant group of species out-competes another group, e.g.:

Pond →(silting) **Marsh** →(drying) **Oakwood**
(with *Elodea, Spirogyra, Daphnia*)   (with bullrush, *Iris*)   (with oaks)

(*b*) *pollution or disease* – may disrupt the food web by causing the death of important organisms, e.g. sooty smoke from industry kills lichens (see Section 16.6); or Dutch-elm disease kills elms.

Causes of instability

If any member of a food chain is removed, it affects the whole chain, e.g. shooting foxes kills their fleas, allows rabbits to increase and grass will become over-grazed. *Thus an effect on one is an effect on all.*

In simple ecosystems (few food chains), e.g. the terrestrial Arctic or man's monocultures on farms, any effect on one species can easily affect the rest. Complex ecosystems are more stable, e.g. tropical forest, owing to a great variety of alternative foods.

15.5   SOIL COMPONENTS

Soil: the layer of earth that harbours life. Consists of:

1 Rock particles, **2** air, **3** water, **4** mineral salts, **5** humus, **6** organisms.

Table 15.2   Comparison of sandy soil and clay soil

	Sandy soil	*Clay soil*
1 Rock particle sizes	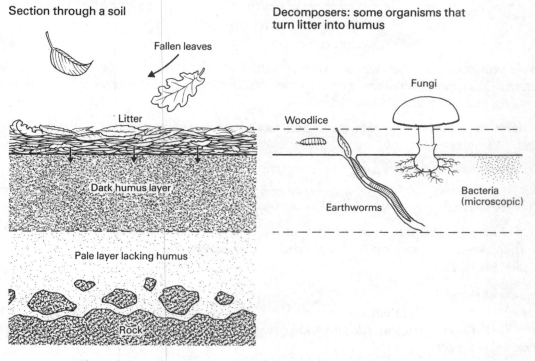	
2 Air: for root respiration (essential for absorption of salts), and for many soil organisms	Abundant	Little
3 Water		
(*a*) *drainage* (waterlogging restricts oxygen supply – important when wet)	Good	Poor ↓↓
(*b*) *capillarity* (i.e. raising water from deeper down – important in drought)	Poor ↑↑	Good
(*c*) *ability to warm up* (air warms quickly, water slowly)	Good – for spring germination; maybe lethal in summer	Poor – a 'cold' soil giving slow growth
4 Mineral salts: for plant growth	Little – leached away	Abundant – retained

Thus a **silty soil,** with its particle size intermediate between sand and clay (0.02–0.002 mm) 'averages out' their properties, giving near-ideal conditions for plant growth.

Fig. 15.7 Structure of soil and the effects of decomposers in incorporating humus

5   Humus – dead organic matter in soil. Mostly decomposing *litter* (fallen leaves) *or manure.*

Improves soil by:

(*a*) providing mineral salts from decay.

(*b*) providing air spaces (improves clay).

(*c*) retaining moisture (improves sand).

(*d*) improving crumb structure (prevents soil from being blown away).

(*e*) encouraging earthworms.

6 Organisms: assist circulation of elements. **Decomposers** in soil are particularly important, turning dead organic matter (unusable by green plants) into inorganic food for them, e.g. salts and CO_2. **Bacteria** have special roles in the circulation of nitrogen and carbon in nature (see Fig. 15.8).

15.6 NITROGEN CYCLE

Green plants need nitrates for protein synthesis.

Nitrates are available to green plants from four sources:

(*a*) man-made fertilisers.

(*b*) lightning – causes a little nitrate to fall in rain.

(*c*) nitrogen-fixing bacteria – the only organisms capable for converting nitrogen gas into compounds.

(*d*) nitrifying bacteria – oxidise ammonium compounds to nitrites and then nitrates, if there is air for them to use.

Nitrates are turned into nitrogen by de-nitrifying bacteria if the soil lacks air, as in waterlogged conditions. Nitrogen is useless to green plants.

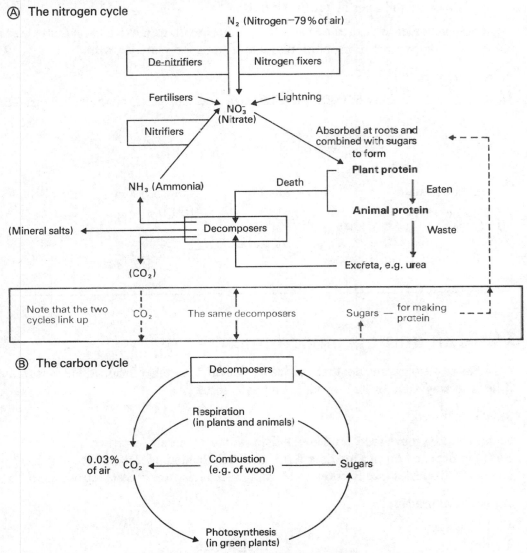

Fig. 15.8 Ⓐ – The nitrogen cycle Ⓑ – The carbon cycle

In green plants, nitrates and sugars form amino acids; these become proteins. Animals convert plant proteins into their own, but in doing so waste some, e.g. as urea, which is excreted.

Decomposers break down dead organisms and their wastes. Nitrogen compounds in them, e.g. proteins, end up as ammonia and then ammonium compounds.

15.7   CARBON CYCLE

Green plants photosynthesise CO_2 into sugars. From sugars most other organic molecules are made, e.g. cellulose in wood, protein in muscles, fats in skin.

This variety of organic molecules is returned to air as CO_2 during respiration in plants, animals, and bacteria of decay; or by combustion.

15.8   EARTHWORMS AND SOIL

Earthworms (*see also* Section 17.7):

(*a*) *aerate* and *drain* soil by tunnelling.
(*b*) *fertilise* soil by:

    (*i*) pulling litter down into tunnels for bacteria to decompose.
    (*ii*) excreting urine.
    (*iii*) decomposing when dead.

(*c*) bring *salts*, leached to lower layers, up again to roots (worm casts).
(*d*) *neutralise* soil acidity by secreting lime into it (from gut glands).
(*e*) *grind* coarse soil finer in gut (in gizzard).

These activities are exactly what a farmer aims to do to make a *loam* (cultivated soil, with all six soil components in proportions suitable for good plant growth).

15.9   WATER CYCLE

In the *water cycle* most of the water circulated does not go through organisms:

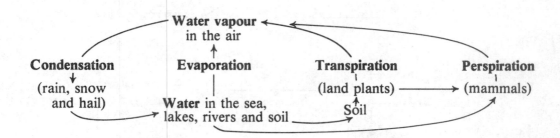

---

16 Man and his environment

Man has two environments: that outside his skin and the other inside it. He must manage both if he is to stay alive as an individual and as a species.

MAN'S EXTERNAL ENVIRONMENT

Man produces more food for himself than nature alone could provide, by farming the land. Farming depends on producing a fertile soil (see Section 15.5); on breeding good plant and animal food-species (see Section 14.6); and on reducing their pests and diseases.

Agricultural practices

1 Ploughing,
2 Liming,   4 Crop rotation,
3 Manuring (= Fertilising),   5 Pest control.

16.1 PLOUGHING

(*a*) aerates and drains soil by creating ridges and furrows.
(*b*) brings leached salts up to near the surface for roots.
(*c*) brings pests, sheltering deep down, up to the surface for frost to kill.
(*d*) allows frost to break up the ridges of soil.
(*e*) turns organic matter, e.g. wheat stubble, into the ground to decay.

16.2 LIMING AND FERTILISING

Liming – addition of powdered $CaCO_3$:

(*a*) neutralises acidity.
(*b*) allows efficient application of fertilisers (see Fig. 16.1).
(*c*) flocculates ('clumps') clay particles together into larger groups ('crumbs') with air spaces between them.

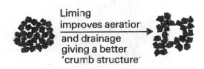

Liming improves aeration and drainage giving a better 'crumb structure'

Fertilising – restoring mineral salts (lost in crops) to the soil.

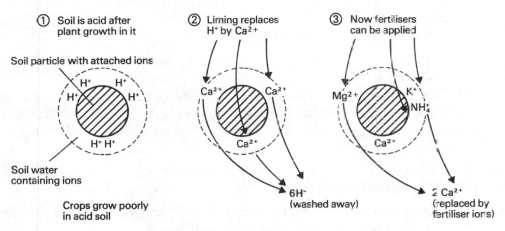

Fig. 16.1 Liming and fertilising – chemical effects

Table 16.1 Comparison of organic and inorganic fertilisers

	Organic: 'green manure' = legumes ploughed in to decay 'Brown manure' = animal dung + urine	Inorganic: factory products, e.g. $(NH_4)_2SO_4$ or wastes, e.g. basic slag
Cost	Cheap	Expensive
Application	Difficult (bulky, sticky)	Easy (powders, granules)
Action	Slow but long-lasting	Quick but short-lasting
Soil structure	Improved (see 'humus')	Not improved
Earthworms	Encouraged	Often detrimental to them

16.3 CROP ROTATION

Crop rotation – growth of different crops on the same land in successive years without manuring each year. The two harvested crops have different mineral requirements and often obtain them from different soil depths. In the 'fallow year' legumes, e.g. clover, are sown to restore *nitrogen compounds* to the soil when the plants decay after being ploughed in. Other minerals (removed in crops) are restored by fertilising.

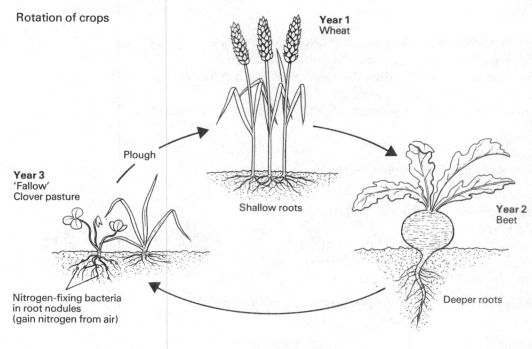

Fig. 16.2 Crop rotation

16.4   Pest control

Pest control – pest organisms reduce man's agricultural efforts or other interests, e.g. locusts, termites, weeds. *Man* created pests by providing organisms, normally held in check in their ecosystems, with unusual opportunities for increase in numbers in a monoculture (e.g. of corn, cotton or cows).

Chemical control – expensive. May eliminate pest but also kills harmless organisms too. Examples: DDT (insects); 2-4D (weeds).

Biological control – cheap. Use of a natural enemy of pest to *control* numbers (some damage must be expected) e.g. guppy fish eat mosquito larvae in ponds.

16.5   Human population crisis (problems)

Man's population growth has been *exponential:*

Year	Population	
1630 (estimated)	500 million	200 years
1830	1000 million	
1930	2000 million	100 years
1975	4000 million	estimated to rise to 6000 million by 2000.

This has been possible because of improvements in:

1 **Agriculture:** improved strains of crops and livestock; mechanisation and fertilisers – more food.

2 **Sanitation:** disposal of excreta, finally via sewage farms.

3 **Water supply:** filtration, finally chlorination.

4 **Medicine:** inoculation, drugs, antibiotics, aseptic surgery.

} reduced death rate from disease

Consequences

Bacteria on an agar plate show exponential growth (log phase). This leads to exhaustion of food and self-pollution resulting in mass death (crash phase) (see Fig. 16.3, graph 1). Man is on the log phase still, but he is both polluting the biosphere and reducing its resources. Unlike bacteria, man has the ability to avoid the crash phase by using a variety of solutions.

16.6   POLLUTION

Pollution: waste substances or energy from human activities which upset the normal balances in the biosphere. Anything from noise (aircraft), and heat (atomic power stations) to various substances in excess (sewage, DDT).

Table 16.2   Air, land and water pollutants

Air pollutants	Origin	Effect	Solution
(a) Sulphur dioxide (SO_2)	Coal burning; sulphide ore smelting	Smog; bronchitis	Burn smokeless fuels; SO_2 extraction units in factories
(b) Soot	Factories, steam engines	Smog; coats leaves, reducing photosynthesis	Smokeless fuels; factory chimney filters
(c) Carbon monoxide (CO)	Car exhausts	Prevents O_2 being carried by haemoglobin	After-burners in car exhausts turn CO →CO_2
(d) Lead (Pb)	Anti-knock in petrol	Harms nervous system	Low-compression engines
(e) Chloro-fluoro-methanes	Aerosol propellants	Allow more u.v. light to penetrate stratosphere by breaking down ozone: may increase skin cancer incidence.	Not yet devised
Land pollutants			
(a) Insecticides	Crop protection; control of disease vectors, e.g. mosquito	May kill top consumers*; lowers photosynthesis rate of marine algae	Ban undesirable ones, e.g. DDT, as U.K. has done†
(b) Radioactive wastes	Nuclear reactor accidents; atom bombs	Mutations ‡	Nuclear waste silos – but some have leaked
Water pollutants			
(a) Sewage	Human	Eutrophication §	Sewage treatment
(b) Artificial fertilisers	Excessive agricultural use	Eutrophication	Use of green and brown manures (Secs. 16.2, 16.3)
(c) Petroleum	Tanker accidents	Oiled sea birds, beaches	Effective accident prevention
(d) Mercury (organic)	Chemical works; fungicides on seeds, wood	Minemata disease (paralysis, idiots born)	Effluent purification

* Tiny amounts in producers are concentrated along a food chain into top consumers. Thus in 1950's eagles had very high DDT levels and laid thin-shelled eggs that broke easily. Their population fell.

† Poor countries cannot afford to do this in the tropics – famine or disease would result. DDT is cheap, effective.

‡ Cobalt is part of vitamin B_{12}, strontium is part of bone. If ^{60}Co or ^{90}Sr enter body, radiations emitted can cause leukaemia.

§ *Eutrophication:* excess sewage creates population explosion in bacteria decaying it. This depletes O_2, killing aquatic animals – which provide even more matter for decay. Decay produces abundant mineral salts which encourage algae to multiply – water goes green.

16.7   DEPLETION OF RESOURCES

(a) *Non-renewable*, e.g. minerals: zinc – may last another 10 years; natural gas – 30 years, at present rates of use from *known* resources.

(b) *Renewable*, e.g. foods: over-fishing of cod, herring, whales. Cutting down of forests exceeds planting.

Destruction of wild-life

Agricultural needs destroy natural habitats; pesticides, poison; and hunting for 'sport' or fashionable items, e.g. skins, ivory, may all lead to extinction of species, e.g. moa, Cape lion.

Lack of food

Two thirds of the world population lack either enough calories or protein or both in their diet. Poor nations are unable to pay for the surplus food of rich ones.

Overcrowded populations (reduced living space)

Leads to greater chance of epidemic diseases and social diseases, e.g. vandalism, baby-bashing, drug-taking.

16.8   HUMAN POPULATION CRISIS (SOLUTIONS)

Solutions

1   **Contraception** (see Section 12.19) and abortion (removing unwanted embryos) would by themselves reduce the rate of increase in population if used world-wide.

2   **Conservation of minerals:** use of substitutes for metals, e.g. carbon-fibre plastics; reversing the throw-away mentality by making durable products, e.g. cars that last; re-cycling metals in discarded items.

Note: lowered industrial production (and fewer jobs) must be accepted as a result of these policies.

3   **Conservation of wild-life and natural scenery:** strict guardianship of Nature Reserves; acceptance that minerals in a mountain may be less valuable than the beauty it affords. Man's need for recreation and enjoyment of nature is as necessary for health as meeting his material needs.

4   **Conservation of renewable resources:** by never taking more than can be replaced (by reproduction).

5   **Finding new (acceptable) energy sources,** e.g. solar power, tide power. Fast-breeder reactors will produce very much more dangerous waste than conventional reactors – a possible mutation hazard. To re-cycle metals, produce substitutes for them, and make artificial fertilisers is very energy-consuming.

6   **New sources of food:** greater dependence on micro-organisms, e.g. 'SCP' (see Section 17.2) and soya bean meat-substitutes.

16.9   PREDICTIONS FOR THE FUTURE OF MANKIND

An international group of scientists called the 'Club of Rome', concerned at the misuse of the biosphere by man, gathered data from 1900–1970 on population, pollution, food and mineral resources in the world. Using a computer they made predictions about present and possible future trends in the world (see Fig. 16.3, graphs 2, 3 and 4).

These predictions do not have to come to pass. Hopefully, solutions will be implemented to avoid the fate of the bacteria shown in Fig. 16.3, graph 1.

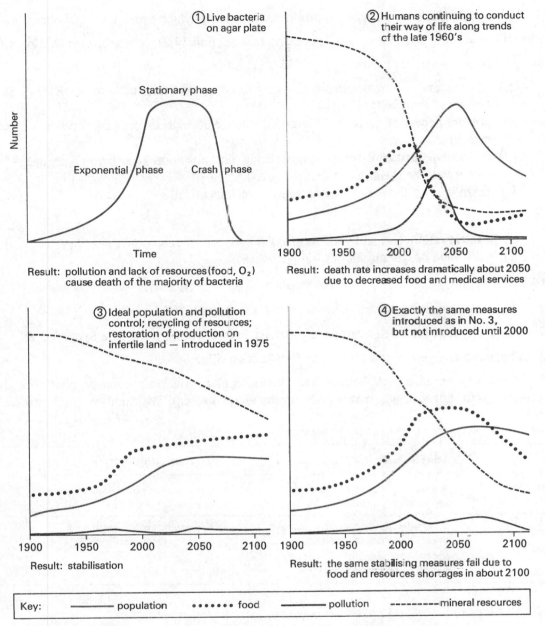

Fig. 16.3 Population graphs: bacteria and humans

Graphs based on those in THE LIMITS TO GROWTH: A report for THE CLUB OF ROME'S Project on the Predicament of Mankind, by Donella H Meadows, Dennis L Meadows, Jørgen Randers, William W Behrens III. A Potomac Associates book published by Universe Books, New York, 1972.

MAN'S INTERNAL ENVIRONMENT

Hormones and nerves (see Section 9.9) help to stabilise the body's internal environment (achieve homeostasis). Any change from normal is called **disease**.

16.10 TYPES OF DISEASE IN MAN

1 Genetic: since these diseases are inherited, they are *incurable*.

Examples: **haemophilia** – a gene mutation (see Section 13.11); **mongolism:** baby has an extra chromosome, i.e. 46 + 1 owing to faulty meiosis in mother. Person has retarded development and dies usually before 40.

2 Diet deficiency: curable by eating a balanced diet.

Examples: lack of iodine (**goitre**, see Section 4.3); or vitamin C (**scurvy**, see Section 4.5); or protein (**kwashiorkor** – matchstick limbs, pot belly, see Section 4.21).

3 Hormonal: curable by artificial supply of hormone.

Examples: lack of thyroxin (**cretinism**) or insulin (**diabetes**) (see Section 9.8).

4   Pathogenic: entry of parasites (pathogens) into body which upset its metabolism.

Examples: viruses (see Section 17.1); bacteria (see Section 17.2); protozoa (see Section 17.4).

(*a*) **prevention** (better than cure)

   (*i*) **kill vectors,** e.g. mosquitoes carrying malaria; or intermediate hosts, e.g. snails carrying biharzia.

   (*ii*) **prevent access** of parasite by hygiene, water chlorination, cooking food or protective measures, e.g. mosquito nets.

   (*iii*) **preventive medicine** (prophylaxis) using immunisation (see below) or drugs, e.g. mepacrine for malaria.

   (*iv*) **quarantine** of those ill (isolates sources of infection)

(*b*) **cure**

   (*i*) **hospitalisation:** rest and good food assist body's own defences.

   (*ii*) **medicines:** drugs, antibiotics kill pathogens.

16.11 NATURAL DEFENCES OF THE BODY AGAINST PATHOGENS

1   Skin: keratin; sweat (which is antiseptic) – (see Section 7.7).

2   Blood clotting: provides a temporary barrier before wound heals (see Section 5.8).

3   Phagocytes: ingest micro-organisms (see Section 5.8).

4   Lymphocytes: make antibodies (see Section 5.8) to kill pathogens or neutralise their poisons (with anti-toxins), make body immune (protected). Mechanism used medically.

Table 16.3   Comparison of active and passive immunity

	Active immunity (body participates)	**Passive immunity** (body passive)
Method	Weakened or dead strain of pathogen introduced, e.g. polio **vaccine**	Antibodies made by another animal, e.g. horse, are injected
Protection	(*a*) long-lasting ('boosters' prolong protection e.g. anti-tetanus every 3 years) (*b*) takes weeks to develop	(*a*) short-lived (body destroys the foreign antibodies) (*b*) immediate

16.12 NOTABLE CONTRIBUTORS TO HEALTH AND HYGIENE

Edward Jenner (1749–1823): practised *vaccination*: scratching cowpox (spots from vaccinia virus on cows) into skin protects person from smallpox. Cowpox – mild spots in dairy maids; smallpox – disfiguring or lethal disease.

Louis Pasteur (1822–1895): father of *bacteriology*. Discovered the bacterial nature of putrefaction and many diseases. Saved silk industry (pebrine disease of silkworms); brewers ('ropy' beer); poultry farmers (chicken cholera) and cattle farmers (anthrax) from severe losses by developing sterile techniques and vaccines. Finally, developed a rabies vaccine to protect humans.

Joseph Lister (1827–1912): developed *antiseptic surgery*. Used fine phenol spray during operations to kill bacteria, dramatically reducing hospitals deaths. Today *aseptic* surgery is used – sterilisation of all equipment before use, in autoclaves (see Section 17.2).

Alexander Fleming (1881–1955): discovered lysozyme (natural antiseptic in tears and saliva) and the *antibiotic* penicillin (see Section 17.5).

Drugs, antibiotics, disinfectants and antiseptics

'Drugs' are chemicals made by man or organisms. Some are harmful and possession of them is illegal, e.g. LSD – which has no medical purpose. Others (in the right doses) assist medically, e.g. sulphonamides for curing bacterial infections; aspirin for headaches; and belladonna for helping people with ailing hearts. The term 'drug' is thus too vague to be very useful.

Antibiotics are chemicals secreted by bacteria or fungi and extracted by man for his own use in killing micro-organisms in his body. *Examples:* penicillin, aureomycin.

Disinfectants are chemicals made by chemists to kill micro-organisms, e.g. neat 'Dettol' in latrines.

Antiseptics are chemicals used in such a dose that they kill micro-organisms but not human cells with which they make contact. May be diluted disinfectants, e.g. weak 'Dettol' for gargling or bathing cuts.

17 A variety of life

17.1 VIRUSES

Size: approximately 0.00001 mm, i.e. 10 nm (1/100 size of bacteria) – visible only by electron microscope.

Structure: protein coat around a DNA strand (a few genes) (see Fig. 17.1).

Living?: no; are not cells; have no metabolism of their own (see Section 2.1).

All are *parasites*, killing host cells as they reproduce within them, using the cell's energy and materials. This causes disease, e.g. rabies.

Disease transmission

(*a*) by water, e.g. polio.
(*b*) by droplet (sneezing), e.g. colds, 'flu.
(*c*) by vector, e.g. mosquito transmits yellow fever and greenfly transmits the T.M.V.

Useful: for biological control of rabbits – myxomatosis virus.

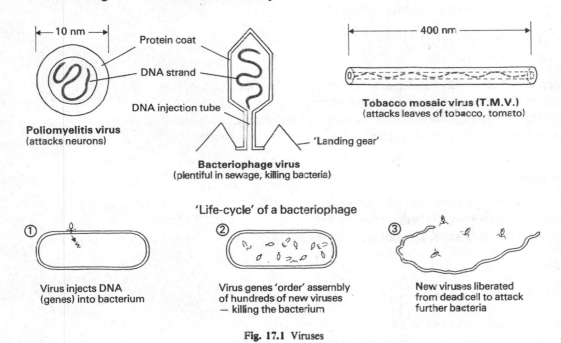

Fig. 17.1 Viruses

17.2 BACTERIA

Size: approximately 1 μm, i.e. 1000 nm (1/100 size of mammal cheek cell) – the smallest cell.

Structure: Cell is unique in not having:

(*a*) nuclear membrane around its single loop chromosome.
(*b*) mitochondria (cell membrane has the same function).
(*c*) endoplasmic reticulum (see Section 2.2).

Cell is unlike green plant cells in having no:

(*a*) chloroplasts (therefore bacteria are either saprophytes or parasites) (see Section 4.11).

(*b*) cellulose in cell walls (made of nitrogenous compounds instead) (see Fig. 17.2).

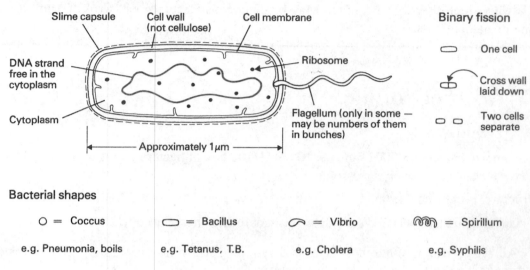

Fig. 17.2 Bacteria

Reproduction

(*a*) by binary fission, every 20 minutes in suitable conditions.

(*b*) use a conjugation tube to transfer DNA from one bacterium to another. Bacteria do *not* reproduce by forming spores. Some bacilli, only, form spores (endospores) for survival when conditions become unfavourable.

Importance of bacteria

Helpful

(*a*) in decay, releasing nutrients for green plants (see Section 4.2).

(*b*) in fixing nitrogen for green plants (see Section 15.6).

(*c*) in industrial processes, e.g. making butter, cheese, vinegar.

(*d*) as food source – single cell protein ('SCP') fed to animals.

Harmful

(*a*) in decaying food (rotting, putrefying).

(*b*) in de-nitrifying the soil, reducing fertility (see Section 15.6).

(*c*) in causing disease to man and his animals.

Requirements

1 Moisture.
2 Organic food.
3 A suitable temperature (warmth).
4 No ultra-violet light (it kills by damaging DNA).

If these conditions are not met, bacteria die (see **1–4** below).

Man's control of harmful bacteria

1 **Dried foods:** peas, raisins, milk, meat – keep for ever.

   Salting: e.g. ham, or *syruping*, e.g. peaches, plasmolyses (see Section 5.3) bacteria.

2 **Hygiene:** removal of bacterial foods by washing body, clothes, food-utensils; by disposing of refuse, excreta and hospital dressings; cleaning homes.

3   Temperature treatment:

(*a*) *refrigeration:* deep-freeze (−20°C) suspends life; fridge (+4°C).slows rotting to acceptable level.

(*b*) *boiling:* kills most, but not spores.

(*c*) *pressure-cooking* ('sterilising' or 'autoclaving') for 10 minutes at 10 kN/m² (15 lbs/in²) kills all, including spores.

(*d*) *pasteurisation* (of milk): heat to 77°C for 15 seconds and rapidly cool to 4°C.

4   Irradiate with ultra-violet light (thin sliced food, surgical instruments) and plan sunny homes (sunlight contains u.v. light).

5   Chemicals are also used to kill bacteria:

(*a*) *chlorine* in drinking water and swimming baths.

(*b*) *disinfectants* in loos.

(*c*) *medical use* of antiseptics, antibiotics, antibodies and drugs in or on man's body (see Section 16.12).

(*d*) *vinegar* for pickling food (pH too acid for bacteria).

17.3   SPIROGYRA

Spirogyra – a filamentous alga living in ponds (see Fig. 17.3).

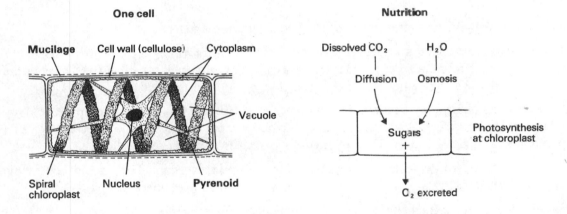

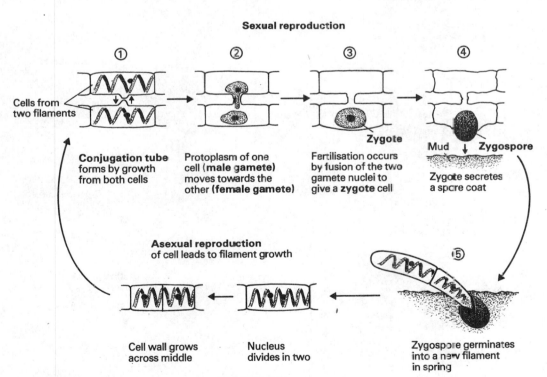

Fig. 17.3 *Spirogyra*

Structure: *Mucilage* stops drying out at surface of water when trapped O_2 from photosynthesis causes tangled mass of filaments to rise during the day.

Pyrenoids turn sugars, made in chloroplasts, into starch.

Functions of other parts are as in any green plant cell (see Section 2.1).

Nutrition: holophytic (see Section 4.2).

Reproduction: since all cells in the filament are identical, and able to reproduce, each one may be regarded as an individual organism that happens not to have separated from its neighbour at cell division. This *asexual* reproduction occurs in summer: *sexual* occurs in autumn.

Zygospore ensures *dispersal* (carried to other ponds in mud on animals) and *survival* over the winter.

Importance of algae

1   **Diatoms** (unicellular algae) are the main plant component of plankton:

(*a*) provide majority of world's O_2.
(*b*) are at base of all marine food chains.

2   Some **sea-weeds** are eaten, e.g. 'Irish moss' by Irish and Japanese.

3   **Extracts:** 'agar' for bacterial culture methods; 'alginates' for ice-cream.

17.4   AMOEBA

Amoeba – a large fresh-water protozoan (up to 1 mm in diameter) (see Fig. 17.4).

Locomotion: cytoplasm in centre (plasmasol) flows forward forming a pseudopodium. At the front plasmasol fountains out, solidifying to a jelly-like tube (plasmagel) through which the centre flows. Plasmagel re-liquefies at rear end, flowing into centre.

Nutrition: holozoic (see Section 4.2). Pursues prey (algae, bacteria, other protozoa) by following the trail of chemicals they exude (chemotaxis, see Section 9.11). Ingests prey using pseudopodia; digests it in food vacuole; egests indigestible matter, e.g. cellulose.

Osmoregulation: water, entering continually by osmosis, is channelled to the contractile vacuole. When full, this bursts, squirting water out. Process uses energy.

Respiration: gaseous exchange (O_2 in, CO_2 out) occurs over whole surface area.

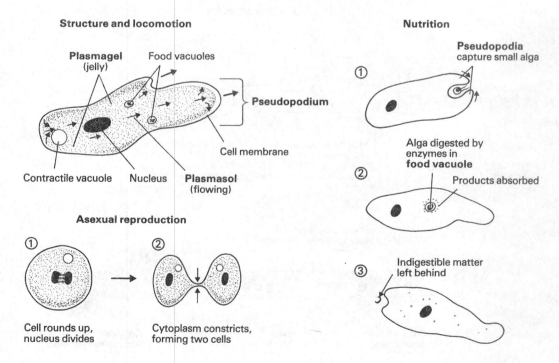

Fig. 17.4 *Amoeba*

Reproduction: asexually by binary fission; no sexual method.

Sensitivity: moves towards food; away from strong light, harmful chemicals and sharp objects.

Importance of protozoa

1   Malaria parasite (*Plasmodium*), transmitted by mosquito, kills millions of people by fever unless protected by drugs, like quinacrine.

2   Sleeping sickness parasite (*Trypanosoma*), transmitted by tse-tse fly, kills millions of people, cattle and pigs in Africa. No drug protection against some types.

3   Dysentery parasite (*Entamoeba*), transmitted by house-fly, causes dysentery (intestinal bleeding and upsets) and liver abscesses.

17.5   RHIZOPUS AND MUCOR

Rhizopus (mould on bread) and *Mucor* (mould on dung) – both 'pin-moulds' (see Fig. 17.5).

Structure: The cytoplasm, with many nuclei in it, lines the cell wall – a continuous tube (of chitin) with no partitions forming separate cells. Inside the cytoplasm is a continuous vacuole. Threads of fungus (hyphae) make up a mycelium.

Nutrition: saprophytic (see Section 4.2). Rootlet hyphae branch through the food secreting digestive enzymes and absorbing the soluble products.

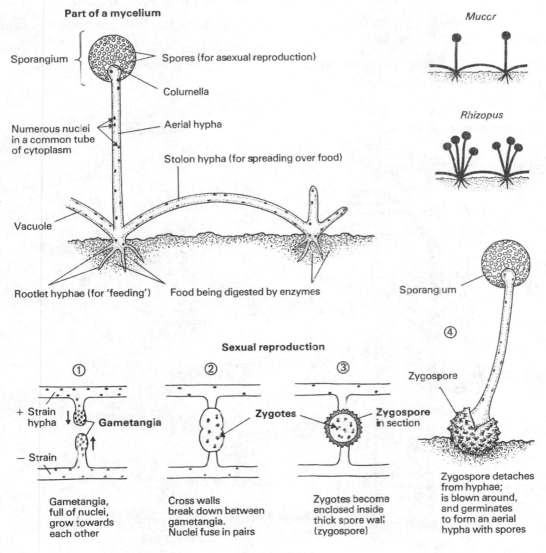

Fig. 17.5 *Mucor*

Reproduction:

(*a*) *asexually* by hundreds of spores from each sporangium. In *Mucor*, sporangium wall dissolves in moisture and spores are distributed in a slime-drop by rain or animals. In *Rhizopus*, wall cracks open when dry and wind distributes dry spores.

(*b*) *sexually* using gamete-nuclei in gametangia of two different strains. A zygospore results – allowing dispersal and survival in unfavourable conditions.

Importance of fungi

Helpful

1 **Decay fungi** liberate nutrients for green plants from dead organisms.

2 **Yeasts,** respiring anaerobically, provide:

(*a*) alcohol for brewers and wine-makers.

(*b*) CO_2 for bakers (yeast acts on sugar in dough, making it rise).

$$C_6H_{12}O_6 \xrightarrow{\text{Enzymes}} 2C_2H_5OH + 2CO_2$$

Glucose   Alcohol   Carbon dioxide

The yeast cells themselves also yield vitamin B extracts (e.g. 'Marmite').

3 **Antibiotic-producers,** e.g. *Penicillium* produces penicillin.

4 **Food fungi,** e.g. mushrooms, chanterelles and single cell protein (from yeasts).

Harmful

1 **Decay fungi** spoil food, e.g. *Rhizopus, Penicillium* on bread, cakes and jam.

2 **Plant diseases,** e.g. potato blight caused millions to die in the Irish potato famine; 'rust' fungi damage cereal crops seriously.

3 **Dry rot** fungus destroys house timbers.

17.6 HYDRA

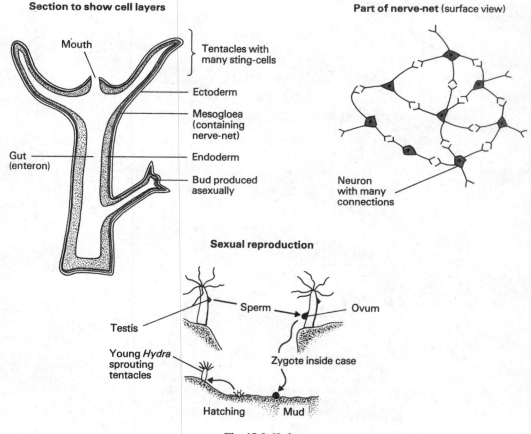

Fig. 17.6 *Hydra*

Hydra is a fresh-water coelenterate (see Fig. 17.6).

Structure: body has only two cell-layers (*ectoderm* and *endoderm*) forming a sack with tentacles at the open end. A *nerve-net* (no nerves or brain) lies between ectoderm and endoderm, in a thin layer of jelly (mesogloea).

Feeding

1 Prey, e.g. *Daphnia* (water flea), is paralysed by sting-cells on tentacles and moved through mouth into gut. Here, gland-cells secrete digestive enzymes to break up food; other cells ingest the bits (as amoebae do) to finish off digestion. Indigestible food is egested through the mouth.

2 Some *Hydra* species have algae living in **symbiosis** within endoderm cells. *Hydra* gains photosynthesised food and O_2; algae gain CO_2 and nitrogenous wastes from *Hydra*.

Reproduction

1 asexually by budding; buds detach.

2 sexually by forming testes and an ovary (containing one ovum) on the same *Hydra*, but ripening at different times. Sperm fertilises the ovum. Zygote secretes a chitin case and falls into the mud. Later the case splits and from it a hollow ball of cells grows into a *Hydra*. Parent usually dies.

17.7 EARTHWORM

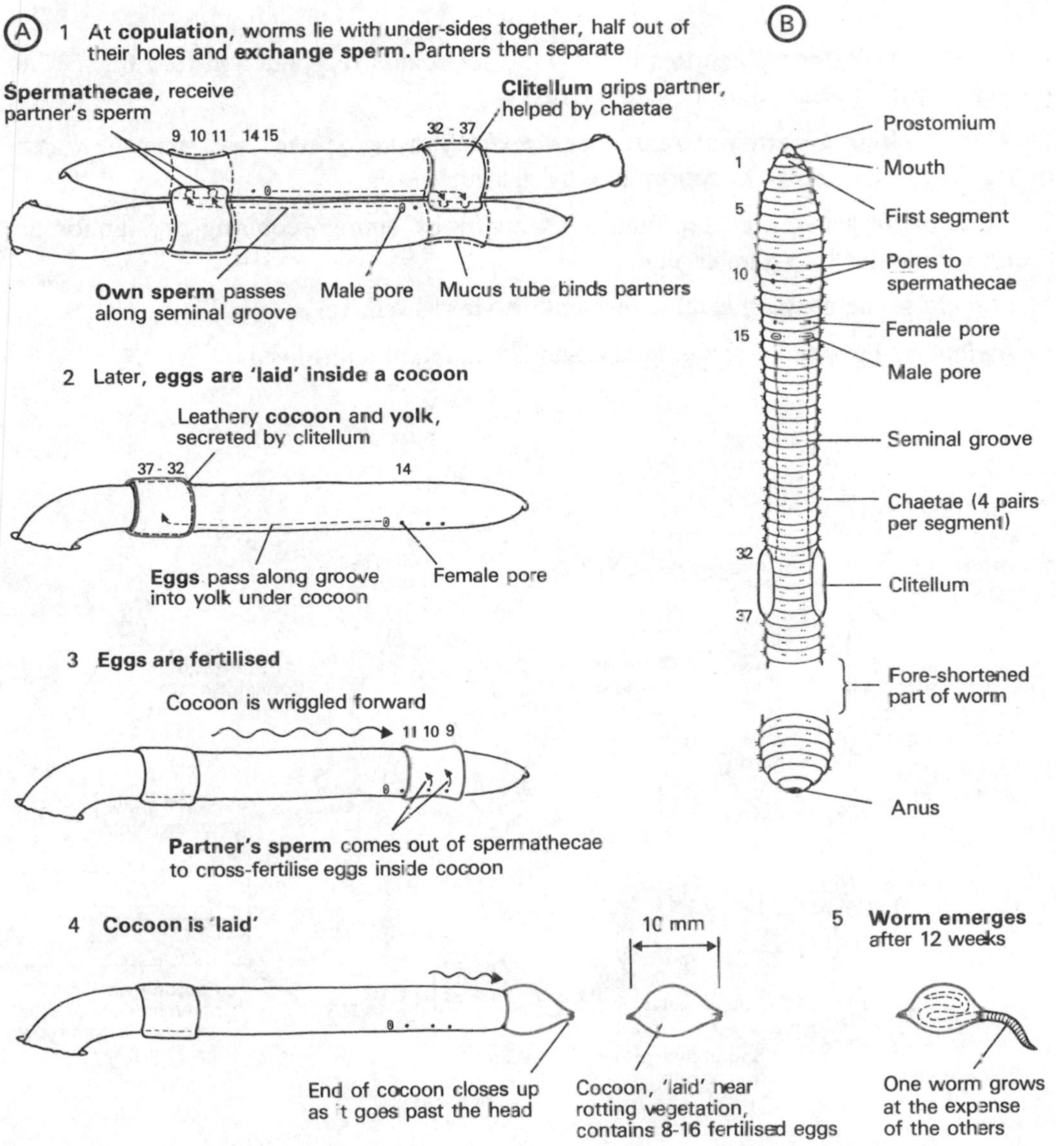

Fig. 17.7 The earthworm. A –reproduction, B –external features from underneath

Earthworm (*Lumbricus terrestris*) is a terrestrial annelid (see Fig. 17.7).

Reproduction

1 worm is *hermaphrodite* (both male and female).

2 *copulates* on warm moist nights to receive and store another worm's sperm in its spermathecae.

3 later, *cross-fertilises* its eggs within a cocoon which it lays.

Locomotion

1 Burrows through soil.

2 Alternately contracts longitudinal muscles (to become short and fat) and circular muscles (to become long and thin), using an internal liquid skeleton (see Section 10.5).

3 Chaetae (bristles) provide anchorage.

4 Mucus (slime) provides lubrication as it slides through tunnel.

Importance of earthworms

Improve soil fertility by their actions (see Section 15.8).

17.8   MOSS AND FERN

Moss and fern – green plants requiring water for sexual reproduction (see Figs. 17.8, 17.9). Life cycle shows **alternation of generations:**

1 **Gametophyte** generation: reproduces *sexually* using sperm that swim in water to the ovum. Zygote gives rise to sporophyte by growth.

2 **Sporophyte** generation: reproduces *asexually* by spores requiring dry air for dispersal. Spore germinates into gametophyte.

Moss plant is the *gametophyte*; sporophyte is short-lived.

Fern plant is the *sporophyte*; gametophyte is small and short-lived.

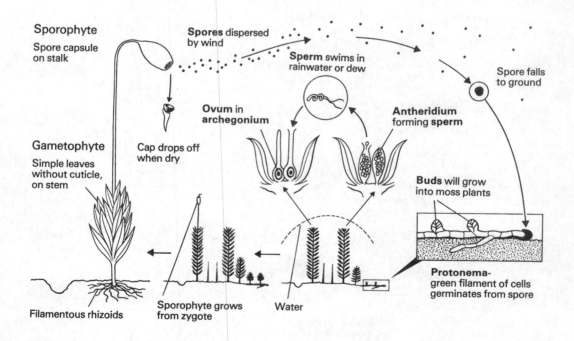

Fig. 17.8 Life cycle of a moss (showing alternation of generations)

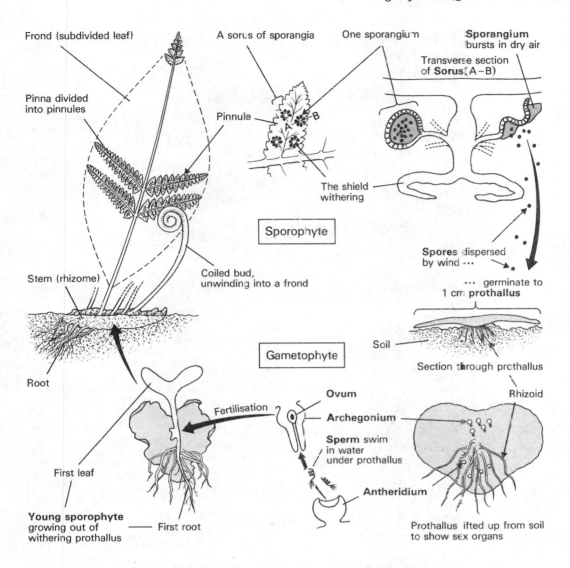

Frond (subdivided leaf)

Pinna divided into pinnules

Pinnule

A sorus of sporangia

One sporangium

Sporangium bursts in dry air

Transverse section of **Sorus** (A–B)

The shield withering

Sporophyte

Stem (rhizome)

Coiled bud, unwinding into a frond

Root

Spores dispersed by wind ⋯

⋯ germinate to 1 cm **prothallus**

Soil

Section through prothallus

Rhizoid

Gametophyte

Fertilisation

Ovum

Archegonium

Sperm swim in water under prothallus

Antheridium

First leaf

Young sporophyte growing out of withering prothallus

First root

Prothallus lifted up from soil to show sex organs

Fig. 17.9 Life cycle of a fern (showing alternation of generations)

17.9 ANGIOSPERMS (GENERAL STRUCTURE)

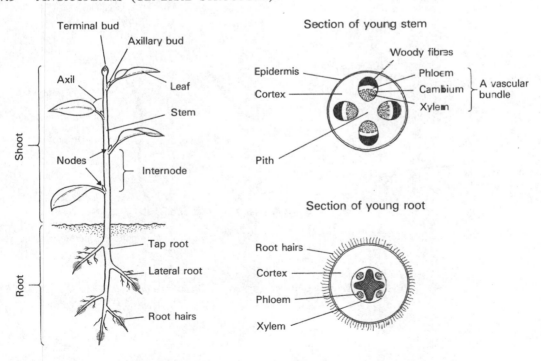

Terminal bud

Axillary bud

Axil

Leaf

Stem

Shoot

Nodes

Internode

Root

Tap root

Lateral root

Root hairs

Section of young stem

Woody fibres

Epidermis

Phloem

Cambium

Cortex

Xylem

A vascular bundle

Pith

Section of young root

Root hairs

Cortex

Phloem

Xylem

Fig. 17.10 Angiosperm – general structural of a dicot plant

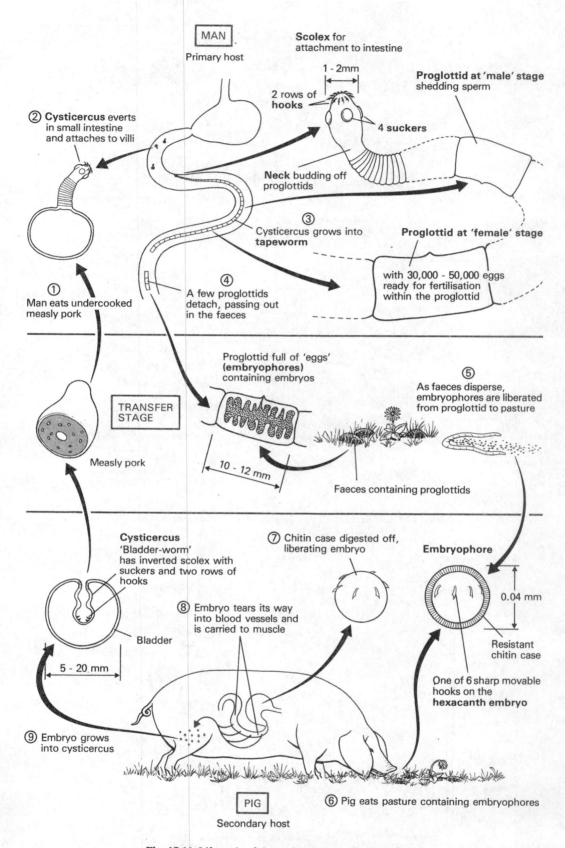

Fig. 17.11 Life cycle of the pork tapeworm, *Taenia solium*

17.10 PARASITIC ADAPTATIONS

Parasitic adaptations (of all parasites):

1 Specialised feeding structures.
2 Lack of usual feeding structures found in the phylum.
3 Structures for attachment to the host.
4 High rate of reproduction to ensure infection.
5 Special stages in the life cycle for distribution and survival. In addition, parasites show individual adaptations.

17.11 PORK TAPEWORM

Pork tapeworm (*Taenia solium*) – parasite of man and pig (see Fig. 17.11).

Life cycle essentials are:

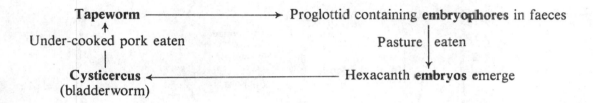

Control – by breaking the life cycle:

(*a*) *cook pork thoroughly* – cysticerci are killed by cooking.
(*b*) *dispose of faeces* sanitarily – pigs cannot be infected.
(*c*) *inspect pork* – meat inspectors prevent sale of 'measly pork'.

Adaptations to parasitic life

1 **Scolex:** hooks and suckers prevent dislodgement by food flowing in intestine.

2 **Thick cuticle** (perhaps also anti-enzymes): prevent digestion by host.

3 **Flat shape:** large surface area for absorption of food (digested by man).

4 **Anaerobic respiration:** little O_2 in intestine.

5 **Hermaphrodite and self-fertilising:** essential because worm is large (2–3 metres), so only one can be accommodated at a time.

6 **High reproductive rate:** makes up for the enormous chances *against* infection of hosts. In a worm's life span of over 25 years it produces over 2000 proglottids per year each containing 30–50 000 hexacanth embryos, each capable of forming a cysticercus to infect man.

7 **Embryophore case:** permits survival of embryo for many weeks.

8 **Two hosts:** gives a double chance of survival and distribution to new hosts.

17.12 PYTHIUM DEBARYANUM

Pythium debaryanum the 'damping off' fungus – a plant parasite (see Fig. 17.12). Kills seedlings and weak plants grown in humid conditions; causes millions of pounds in losses and control measures in the horticultural industry. Difficult to control since:

1 Fungus is both parasitic on live plants and saprophytic on dead ones.

2 Humid, well-watered conditions in greenhouses favour rapid spread of fungus by zoospores (swim by flagella in minute films of water).

3 Zygospores survive for long periods even in dry soil not being used.

Control measures therefore include:

(*a*) growing seedlings in well ventilated conditions (zoospores not formed).

(*b*) burning all infected seedlings.

(*c*) using fungicides or steam-sterilising soil that contained infected plants before re-use in seedling boxes (to kill zygospores especially).

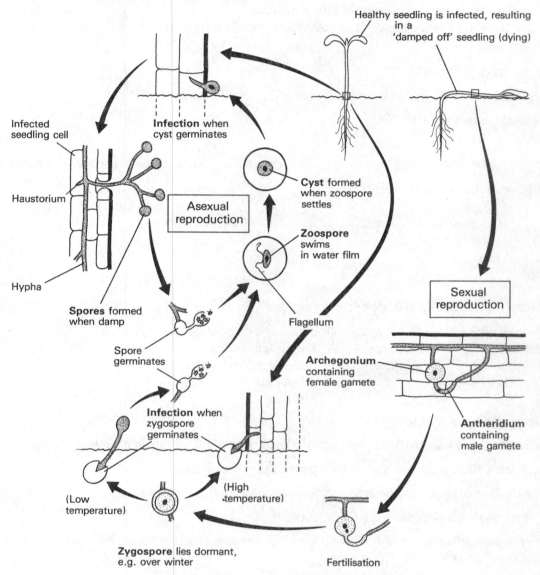

Fig. 17.12 Life cycle of *Pythium debaryanum*

Feeding in parasitic fungi

Usually, rootlet hyphae called **haustoria** penetrate into or between the host cells, absorbing food from them.

17.13 Dodder

The dodder (*Cuscuta epithymum*) – parasite of gorse, broom, clover and heather.

Leaves: small scales without chlorophyll.

Stem: a pink thread twining around the host's stem and sending haustoria ('suckers') into it (see Fig. 17.13). Parasite's conducting tissue joins up with host's, gaining water and mineral salts from xylem and organic food from phloem.

Roots: none.

Flowers: pink-petalled, small and numerous; produced in second year.

Seeds: large numbers; germinate only in summer, giving time for spring growth of hosts.

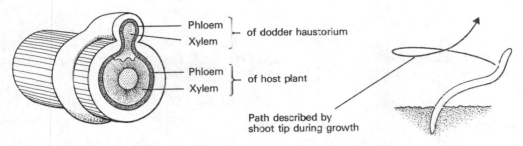

Section through a haustorium   Dodder seedling nutating

Fig. 17.13 Parasitic adaptations of the dodder, *Cuscuta epithymum*

Seedling: sends down root; shoot nutates (twists in a wide arc as it grows) so as to contact a suitable host stem to penetrate with a haustorium. If successful, root withers; otherwise seedling dies.

Cuscuta overwinters as nodules of tissue around each haustorium. Lives for two years or more. Not a parasite of economic importance.

17.14 INSECTS (LIFE CYCLES AND EXTERNAL FEATURES)

Insects: have two contrasting life cycles (see Fig. 17.14):

1 Incomplete metamorphosis, e.g. locust, cockroach, dragonfly. Growing stage (**nymph**) is similar to adult, lacking only wings and ability to reproduce. Last moult gives adult.

2 Complete metamorphosis, e.g. fly, butterfly, bee (most insects). Growing stage (**larva**) so unlike adult that reorganisation into an adult must be achieved as a **pupa**.

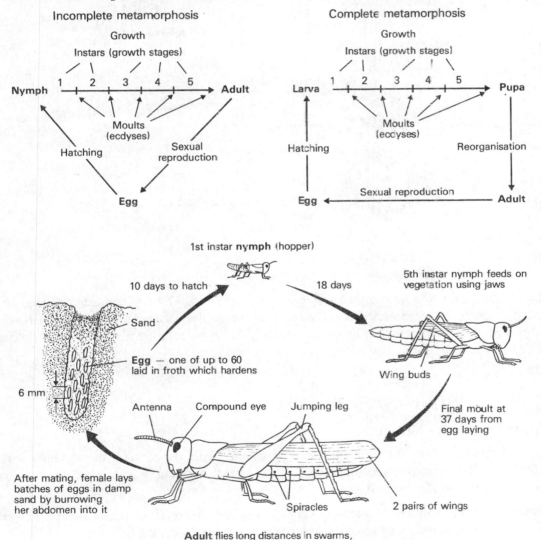

Fig. 17.15 The locust, *Schistocerca gregaria*

17.15 LOCUST

The desert locust (*Schistocerca gregaria*) – found from North Africa to India. Devastates vegetation of all kinds, both as 'hopper' (nymph) and adult. Controlled by laying bran, soaked in insecticide, in path of hoppers (see Fig. 17.15).

17.16 HOUSE FLY

House fly (*Musca domestica*) (see Fig. 17.16).

Adults transmit diseases (e.g. dysentery, certain worms) by visiting faeces and then human food. Here they deposit the infecting organisms via their feet or saliva (see Fig. 4.10) or by their own droppings ('fly-spots'). Flies controlled by good garbage disposal and sanitation (removes breeding sites); insecticides. In tropics: use muslin or wire gauze fly-screens to cover food and drink.

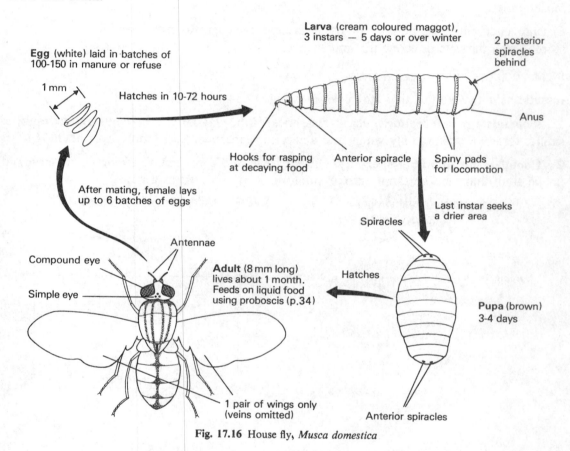

Fig. 17.16 House fly, *Musca domestica*

17.17 LARGE CABBAGE WHITE BUTTERFLY

Large cabbage white butterfly (*Pieris brassicae*) (see Fig. 17.17). Damages cabbage-family plants. Controlled by insecticides and a parasitic 3 mm black wasp (*Apanteles glomerata*). Its eggs, injected into caterpillar, hatch into larvae feeding on caterpillar's tissues, thus killing it. Pupates within bright yellow cocoons on caterpillar's skin.

17.18 HONEY BEE

Honey bee (*Apis mellifera*) (see Fig. 17.18).

Organisation in the hive

No individual bee can live for long without assistance from the others. Thus the hive, with its 5000–100 000 bees, is comparable to a socially-organised unit, e.g. a town, or to a multicellular organism (bee ≡ cell).

The queen is the only fertile female (*a*) laying eggs and (*b*) secreting 'queen substance', which is passed from bee to bee by mouth and keeps the colony working together.

Drones are fertile males; do no hive work; fed by workers; driven out to die in autumn.

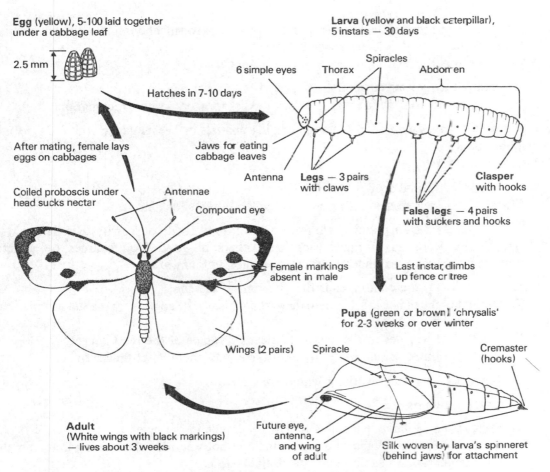

Fig. 17.17 Large cabbage white butterfly, *Pieris brassicae*

Workers are infertile females with a sequence of duties as they get older:

(*a*) *nurse:* cleans out used cells; secretes protein-rich 'royal jelly' from head-glands to feed young larvae; feeds honey and pollen to older larvae.

(*b*) *food storer:* receives from foragers and stores in cells: pollen ('bee bread'); and nectar (mainly sucrose solution), which they change to honey by:

  (*i*) digesting sucrose to simple sugars.

  (*ii*) evaporating its water (at 84% sugar, no bacteria or fungi can ferment it).

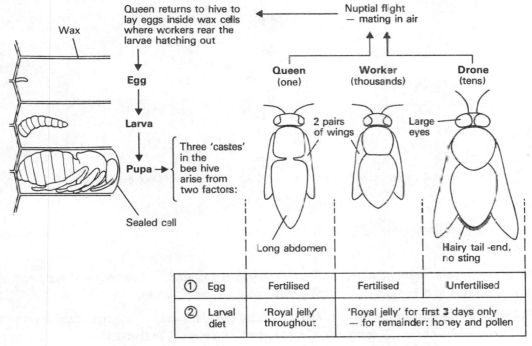

		Queen	Worker	Drone
①	Egg	Fertilised	Fertilised	Unfertilised
②	Larval diet	'Royal jelly' throughout	'Royal jelly' for first 3 days only — for remainder: honey and pollen	

Fig. 17.18 Honey bee, *Apis mellifera*

(c) *comb builder:* secretes wax, oozing out as plates between abdominal segments; chews these into hexagonal cylinder shaped cells.

(d) *ventilator:* stands, beating wings at hive entrance to:

   (i) create outward air current.

   (ii) carry scent from abdominal glands, to assist foragers in hive-recognition.

(e) *guard:* challenges incomers, stinging invading animals or bees unladen with food (usually robber bees).

(f) *forager:* gathers

   (i) nectar in special crop.

   (ii) pollen stuck together with nectar in 'pollen baskets' of hind legs.

Communicates distance and angle from hive of good food sources by 'bee dances' (see Fig. 17.19). Returning forager bees 'tell' others of good food sources by agitated movements. Other bees understand the messages as follows:

   (i) vertically up the comb means the **direction of the sun.**

   (ii) pattern of the dance in relation to the vertical means the **angle from the sun** at which bees must set off.

   (iii) number of waggles of the abdomen means **distance of the food source.**

   (iv) regurgitation of some nectar to bees nearby tells them **what flower to seek.**

   Most bees die while working within six weeks.

(g) *old forager:* gathers

   (i) plant resins to make 'propolis' (to seal up cracks in the hive).

   (ii) water to wet cells (evaporation cools them in hot weather, cf. sweating in mammals). Hive temperature usually maintained at 31–33°C.

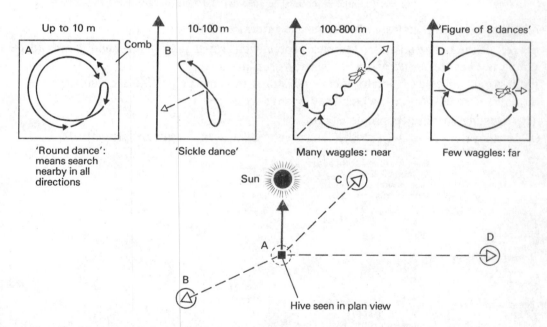

Fig. 17.19 Bee 'dances' on honey combs. Messages A – D are translated into bee flight paths

17.19 IMPORTANCE OF INSECTS TO MAN

Helpful

1 **Bees: pollinators** (without which orchard fruit yields are greatly reduced) and **suppliers of honey** (sweetener) and **beeswax** (for high-grade polishes and lipstick).

2 **Biological control** of pests, by *lady-birds* (control aphids, mealy-bugs and scale insects in gardens, coffee and citrus plantations); *Cactus moth* caterpillars (eat prickly-pear cactus invading agricultural land).

Harmful

1   Food destroyers, e.g. *locust* (crops) *grain weevil* (stored grain).

2   Materials destroyers, e.g. *termites* (wooden buildings) *cotton boll weevil* (cotton flower) *clothes moth* (woollen clothes).

3   Disease vectors, e.g. *mosquitoes* (yellow fever virus' malaria protozoan and elephantiasis nematode worm), *tse-tse flies* (human sleeping sickness and similar sicknesses in domesticated animals), *housefly* (dysentery protozoa and bacteria), *fleas* (plague bacteria), *wood-boring beetle* (dutch-elm disease fungus), *aphids* (plant virus disease).

4   Nuisances, e.g. *cockroaches* and *ants* (spoiling food).

17.20 BONY FISH

Adaptations to an aquatic environment

1   Locomotion (see Fig. 17.20):

(*a*) *shape:* streamlined. Skin, secreting mucus, covers overlapping bony scales.

(*b*) *propulsion:* sideways movement of muscular body exerts a backward and sideways force on the water via the large surface area of the *tail*. Vertebrae have balls of cartilage between them allowing great flexibility; muscles on either side contract alternately to give sideways movement. In fast swimming, side fins kept flat against body. When static, thrusts from pectoral (and pelvic) fins adjust position.

(*c*) *stability: fins* prevent roll, pitch and yaw (see Fig. 17.21).

(*d*) *control:* pectoral and pelvic fins act as *hydroplanes* according to angle; when both are held at right angles to body, act as *brakes*.

(*e*) *buoyancy: air-bladder* (contents adjustable) keeps fish at required depth. Saves energy (cartilaginous fish, e.g. sharks, have no air-bladders and must keep swimming to prevent sinking).

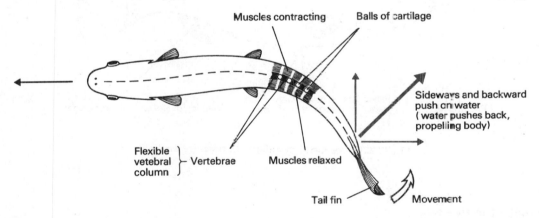

Fig. 17.20 How a fish moves

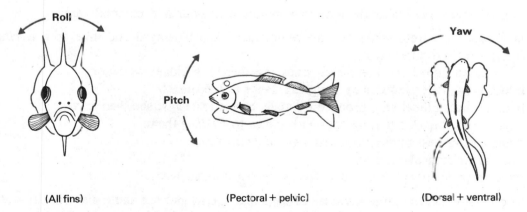

Fig. 17.21 How fish fins prevent instability

2 Respiration

Water enters mouth, is sieved by gill-rakers, allowing gaseous exchange over gills, and leaves under bony operculum. Rakers may provide feeding method too (see Fig. 4.8b).

3 Sensitivity

(a) *'smelling': two nostrils* are double, leading water through a U-shaped cavity lined with cells sensing chemicals.

(b) *seeing:* two unblinking *eyes.*

(c) *'hearing': lateral line* canal contains hair-cells, in bunches, sensitive to pressure waves in water – from obstacles and from moving organisms.

The *cloaca* (a chamber) receives faeces, urine and gametes from separate tubes; discharges to the water via a single opening.

17.21 THREE-SPINED STICKLEBACK

The three-spined stickleback (*Gasterosteus aculeatus*) (see Fig. 17.22).

Habitat: margins of rivers, lakes – amongst weeds.

Food: worms, crustacea and insect larvae (carnivorous). Is eaten by perch, pike and heron.

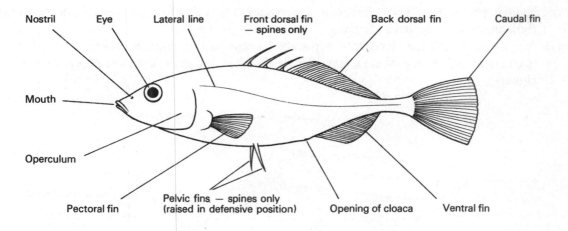

Fig. 17.22 Three-spined stickleback, *Gasterosteus aculeatus*

Specialised in two ways:

1 **Fins:** front dorsal fin and pelvic fins have no webs (spines used in defence when erected).

2 **Reproduction:** has elaborate instinctive mating behaviour and parental care:

(a) in February–March, *males* become red-breasted and blue-eyed and take up a *territory* (defended from other males).

(b) build a *nest*-tunnel of water-weeds stuck together by a kidney secretion.

(c) lead fat, egg-laden females by a zig-zag dance to the tunnel.

(d) female enters tunnel and, prodded by male, lays a few *eggs*; she then leaves.

(e) male enters tunnel, squirting eggs with sperm to *fertilise* them.

(f) male *aerates* nest by fin movements and *defends* it.

(g) eggs *hatch* after about a week.

(h) male keeps *fry* together in a defended shoal for another week.

(Most bony fish lay large numbers of eggs and sperm into the same place in the water, trusting to luck that sufficient fertilisation of eggs and survival of the young will take place.)

17.22 FROG

The frog (*Rana temporaria*) – an amphibian (see Fig. 17.23).

Life cycle

(*a*) in March, male frogs croak, inviting females into shallow water.

(*b*) male grips female under arm-pits with swollen black 'nuptial pads' on thumbs.

(*c*) female lays a few hundred *eggs*; male squirts *sperm* over them as they emerge in a continuous stream.

(*d*) sperm must penetrate eggs to effect *fertilisation* before albumen swells.

(*e*) albumen gives egg *protection* from injury and predators; *camouflage* (by being transparent); and a *large surface area* for gaseous exchange.

(*f*) *larvae* hatch (according to temperature) in about 10 days. In a *continuous* process of change (little happens overnight) larvae go through *three stages* (see Table 17.1 and Fig. 17.24).

(*g*) after about 90 days *young frogs* with stumpy tails hop onto land and start to catch insects with a sticky tongue. Hibernate in mud at bottom of ponds or in sheltered crevices, to avoid freezing each winter.

(*h*) frogs are *adult* by their fourth season.

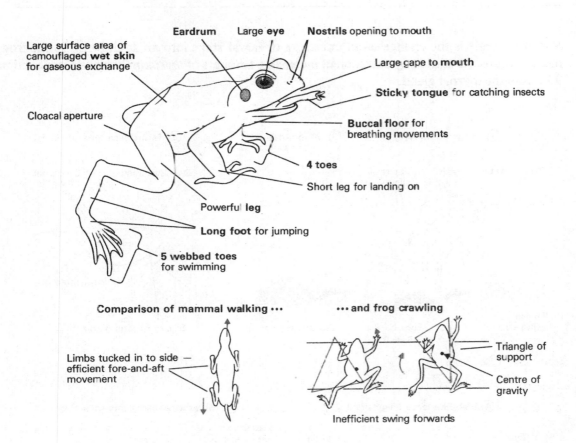

Fig. 17.23 Frog, *Rana temporaria* – external features

Adaptations for jumping

1 Long hind limbs with powerful muscles.
2 Strong pelvic girdle strengthened by a central rod, the urostyle.
3 Stout pectoral girdle with large sternum cartilage to protect heart on landing.
4 Forelimbs designed to take impact of landing.
5 Very short vertebral column to avoid dislocation on take-off and landing.

The three larval stages of a frog

Table 17.1   The three larval stages of a frog

	Mouthless	*Fish-like*	*Metamorphosing*
Size	6 mm long	20 mm long	40 mm long
Duration	2–3 days	40 days	40 days
Feeding	On yolk in gut only	Herbivorous: uses horny jaws to scrape off algae	Carnivorous: scavenger and even cannibal
Breathing (*gas exchange*)	3 pairs of external gills; skin	4 pairs of internal gills next to gill slits; skin	Lungs; buccal cavity; skin
Locomotion	Nil (stuck by mucus to water weed)	Uses tail with broad fin to swim	Tail swimming; hind limbs at times
Sense organs	Nil (still developing)	Lateral line (Fig. 17.22); eyes	Eyes very large

Metamorphosis is the change of an immature or larval stage into an adult form. In the frog, metamorphosis is started by secretion of increasing amounts of *thyroxin* (hormone, see Section 9.8) from the thyroid gland.

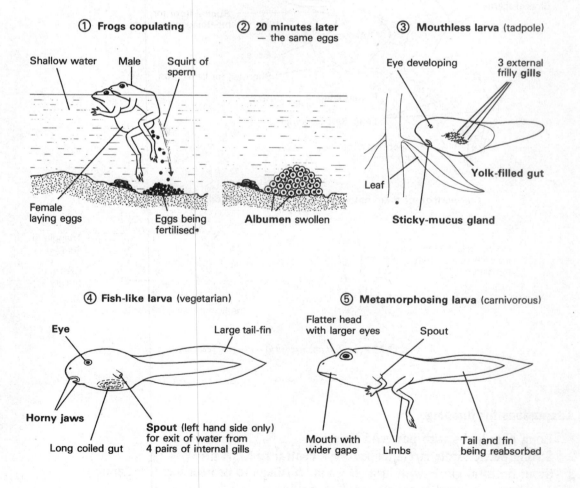

Fig. 17.24 Frog – life history

17.23 BIRDS

Locomotion – adaptations for flight (see Fig. 17.25)

1 **Light bones** – some air-filled and linked to air sacs; no teeth (heavy).

2 **Streamlined** – general body shape; contour feathers smoothing outline.

3 **Feathered wings** – large surface area to exert force on air.

4 **Large flight muscles** – big ones for down-flap; smaller ones for up-flap, together 20% of body weight.

5 **Large keeled sternum** – for attachment of flight muscles.

6 **Breathing system** (see Section 6.5) and **large heart** – highly efficient at supplying food and O_2 to flight muscles at a rate high enough to provide sufficient energy for flight.

7 **High body temperature** – ensures rapid respiration.

Flightless birds, e.g. ostrich, kiwi, lack one or more of these adaptations.

Three kinds of feather:

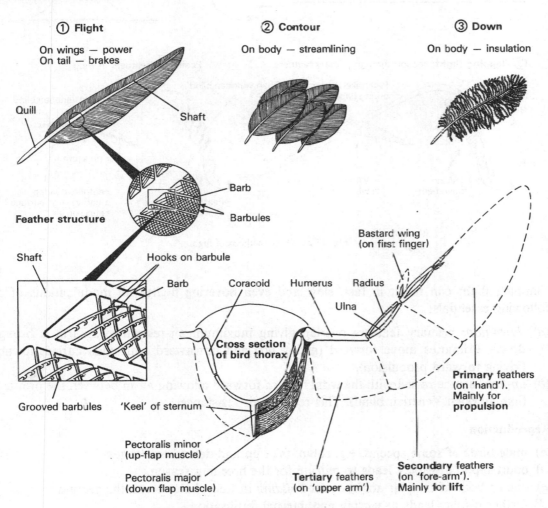

Fig. 17.25 Structures required for flight in birds

Flight

Birds cannot develop buoyancy (compare air-bladder of fishes, see Section 17.20).

Lift is generated by creating low pressure above wing and higher pressure below it. This requires (a) an aerofoil wing and (b) movement of air over aerofoil. Movement of air over the wing can be produced in three ways:

1 **Gliding:** wing rigid, air still; bird moves through air because it is falling.
2 **Soaring:** wing rigid, air moving, e.g. cliff-side winds or hot up-currents from the ground.
3 **Flapping flight:** wing moves, exerting forces on air.

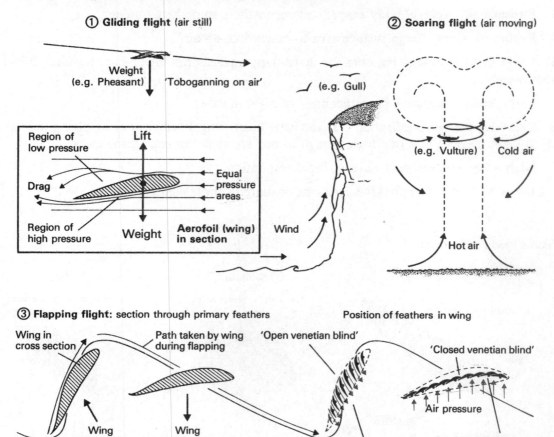

Fig. 17.26 Three methods of flight

Flapping flight can result in fast, slow and even hovering flight – all modifications of the following essentials:

(*a*) *down-flap:* primary feathers overlap giving maximum air-resistance as arm is brought down. Primaries move forward (giving lift) and downward with ends curled upwards (giving forward propulsion).
(*b*) *up-flap:* arm is raised with the wrist *rotated* forward allowing air in between the primaries (like an open Venetian blind). This reduces air resistance.

Reproduction

(*a*) male birds of some species, e.g. robin, take up and defend *territories*.
(*b*) courtship and display leads to *pairing* for the breeding season.
(*c*) one or both of the pair achieve *nest building* in trees, holes or on the ground.
(*d*) further display leads to *mating* and internal fertilisation.
(*e*) *eggs* are laid in nest singly, over a period of days, till clutch is complete.
(*f*) eggs gain O_2 through shell from environment, and warmth from female's featherless brood-patches. She also turns the eggs daily, before *incubation* ('sitting').
(*g*) embryo develops, cushioned within the *amnion* (water bag), getting food from *yolk-sac*. *Allantois* stores excreted uric acid; absorbs O_2 (see Fig. 17.27).
(*h*) chick *hatches* with help of egg-tooth (discarded after use).
(*i*) *parental care* of young extends to removal of droppings, defence and feeding (instinctive behaviour induced by yellow gape of chick's mouth and chirruping, see Section 12.17).

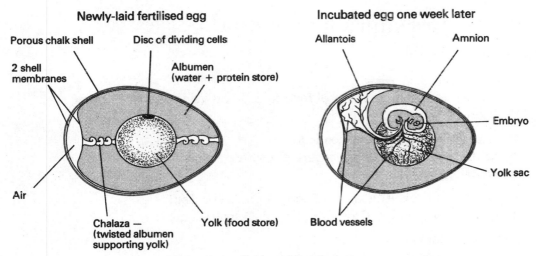

Fig. 17.27 Bird's egg – internal features

17.24 MAMMAL CHARACTERISTICS

Reproduction

1 *Suckle* their young on milk from mammary glands.
2 *Viviparous* – give birth to young, not eggs (exceptions: Echidna and Platypus).

In the head

3 *Large cerebrum* – the most intelligent vertebrates.
4 *Ear pinna* – external ear.
5 *Three ear ossicles* – in the middle ear.
6 *Four kinds of teeth* – incisors, canines, premolars and molars.
7 *Hard palate* – allows chewing and breathing simultaneously.

Temperature regulation

8 *Endothermic* (homeothermic) – constant body temperature (birds also).
9 *Hair* – for insulation.
10 *Sweat glands* – for cooling.

Respiration

11 *Diaphragm* – muscular sheet separating heart and lungs from other organs.
12 *Erythrocytes* (red blood cells) – lack nuclei.

Most mammals are **placentals** – embryos grown inside uterus (womb), nourished via the placenta. Others are **marsupials** – embryos born early and grow mainly within a pouch, e.g. kangaroo. Two types only (Echidna and Platypus) lay eggs much like those of reptiles, but then give milk to the hatched young. These egg-layers are the **monotremes**.

17.25 RABBIT

The rabbit (*Oryctolagus cuniculus*)

Life history:

(a) males pursue females in '*courtship* chases'.
(b) *mating* occurs mainly in January–June (but can be in any month).
(c) female often digs a short (30–90 cm) 'stop' burrow away from warren at blind end of which she makes a *nest* of hay, straw and her own chest fur.
(d) *gestation* of young takes 28–31 days; 3–7 blind young born.
(e) female is often *mated* again within 12 hours of dropping litter.
(f) young are *suckled* for about 21 days; fiercely protected from enemies.
(g) young are *sexually mature* at 3–4 months; fully grown by 9 months.
(h) *life expectancy* in wild about 1 year.

Part III Test yourself

Test yourself on chapter 2

1 Nutrition means:
   A building up sugars **B** intake of food to build up living matter **C** eating food
   D absorbing vitamins   *B*

2 The main purpose of respiration is to:
   A use oxygen in cells **B** burn sugars **C** provide energy for cells
   D give off carbon dioxide   *C*

3 Maintaining a suitable quantity of water in cells is called:
   A excretion **B** drinking **C** osmoregulation **D** hydration   *C*

4 Metabolism does *not* take place in:
   A death **B** digestion **C** growth **D** respiration   *A*

5 A cell wall is *not*:
   A freely permeable **B** non-living **C** selectively permeable **D** found in plants   *B*

6 Chloroplasts are found in:
   A animal cells **B** all plant cells **C** the vacuole **D** green plant cells   *D*

7 Protoplasm does not include:
   A cytoplasm **B** nucleus **C** cell wall **D** protein and water   *C*

8 The organelle which 'controls' the cell is the:
   A cell membrane **B** nucleus **C** cytoplasm **D** ribosome   *B*

9 Name plant and animal cells which fit the descriptions below:

	Plant	Animal
(*a*) long and thin	_____	_____
(*b*) have no nucleus	_____	_____
(*c*) are not green (plant) are red (animal)	_____	_____

10 **The following are various sub-units into which a species of plant or animal can be divided:**
   A cell **B** organ **C** organelle **D** organism **E** organ system **F** tissue
   (*a*) Arrange them in order starting with the simplest and ending with the most complex:

   _A_   _C_   _B_   _E_   _F_   _D_

   (*b*) Which of the above can be applied to the following?
   (*i*) cat___*D*___ (*ii*) *Amoeba*___*D*___ (*iii*) leaf___*E*___ (*iv*) chloroplast___*C*___
   (*v*) muscle___*F*___ (*vi*) alimentary canal (gut)___*E*___

Test yourself on chapter 3

1 Which of the following is an animal?
   A sea-anemone **B** sea-weed **C** bee-orchid **D** horse-tail   ___

2 Which of the following possesses no chlorophyll?
   A copper-beech tree **B** dandelion **C** lichens **D** *Penicillium* mould   ___

3 Which of the following is a mammal?
   A sea-horse **B** dolphin **C** sea-butterfly **D** tarantula   ___

4 Which plant reproduces by forming seeds?
   A fern **B** mushroom **C** oak **D** moss   ___

5 Here is a range of animals:

A spider **B** starfish **C** Protozoa **D** tapeworm **E** locust
F *Lumbricus terrestris* **G** crab **H** snail

  (*i*) To which of the above do the following descriptions apply?
  (*a*) is the name of a phylum   F
  (*b*) is the name of a species   C
  (*c*) has eight legs   A
  (*d*) belongs to the phylum Mollusca   D
  (*e*) belongs to the phylum Arthropoda   ___ ___ E A
  (*f*) is a flat-bodied worm   C
  (*g*) has a body built on a five-rayed plan   B
  (*ii*) What kind of animals are **A–H**? _____

6 Here is a range of organisms:

A bat **B** bacterium **C** blue whale **D** frog **E** sea anemone
F sparrow **G** alligator **H** salmon **J** *Amoeba*

To which of the above do the following descriptions apply?

  (*a*) unicellular   ___ ___
  (*b*) feathered   ___
  (*c*) mammal   ___ ___
  (*d*) body temperature is constant and warm   ___ ___ ___
  (*e*) larva uses gills for gaseous exchange   ___ ___
  (*f*) lays eggs out of water   ___ ___
  (*g*) belongs to class Amphibia   ___
  (*h*) animals not in the phylum Chordata   ___ ___ ___
  (*j*) has cell walls   ___

Test yourself on chapter 4

1 The following terms describe various methods of nutrition:
  A autotrophic **B** heterotrophic **C** parasitic **D** saprophytic **E** holozoic **F** carnivorous
  (*i*) With which of the above are the following statements about organisms associated?
  (*a*) All their energy comes from respiration   ___(includes___ ___ ___ ___)
  (*b*) They require only inorganic food   ___
  (*c*) They digest their food externally but have no gut   ___
  (*d*) A dog's method of nutrition   ___ ___ ___
  (*e*) Food is taken from a living organism, which survives   ___ ___
  (*ii*) Apart from **B** and **E**, what term not mentioned above best
       describes man's nutrition? _____

2 The following kinds of substances may be found in organisms:
  A fats **B** carbohydrates **C** water **D** salts **E** protein

  (*a*) Which are organic?   ___ ___ ___
  (*b*) Which of the organic substances contain C, H and O alone?   ___ ___
  (*c*) Which of the organic substances contains N?   ___
  (*d*) Which substance forms the major part of living cells?   ___
  (*e*) Which possess H and O in the ratio of 2 to 1?   ___ ___
  (*f*) Name an organic food class not mentioned in **A–E** above _____

3 The following are items of diet for man:
  A oranges **B** butter **C** lean steak **D** table salt **E** boiled potatoes

  (*a*) Which is mainly protein?   ___
  (*b*) Which is mainly carbohydrate?   ___
  (*c*) Which is mainly fat?   ___
  (*d*) Which contain cellulose?   ___ ___

(e) Which are 'energy' foods? —— ——

(f) Which contains iodine? ——

(g) Which contains vitamin C? ——

(h) Which is a body-building food? ——

4 The following substances may be found in the mammal gut:
A amino acids B vitamins B and C C fatty acids D starch E vitamins A and D
F glucose

(a) Which can be absorbed into villi? —— —— —— —— ——

(b) Which are absorbed into lacteals in the villi? —— ——

(c) Which are simple units of proteins? ——

(d) Which are digested by ptyalin (salivary amylase)? ——

(e) Which are simple units of carbohydrates? ——

(f) Which are required in diets in minute amounts? —— ——

5 The following are included in man's diet in small quantities:
A calcium B fluorine C iron D vitamin C E vitamin D F vitamin A G iodine

(i) Which of these are needed for:

(a) making red blood cells? ——

(b) making strong bones? —— ——

(c) good vision at night? ——

(d) making hard teeth? ——

(e) preventing scurvy? ——

(f) addition to margarine (by law)? —— ——

(g) making the hormone thyroxin? ——

(ii) Which of the above can man synthesise by sunbathing? ——

6 The following terms are associated with the way in which mammals deal with their food:
A physical digestion B chemical digestion C canines D cellulases E hydrolysis
F condensation G egestion H rumen or caecum
With which of the above are the following linked?

(a) enzymes in the gut of all mammals —— ——

(b) digestion of plant cell walls —— —— —— —— ——

(c) bile ——

(d) killing prey ——

(e) storing glucose as glycogen ——

(f) molars ——

(g) elimination of roughage and excess gut bacteria ——

7 The following are parts of the mammal gut:
A stomach B colon C duodenum D rectum E lower part of small intestine
F buccal cavity G oesophagus

(a) Place them in sequence, starting at the mouth end _____

(b) Where would you find teeth? ——

(c) Where would you find villi? —— ——

(d) Between which parts is the epiglottis? —— ——

(e) Between which parts is the pyloric sphincter? —— ——

(f) Between which parts is the caecum? —— ——

(g) Which parts of the intestine are long and narrow? —— ——

(h) Which parts of the intestine are short and wide? —— ——

(j) Which part receives bile? ——

(k) Which part receives gastric juice? ——

8 Parts concerned with digestion in the buccal cavity include:
A salivary glands B enamel C pulp cavity D dentine E molars F incisors
G premolars H canines.

(a) Arrange the types of teeth in sequence from front to back   —— —— —— ——

(b) Arrange the parts of a tooth in order of hardness starting with the hardest part   —— —— ——

(c) Which type of tooth is not present in the milk set?   ——

(d) Which type of tooth is not present in herbivores?   ——

(e) Which part contains ptyalin?   ——

(f) Which part of a tooth contains blood vessels?   ——

(g) Which class of food is digested by the secretion from A?   ————

9   Green plant nutrition is affected by the following factors:
A water **B** chlorophyll **C** nitrates **D** carbon dioxide **E** sunlight **F** darkness
G magnesium ions.

(a) Which are essential for making sugars?   —— —— —— ——

(b) Which additional factor is needed to make amino acids, once sugars have been made?   ——

(c) Which supplies the energy for photosynthesis?   ——

(d) Which are 'food' for the plant?   —— —— ——

(e) Which of the 'foods' will not be absorbed efficiently unless there is oxygen around the roots?   —— ——

(f) For which factor, needed for photosynthesis, is **G** particularly important?   ——

(g) Which factor stops photosynthesis every 24 hours?   ——

(h) Which foods enter by diffusion alone?   ——

10   Experiments on photosynthesis may involve the following:
A variegated leaves **B** soda lime or caustic soda **C** ethanol **D** iodine **E** oxygen **F** starch

(i) Which would you use to:

   (a) prevent leaves getting carbon dioxide?   ——

   (b) remove chlorophyll from leaves?   ——

   (c) test whether chlorophyll is essential for photosynthesis?   ——

   (d) test a decolourised leaf for starch?   ——

(ii) Which are products of photosynthesis?   —— ——

(iii) if water containing ^{18}O were fed to a photosynthesising plant, in which product would the ^{18}O appear?   ——

(iv) Before doing any photosynthesis experiment with a pot plant, what must first be removed from its leaves?   ——

11   The following are parts of leaves:
A stomata **B** palisade cells **C** xylem cells **D** spongy cells **E** epidermis cells
F phloem cells **G** cuticle **H** guard cells

(i) Which cells allow transport of:

   (a) water into the leaf?   ——

   (b) gases out of the leaf?   ——

   (c) sucrose out of the leaf?   ——

(ii) After excluding your answers to (i) (a)–(c), arrange the remaining parts in the correct sequence to label a vertical section of a leaf, starting with the upper surface:

    —— —— —— —— —— ——

(iii) Which cells can photosynthesise?   —— —— ——

(iv) Which cells provide most of the strength in veins?   ——

(v) Which are small pores?   ——

Choose the best answer to the alternatives given in questions 12–19.

12   Assimilation is the process in which food is:
    A taken in **B** used or stored within the body **C** excreted **D** broken up   ——

13   The elements carbon, hydrogen, oxygen and nitrogen can all be found in:
    A fats **B** glycogen **C** proteins **D** carbohydrates   ——

14   Glycogen is stored in the:
      A liver **B** stomach **C** pancreas **D** brain   ___

15   The liver does not:
      A break down red blood cells **B** make urea **C** make bile **D** make insulin   ___

16   A food tested by boiling with Benedict's (or Fehling's) solution gave an orange precipitate. This showed it contained some:
      A protein **B** fat **C** reducing sugar **D** sucrose   ___

17   A protein when boiled with Millon's reagent gives the following colour:
      A brick red **B** blue-black **C** orange **D** brown   ___

18   Fats and oils do not:
      A leave translucent stains on paper **B** taste sweet **C** float in water
      D attract Sudan III solution.   ___

19   Chlorophyll is removed from leaves before they are tested for starch because:
      A otherwise the iodine would not react
      B the green colour would make it difficult to see any blue-black colour
      C this helps the alcohol to penetrate the leaf
      D boiling in water kills the leaf   ___

Test yourself on chapter 5

1   Match the biological functions of water given as **A–E** below with processes (*a*)–(*g*) by putting the correct letters in the spaces provided (You may use **A–E** more than once)
     A reactant **B** glucose transporter **C** lubricant **D** coolant **E** supporter

     (*a*) blood flowing   B
     (*b*) sweating   D
     (*c*) digestion   E
     (*d*) plant cells becoming turgid   E
     (*e*) movement at a synovial joint   C
     (*f*) photosynthesis   A
     (*g*) transpiration   D

2   (*i*) State the name of the process by which plant cells gain most of their:

        (*a*) mineral salts   Roots
        (*b*) water   Air / roots.
        (*c*) carbon dioxide   Mbs

     (*ii*) Which of the above processes:

        (*a*) requires a semi-permeable membrane?   b
        (*b*) is slow?   a
        (*c*) requires cell respiration?   c

3   A strip of epidermis was taken from a leaf and cut into three parts. Each piece was placed for 5 minutes in one of three beakers containing either distilled water, or 0.5 molar sugar solution, or 1.0 molar sugar solution. After 5 minutes a representative cell from each piece of epidermis was drawn – as shown in the diagram:

A   B   C

Which cell(s):
(a) had been in the distilled water?   *C*
(b) had been in the 1.0 M sugar solution?   *B*
(c) has a high wall pressure?   *C*
(d) are plasmolysed?   *A b*
(e) has the most concentrated cell sap?   *B*
(f) is turgid?   *C*
(g) could have come from a wilted leaf (rather than from this experiment)?   *A b.*

4 (i) Match the plant parts **A–F** below with their descriptions (a)– (f)
   A xylem **B** stomata **C** cork **D** phloem **E** cuticle **F** lenticels

   (a) external holes in an old stem   *F*
   (b) woody cells (vessels)   *D*
   (c) wax secreted by cells   *E*
   (d) cells of outer bark   *C*
   (e) leaf pores   *B*
   (f) sieve tube cells   *A*

   (ii) Which pairs of plant parts **A–F** above are associated with (a)–(e) below?
   (a) are transporting tissues   *A D*
   (b) allow gaseous exchange   *B C*
   (c) waterproof the plant   *C E*
   (d) permit supply of raw material for photosynthesis   *A D*
   (e) are dead cells   *C F*

5 Which of the following is *not* a process linked with transpiration?
   A transporting sugars **B** absorption of water by roots **C** cooling the leaf
   D evaporation of water at leaves   ___

6 Which of the following factors increases the rate of loss of water vapour at the surface of leaves?
   A still air **B** sunlight **C** high humidity **D** cool temperature   ___

7 Select from **A–M** those items which apply to (a)–(d):
   A epidermis cell **B** guard cell **C** CO_2 **D** O_2 **E** spongy mesophyll cell
   F xylem vessel **G** dry soil **H** palisade cell **J** phloem sieve tube **K** cuticle
   L water vapour **M** closed stoma

   (a) three types of cell that photosynthesise   ___ ___ ___
   (b) three types of cell that cannot photosynthesise   ___ ___ ___
   (c) three factors that reduce transpiration   ___ ___ ___
   (d) stomata during the day allow the entry of ___ into the leaf
   and the exit of ___ and ___

8 Which of the following is the correct definition of osmosis?
   A absorption of water by roots
   B diffusion of water from where it is in high concentration to where it is in low concentration across a semi-permeable membrane
   C diffusion of a weak solution into a strong one across a semi-permeable membrane
   D absorption of salts into a weak solution across a cell membrane   ___

9 Write **T** (for true) or **F** (for false) against the following statements about a sea-water alga the cells of which are becoming turgid:

   (a) the cells will shortly burst   ___
   (b) the sea water is a stronger solution than that inside the
      cell vacuoles   ___
   (c) the cell membrane is fully permeable to the water but not to
      the salts   ___
   (d) the cell wall is fully permeable to sea water   ___

10   Which of the following is the principal reason why multicellular animals have a blood system?
      A they need to cool themselves when they are active
      B diffusion alone is too slow a process to supply food and remove wastes from their cells
      C hormones cannot be transported any other way
      D the heart would have nothing to do otherwise   ___

11   Mammal blood can be separated into various components.

      (*i*) What is the main chemical component of:
          (*a*) whole blood?   _____
          (*b*) dried plasma?   _____
          (*c*) dried erythrocytes?   _____

      (*ii*) What is the main type of cell in
          (*a*) the cellular part of blood?   _____
          (*b*) the leucocyte portion?   _____

12   In mammal blood name:

      (*a*) a gas transported mainly as bicarbonate ions   _____
      (*b*) a gas transported mainly in red cells   _____
      (*c*) a waste made principally in the liver   _____
      (*d*) the main food respired in cells   _____

13   Which of the statements below apply to lymph nodes?
      A they produce white blood cells B they filter out bacteria from lymph
      C they store carbohydrates D they pump lymph E they assist in making antibodies

                                                                        ___ ___ ___

14   Where appropriate, match statements A–G with blood vessels (*a*)–(*c*)
      A non-return valves B blood under low pressure C thick walls with muscle
      D walls one cell thick E blood loses volume F blood flows in pulses
      G provide a very large surface area

      (*a*) arteries ___ ___   (*b*) veins ___ ___   (*c*) capillaries ___ ___ ___

15   Which of the following is the medium which carries dissolved food to the cell membranes of tissues?
      A serum B lymph C blood D water E extracellular fluid (tissue fluid) F plasma ___

16   Which of items A–H below in the blood are:

      (*a*) lost at the lungs   ___ ___ ___
      (*b*) used by growing muscles   ___ ___
      (*c*) removed permanently from blood in the kidneys   ___ ___ ___ ___
      (*d*) gained at a sunbather's skin   ___ ___

      A O_2 B CO_2 C urea D amino acids E water F vitamin D G glucose H heat

17   A blood cell is on the point of entering the mammal heart. Trace the route it will take to reach the aorta by arranging those of the following letters that apply in the correct sequence:
      A lung B left ventricle C right ventricle D pulmonary vein E right auricle
      F left auricle G hepatic portal vein H pulmonary artery J renal artery

                                                            ___ ___ ___ ___ ___ ___ ___

18   Trace the journey of a blood cell from the aorta to just outside the heart assuming that it contributes to the processes involved in the absorption and storage of digested food in the liver on the way. Arrange those of the following letters that apply in the correct sequence:
      A renal artery B hepatic portal vein C mesenteric artery (to intestine)
      D hepatic vein E vena cava F hepatic artery G villi H liver J lungs

                                                            ___ ___ ___ ___ ___ ___

19　Which of the following blood vessels **A–H** are associated with (*a*)–(*e*) below?
　　A renal artery **B** leg vein of a sprinting man **C** pulmonary artery **D** renal vein
　　E hepatic portal vein **F** aorta **G** hepatic vein **H** pulmonary vein

　　(*a*) lowest urea content　　　　　　　＿＿　　(*d*) warmest blood　　　　　　＿＿
　　(*b*) highest food content after a meal　　＿＿　　(*e*) highest blood pressure　　＿＿
　　(*c*) lowest oxygen content　　　　　　＿＿

20　Select the figures from the right hand column which most closely approximate to the
　　statements in the left hand column and insert them in the spaces provided:

　　(*a*)＿＿＿＿＿＿: number of red blood cells per mm³ of blood　　70
　　(*b*)＿＿＿＿＿＿: number of white blood cells per mm³ of blood　　98.4
　　(*c*)＿＿＿＿＿＿: resting adult heart-beat rate per minute　　0
　　(*d*)＿＿＿＿＿＿: number of heart chambers　　1
　　(*e*)＿＿＿＿＿＿: number of nuclei in a red blood cell　　4
　　(*f*)＿＿＿＿＿＿: man's 'normal' under-tongue temperature in °C　　10 000
　　　　　　　　　　　　　　　　　　　　　　　　　　　　5 000 000
　　　　　　　　　　　　　　　　　　　　　　　　　　　　37

Test yourself on chapter 6

1　Pair terms **A–E** with the descriptions (*a*)–(*e*):
　　A internal respiration **B** breathing **C** external respiration **D** respiration
　　E gaseous exchange

　　(*a*) movements in animals bringing oxygen to where it can be absorbed
　　　　into the body　　　　　　　　　　　　　　　　　　　　　＿＿
　　(*b*) a physical process which includes **B** and **E**　　　　　　　＿＿
　　(*c*) exchange of O_2 for CO_2　　　　　　　　　　　　　　　＿＿
　　(*d*) chemical reactions in cells that release energy from organic molecules　＿＿
　　(*e*) a process which includes **A**, **B** and **E**　　　　　　　　＿＿

2　Below is a list of structures in organisms. Against them write the appropriate letter from
　　A and **E** in question 1 above to signify their main purpose in respiration:

　　(*a*) gills　　　　　＿＿　　　　(*e*) tracheoles　　　　　　＿＿
　　(*b*) mitochondria　　＿＿　　　　(*f*) ribs　　　　　　　　＿＿
　　(*c*) capillaries　　＿＿　　　　(*g*) *Amoeba*'s cell membrane　＿＿
　　(*d*) diaphragm　　　＿＿　　　　(*h*) leaves　　　　　　　＿＿

3　Small animals like *Amoeba* and *Paramoecium* do not need gills because:
　　A they would get in the way
　　B there is no oxygen in the water in which they live
　　C only fish evolved with gills
　　D their surface area for obtaining oxygen is large in relation to
　　　　their volume
　　E they do not move very far and so need little oxygen　　　　　＿＿

4　Air inhaled by man on a dry day differs from air exhaled in the following respects.
　　It contains:
　　A more CO_2 **B** less CO_2 **C** less O_2 **D** less water vapour **E** more water vapour
　　F more O_2 **G** more nitrogen **H** same amount of nitrogen **J** more dust

　　　　　　　　　　　　　　　　＿＿ ＿＿ ＿＿ ＿＿ ＿＿

5　Air breathed in by man passes the structures of the respiratory system listed below
　　in what order?
　　A bronchioles **B** bronchi **C** nostrils **D** pharynx **E** alveoli **F** epiglottis **G** trachea

　　　　　　　　　　　　　　＿＿ ＿＿ ＿＿ ＿＿ ＿＿ ＿＿ ＿＿

6   Write **T** (true) or **F** (false) against the following statements. As a man breathes in:

(*a*) the volume of his chest cavity increases ____
(*b*) the pressure within his chest cavity decreases ____
(*c*) the lungs expand, pushing out the ribs ____
(*d*) the diaphragm becomes flatter ____
(*e*) the ribs move downwards and inwards ____
(*f*) the deflated alveoli fill with air ____

7   (*i*)   Which of the following statements do you feel is the *most* accurate? ____
    A   Man breathes out carbon dioxide ____
    B   Man breathes in oxygen ____
    C   Man breathes out nitrogen ____
    D   Man breathes out air

(*ii*) In the spaces provided above indicate the approximate percentage of gases applicable to statements **A** to **C**.

(*iii*) If statements **A** and **B** above were *literally* true what would happen to:
(in **A**) a man being revived by the 'kiss of life'?

_____

(in **B**) a man smoking a cigarette?

_____

8   Write **T** (true) or **F** (false) against the following statements. Anaerobic respiration in yeast:

(*a*) produces CO_2 ____   (*d*) needs O_2 ____
(*b*) produces bread ____   (*e*) liberates more energy
(*c*) uses glucose ____   than aerobic respiration ____

9   If an animal is respiring aerobically, which of the following is it *not* doing?
A using glucose **B** performing gaseous exchange **C** using O_2 **D** giving out CO_2
E making ethanol **F** releasing heat ____

10 Pair organisms **A–H** with their structures for gaseous exchange (*a*)–(*e*):
A earthworm **B** *Amoeba* **C** insect **D** mammal **E** fish **F** frog **G** flowering plant
H yeast

(*a*) tracheoles ____   (*d*) cell membranes only ____ ____
(*b*) alveoli ____   (*e*) skin capillaries ____ ____
(*c*) gill lamellae ____

11 From the list of organisms in question 10 above select those that:

(*a*) assist their gaseous exchange by breathing ____ ____ ____ ____
(*b*) do *not* use blood to assist gaseous exchange ____ ____ ____ ____
(*c*) respire aerobically _____

12 The cells (*a*)–(*c*) of an angiosperm perform some of the processes **A–F**. Insert the appropriate letters from **A–F** in the spaces provided:
A respire at all times **B** produce O_2 at all times **C** produce CO_2 at night
D absorb CO_2 in sunlight **E** produce O_2 by day **F** do none of these

(*a*) green cells in a leaf ____ ____ ____ ____
(*b*) non-green cells of pith ____ ____
(*c*) xylem vessels of wood ____

Test yourself on chapter 7

1 Select from **A–F** below those that are *not* major excretory products in:

   (*a*) an insect   —— —— —— ——
   (*b*) an oak tree by day   —— —— —— ——
   (*c*) a mammal   —— —— —— ——
   A O_2 **B** CO_2 **C** water **D** autumn leaves **E** uric acid **F** urea

2 Select from **A–E** below those that are *not* excretory organs in man:
   A liver **B** anus **C** kidneys **D** salivary glands **E** lungs   —— ——

3 Urea is excreted by mammals. Name the organ where it is:

   (*a*) made   _____
   (*b*) stored temporarily   _____
   (*c*) excreted   _____

4 Trace the pathway of a urea molecule from a person's aorta to its elimination from the body by arranging structures **A–L** in the correct sequence:

A collecting duct	**E** renal vein	**J** bladder
B Bowman's capsule	**F** loop of Henle	**K** urethra
C glomerulus	**G** first coiled tubule	**L** ureter
D renal arterioles	**H** second coiled tubule	

   (*a*) inside the kidney   —— —— —— —— —— —— ——
   (*b*) beyond the kidney   —— —— ——

5 Match the items **A–F** below with (*a*)–(*f*) – biological materials present in man's kidney:
   A 2–4% solution of urea **B** pressure-filtrate of blood
   C hormone ADH influences its uptake **D** blood in renal vein
   E totally reabsorbed in first coiled tubule **F** blood leaving glomerulus

   (*a*) water   ——
   (*b*) urine   ——
   (*c*) tissue fluid   ——
   (*d*) small food molecules   ——
   (*e*) blood unusually rich in blood cells   ——
   (*f*) blood containing almost no urea   ——

6 Which of the following are *not* normally present in urine?
   A glucose **B** amino acids **C** fatty acids **D** water **E** sodium chloride **F** protein
   G blood cells **H** bile pigments

                                                —— —— —— —— ——

7 More glucose enters the kidney than leaves it because:
   A the kidney cells use glucose in respiration
   B the kidney converts glucose to amino acids
   C glucose is retained by the kidney to maintain a high osmotic pressure
   D the kidney stores glucose as glycogen   ——

8 No glucose is normally present in urine. This is because:
   A glucose is not filtered out into Bowman's capsules
   B the glucose is excreted as sucrose
   C the bladder reabsorbs the glucose
   D kidney tubules reabsorb glucose   ——

9 The volume of urine produced by a healthy person fluctuates. Assuming no extra drinking takes place, indicate the effect of factors (*a*)–(*e*) on urine volume by inserting **I** (increase), **D** (decrease) or **O** (no change) in the spaces provided:

(*a*) strenuous exercise   ____
(*b*) drinking a litre of water   ____
(*c*) eating a lot of salted peanuts   ____
(*d*) a hot day   ____
(*e*) eating 1 kg of steak   ____

10 (*i*) Water loss accompanies most forms of excretion. Name the processes **A–E** described below and an excretory product which is lost at the same time:

	Process	*Product*
A water vapour loss by a daisy in sunlight:	_____	_____
B water vapour loss at skin in man:	_____	_____
C water vapour loss from lungs in man:	_____	_____
D water loss by a bear in winter:	_____	_____
E water loss by *Amoeba*:	_____	_____

(*ii*) Select from **A–E** above pairs of processes which have as a main function:
(*a*) keeping the strength of body fluids stable   ___ ___
(*b*) causing loss of heat   ___ ___

(*iii*) Select from **A–E** above pairs of processes in which:
(*a*) loss of excretory substances is of minor importance   ___ ___
(*b*) the excretory substances are gases   ___ ___

11 Heat can be gained or lost from an organism's environment in a number of ways. By which of the following methods can heat only be *lost*?
A evaporation of water **B** radiation **C** conduction **D** convection   ____

12 Which of the descriptions of organisms **A–D** below *best* describes:

(*a*) an insect?   ____   (*b*) a mammal?   ____

A body temperature remains constant **B** ectotherm (poikilotherm) **C** cold-blooded **D** warm-blooded

(*c*) If an insect experiences a warm sunny day followed by a chilly night, which of the following terms best describes it during those 24 hours?

A warm-blooded **B** cold-blooded **C** both warm- and cold-blooded   ____

13 The methods of temperature regulation used by a mammal are listed below as (*a*) to (*d*). Indicate which of items **A–F** below assist in methods (*a*)–(*d*):
A shivering **B** vasoconstriction **C** subcutaneous fat **D** radiation **E** sweating **F** liver metabolism **G** contact with warm rocks

(*a*) heat loss   ___ ___
(*b*) heat generation   ___ ___
(*c*) heat conservation   ___ ___
(*d*) heat gain from outside   ___ ___

14 The basic reason for the inactivity of ectotherms (poikilotherms) during cold weather is:
A they are hibernating **B** there is no food available **C** their enzymes work slowly **D** their body water is frozen   ____

15 The following activity in an organism does *not* contribute to homeostasis:
A removal of CO_2 **B** provision of adequate food **C** provision of adequate O_2 **D** removal of excess water **E** continuance of growth   ____

Test yourself on chapter 8

1 The structures of the eye listed as (*a*)–(*g*) have various properties and functions listed as
   A–N. Match the two by putting the letters **A–N** in the spaces provided:
   A is very sensitive to touch **B** regulates amount of light reaching back of eye
   C does most of the light focusing **D** is tough and opaque **E** is black
   F is tough and translucent **G** nourishes the retina **H** is muscular
   J is attached at the blind spot **K** is light-sensitive **L** is white
   M is the front surface layer **N** is the innermost surface

(*a*) sclera ___ ___	(*d*) choroid ___ ___	(*f*) iris ___ ___	
(*b*) cornea ___ ___	(*e*) retina ___ ___	(*g*) optic nerve ___	
(*c*) conjunctiva ___ ___			

2 Which of the following is true?
   When an eye of a mammal focuses on a near object:
   A the lens becomes thinner **B** the lens becomes a fatter shape once the tension is taken
   off it
   C the cornea is bent further by the ciliary muscles
   D the ciliary muscles contract, squashing the lens into a more convex shape   ___

3 Which of the following statements about the fovea is untrue?
   A contains rods and cones **B** contains cones only **C** is on the optical axis of the eye
   D is where objects being viewed are normally in focus   ___

4 Pair up structures (*a*)–(*d*) properties **A–D**:
   A region of acutest vision **B** allow colour vision only
   C allow black and white vision only **D** where retina is absent

   (*a*) cones   ___
   (*b*) rods   ___
   (*c*) optic nerve   ___
   (*d*) fovea   ___ ___

5 Fill in the blanks in the following table:

Focusing abnormalities of the human eye

	Abnormality	*Eyeball length*	*Eye lens*	*Corrective lens*
(*a*)			Cannot get fat enough to focus on a nearby object	
(*b*)		Normal		Bifocal lenses
(*c*)			Cannot get thin enough to focus on a high-flying jet	

6 Arrange letters **A–G** in the spaces provided to convey the roles that each structure plays
   in hearing processes (*a*)–(*e*):
   A ear ossicles **B** hair cells in cochlea **C** perilymph **D** tympanum **E** endolymph
   F pinna **G** auditory centre of brain

   (*a*) sound gathering   ___   (*d*) sound detection   ___
   (*b*) sound conduction ___ ___ ___ ___   (*e*) sound appreciation   ___
   (*c*) sound amplification   ___ ___

7 By arranging letters **A–J** in sequence, indicate the order in which a noise would affect the
   parts of the ear:
   A endolymph **B** perilymph **C** round window **D** oval window **E** hair cells **F** stapes
   G ear drum **H** malleus **J** incus

   ___ ___ ___ ___ ___ ___ ___ ___ ___

8   The parts of the ear that assist in telling a person he is changing position are:
     A endolymph B perilymph C cochlea D semicircular canals E ampullae F cupula
     G cones H hair cells J cerebellum

     —— —— —— —— ——

Test yourself on chapter 9

1   Organisms gather information about their environment using sensory cells which send 'messages' to other parts of their bodies which, in turn, respond. Compare this chain of events in respect of gravity acting on a pot plant that has been knocked over, and a cat which has overbalanced, by filling in the table below.

	(a) Location of sensory cells	(b) Type of 'message' sent	(c) Speed of 'message'	(d) Main response
Plant				
Cat				

2   The following terms A–G are associated with the reception and response to stimuli in plants and animals. Select those which do *not* apply to:
     (*a*) flowering plants   —— —— —— ——
     (*b*) insects   ——
     A sensory cells B sense organs C nerves D hormones E reflexes F tropisms G taxis

3   Select from A–E below the kinds of cell in a mammal that:
     (*a*) are sensitive to their environment   ——
     (*b*) receive 'messages' from sensory cells   ——
     (*c*) transmit 'messages' to effectors   ——
     (*d*) take 'messages' to the brain from the spinal cord   ——
     (*e*) store information   ——
     A sensory cells B relay neurons C brain cells D sensory neurons E motor neurons

4   (*i*) Arrange the appropriate four kinds of cell from A–E in question 3 above in the correct sequence to make up the main part of a reflex arc: —— —— —— ——
     (*ii*) Name a fifth kind of cell needed to complete the arc: —————————

5   Which parts of the mammal brain, A–F below, are concerned principally with:
     (*a*) sense of balance   ——   (*d*) controlling breathing-rhythm   ——
     (*b*) intelligent decisions   ——   (*e*) secreting hormones   ——
     (*c*) controlling body temperature   ——   (*f*) interpreting what is seen   ——
     A hypothalamus B pituitary C cerebrum D optic lobes E medulla oblongata
     F cerebellum

6   Which description from A–E best fits the parts of a neuron listed (*a*)–(*e*)?
     A secrete a chemical into a gap B long, in sensory neurons C long, in motor neurons
     D major part of white matter in spinal cord E major part of grey matter in spinal cord

     (*a*) cell bodies   ——   (*c*) synaptic knobs   ——   (*e*) fatty sheaths   ——
     (*b*) dendrons   ——   (*d*) axons   ——

7   Arrange parts (*a*)–(*d*) in question 6 in the order in which they would pass an impulse:

     —— —— —— ——

8   State which of A–D below does *not* describe a conditioned reflex action:
     A rapid B unlearned C inappropriate response D response to a stimulus   ——

9   State which of **A–D** below does *not* apply to a reflex action:
    A is an inherited response **B** involves a maximum of three kinds of neuron
    C always involves the brain **D** for example blinking **E** is of high survival value ____

10 During the control of blood sugar in a mammal two antagonistic hormones are employed. Fill in the table about them:

	Raises blood sugar	*Lowers blood sugar*
(*a*) *Hormone's name*		
(*b*) *Hormone's source (gland)*		
(*c*) *Means of stimulating gland to secrete*		
(*d*) *Main organ stimulated by hormone*		

11 The maintenance of a constant internal environment in an organism is called:
    A osmoregulation **B** homeostasis **C** temperature control **D** enteritis ____

12 A number of metabolic diseases in mammals arise as a result of abnormal endocrine function. Complete the table below concerned with this:

Name of abnormality	*Caused by lack of*	*From*
(*a*) Dwarfism		
(*b*)	Insulin	
(*c*) Water diabetes (diabetes insipidus)		
(*d*)		Thyroid of baby
(*e*) Goitre		

13 Choose from the items **A–H** below those that apply to secretion of:
    (*a*) hormones   __ __ __ __ __
    (*b*) digestive enzymes   __ __ __
    A organic **B** inorganic **C** secreted in minute quantities
    D secreted in relatively large quantities **E** secreted into ducts
    F secreted into blood **G** secreted from endocrine glands
    H amount secreted often subject to 'feedback'

Test yourself on chapter 10

1   (*i*) Select the component *not* concerned with support of aerial parts of a currant-bush:
    A turgor pressure **B** xylem **C** cellulose **D** cork   ____

    (*ii*) which of the above provide the *main* support for:

    (*a*) leaves ?   ____ ____   (*b*) stem ?   ____

2   Select the component *not* concerned with support in a mammal:
    A protein fibres **B** chitin **C** bone **D** cartilage   ____

3   **A–E** below are functions of skeletons. Select those that are *exclusively* functions of:
    (*a*) mammal skeletons   ____
    (*b*) insect skeletons   ____ ____

    A levers for locomotion **B** protection **C** making red blood cells
    D providing camouflage **E** determining body shape exactly

4   Name the materials in an insect's skeleton that perform the following functions:

    (*a*) waterproofing   _____
    (*b*) hardness   _____
    (*c*) flexibility   _____

5   Name the part of a mammal's locomotory system that:

    (*a*) links bone to bone   _____
    (*b*) links bone to muscle   _____
    (*c*) provides lubricating fluid at joints   _____
    (*d*) provides cushioning at movable joints   _____

6   When a human forearm is raised, certain events take place. From the following, select
    those that are true:
    A triceps muscle pushes the elbow down
    B nerve impulses go to biceps muscle causing contraction
    C nerve impulses pass to both biceps and triceps
    D biceps shortens
    E triceps shortens
    F triceps is prevented from shortening by reflex action   ____ ____ ____ ____

7   Select from the following descriptions those that are *not* true concerning locomotion of
    an earthworm in its burrow:
    A has no skeleton
    B pulls itself up to its anchored prostomium
    C when circular body-muscles contract, body becomes short and fat
    D segments can be anchored with eight chaetae each
    E when circular muscles contract, longitudinal muscles relax
    F segments that are extending pull in their chaetae   ____ ____ ____

8   (*i*) Vertebrae consist of a number of parts each of which performs an important func-
    tion. Fill in the name of the part and its function against the descriptions given below:

Description	Name	Function
A main cylinder of bone		
B largest hole		
C main dorsal projection of bone		
D small projections of bone in pairs, front and back		

(*ii*) Which of **A–D** above is nearest to the:

(*a*) dorsal aorta　　＿＿＿　　　　(*b*) intervertebral disc　　　＿＿＿

9　Name the type of vertebrae or individual vertebra in mammals which:

(*a*) allows most of the mobility in the back　　　　＿＿＿＿＿＿＿

(*b*) is fused to the pelvic girdle　　　　＿＿＿＿＿＿＿

(*c*) allows swivelling of the head right and left　　　　＿＿＿＿＿＿＿

(*d*) is behind the anus　　　　＿＿＿＿＿＿＿

(*e*) bears ribs　　　　＿＿＿＿＿＿＿

10　State as precisely as you can where in a human you would find:

A　the radius　　＿＿＿＿＿＿＿＿＿＿＿＿＿＿＿＿

B　synovial fluid　　＿＿＿＿＿＿＿＿＿＿＿＿＿＿＿＿

C　the humerus　　＿＿＿＿＿＿＿＿＿＿＿＿＿＿＿＿

D　the tibia　　＿＿＿＿＿＿＿＿＿＿＿＿＿＿＿＿

E　phalanges　　＿＿＿＿＿＿＿＿＿＿＿＿＿＿＿＿

F　the femur　　＿＿＿＿＿＿＿＿＿＿＿＿＿＿＿＿

G　carpals　　＿＿＿＿＿＿＿＿＿＿＿＿＿＿＿＿

H　the scapula　　＿＿＿＿＿＿＿＿＿＿＿＿＿＿＿＿

11　Between which bones in question 10 would you find the following kinds of joint?

(*a*) hinge　　　＿＿＿＿＿＿＿　　　　(*c*) slipping　　＿＿＿＿＿＿＿

(*b*) ball and socket　　＿＿＿＿＿＿＿　　　　(*d*) fixed (suture)　　＿＿＿＿＿＿＿

Test yourself on chapter 11

1　Growth includes certain of the following processes, depending on the organism concerned:
A mitosis **B** meiosis **C** formation of protein **D** formation of new cell walls
E vacuolation **F** differentiation

Fill in the appropriate letters as the processes apply to:

(*a*)　most animals　　＿＿ ＿＿ ＿＿　　　　(*b*) most plants　　＿＿ ＿＿ ＿＿ ＿＿ ＿＿

2　Complete the following passage by inserting suitable words in the blanks:

Angiosperms grow into a＿＿＿＿＿shape with a＿＿＿＿＿surface area
to assist in absorption of＿＿＿＿＿and＿＿＿＿＿through their
leaves and of＿＿＿＿＿and ＿＿＿＿＿from the soil in which
they are anchored. By contrast animals have ＿＿＿＿＿bodies
with limbs to assist them in ＿＿＿＿＿to get their food.

3　Study **A–G** below as they apply to primary and secondary growth in angiosperms:
A growth in length **B** cambium divides **C** apical meristem divides **D** growth in diameter
E cork formed **F** some cortex splits off **G** forms xylem and phloem

Enter letters **A–G** as they apply mainly to:

(*a*) primary growth ＿＿ ＿＿ ＿＿　　　　(*b*) secondary growth ＿＿ ＿＿ ＿＿ ＿＿ ＿＿

4　**A–H** below apply to seeds. Enter the correct letters in the spaces provided where they are
associated with structures (*a*)–(*d*):

(*a*) cotyledon　　　＿＿ ＿＿　　　　(*c*) plumule　　　＿＿ ＿＿

(*b*) radicle　　　＿＿ ＿＿　　　　(*d*) testa　　　＿＿ ＿＿

A root **B** hilum **C** shoot **D** micropyle **E** grows out first on germination
F are the first true leaves **G** leaf that absorbs endosperm **H** there are two in bean seed

5　Which of the items (*a*)–(*d*) in question 4:

(*i*) make up the embryo in a seed　　　　＿＿＿＿＿＿＿

(*ii*) grow from the ovule　　　　＿＿＿＿＿＿＿

6   Complete the following passage:

When an endospermic seed is germinating it gets its food from the _____ by digesting it with _____ and absorbing it via the _____.

For these processes to occur the seed needs three essential conditions:
_____, _____, and _____

7   When a seed germinates epigeally, certain events occur. Which of the following do these include?:

A the testa splits **B** the hypocotyl grows fast **C** the cambium divides
D the epicotyl grows fast **E** the cotyledons appear above ground
F the apical meristems divide **G** the cotyledons remain below ground
H new cells vacuolate

___ ___ ___ ___ ___

8   State which of items **A–H** in question 7 apply to:

(*a*) *all* types of germination ___ ___ ___   (*b*) hypogeal germination only ___ ___

9   Which of the following do *not* apply to the way an insect grows?
A   skeleton and other tissues grow at the same rate
B   skeleton does not grow but is replaced
C   animal's mass increases gradually to adulthood
D   mass increases suddenly at each moult
E   length of the body increases suddenly at each moult

___ ___

Test yourself on chapter 12

1   Gametes can never be:
A the protoplasm of *Spirogyra* cells **B** pollen grains **C** spermatozoa
D nuclei inside the gametangia of *Mucor* **E** haploid **F** the whole egg of a hen ___ ___

2   Zygotes are:
A certain kinds of gamete **B** cells produced when gametes fuse **C** dividing cells
D certain kinds of spore **E** the first cells of asexually produced organisms   ___

3   Fertilisation has occurred when:
A   a sperm has just reached an ovum
B   pollen grains of the right species have reached a stigma
C   a zygote has just been formed
D   the pollen tube nucleus has reached the ovule
E   nuclei of the male and female gametes have become one   ___ ___

4   State which of the terms **A–F** you would associate with:
A meiosis **B** identical offspring **C** spores **D** flowers **E** a variety of offspring **F** tubers

(*a*) asexual (non-sexual) reproduction   ___ ___ ___
(*b*) sexual reproduction   ___ ___ ___

5   State which of the following would *not* be produced by mitosis:
A fungal spores **B** sperm **C** bulbs **D** runners **E** pollen **F** zygospores.   ___ ___

6   Pair organisms (*a*)–(*e*) with descriptions **A–G**:
A reproduces both sexually and asexually **B** does not reproduce asexually
C does not reproduce sexually **D** male gamete does not swim
E 'conjugation' precedes fertilisation **F** reproduces by 'budding'
G reproduces by binary fission

(*a*) *Amoeba*   ___ ___   (*d*) *Spirogyra*   ___ ___ ___
(*b*) daffodil   ___ ___   (*e*) rat   ___
(*c*) *Hydra*   ___ ___

7   In a winter twig, name the parts that:

  (*a*) protect delicate parts of a bud   _____

  (*b*) permit gaseous exchange   _____

  (*c*) have waterproof scars   _____

  (*d*) show where the flower stalks fell off   _____

  (*e*) show where leaves fell off at bud-burst _____

8   Apply the appropriate descriptions **A–D** to the terms (*a*)–(*c*) (which concern plants):
   A survives winter as seed in its second year **B** flowers twice a year
   C survives winter as seed each year **D** survives for many years

  (*a*) perennial   ____   (*b*) biennial   ____   (*c*) annual   ____

9   Name the part(s) of an insect-pollinated flower that usually:

  (*a*) 'advertises' by colour and scent   _____

  (*b*) rewards insects with sugar solution   _____

  (*c*) enables the stigma to brush against the visiting insect   _____

  (*d*) protects the flower in bud   _____

  (*e*) contains ova (female gametes)   _____

  (*f*) contains ovules   _____

10   Cross-pollination is best described as:
   A the arrival of pollen on a stigma from a second flower
   B the liberation of gametes at the ovule
   C pollen transfer from one species to the next
   D pollen reaching the stigma of a flower from a second plant of the same kind
   E none of these   ____

11   Indicate the origin of (*a*)–(*d*) by pairing them up with **A–D**
   A receptacle **B** integuments **C** ovary **D** ovule

  (*a*) seed   ____   (*c*) false fruit   ____

  (*b*) true fruit   ____   (*d*) testa   ____

12   Opposite the following parts of a wind-pollinated flower write *two* descriptive terms
   which might indicate what the parts would look like:

  (*a*) stigma   _____   _____

  (*b*) pollen   _____   _____

  (*c*) petals   _____   _____

13   (*a*)–(*c*) below describe stages in mammal reproduction. Select from **A–D** the location of
   those stages within the reproductive tract of the female:
   A ovary **B** uterus **C** oviduct **D** vagina

  (*a*) fertilisation takes place   ____

  (*b*) a blastula develops into an embryo   ____

  (*c*) new ova are shed   ____

14   Name the parts of an angiosperm and of a mammal which:

	Angiosperm	Mammal
(*a*) make pollen/sperm	_____	_____
(*b*) receive pollen/sperm	_____	_____
(*c*) allow development of the embryo within	_____	_____
(*d*) are the immediate source of food for the embryo	_____	_____
(*e*) are responsible for expulsion of the embryo when it is fully developed	_____	_____

15   At the stage when a mammal is a developing embryo, name the part(s) which:

(*a*) cushion the embryo from blows   _____

(*b*) passes wastes from embryo to mother   _____

(*c*) will be severed after birth   _____

(*d*) receives oxygen from the mother   _____

(*e*) is normally the first to appear outside the mother at birth _____

(*f*) is the very last to leave the uterus   _____

Test yourself on chapter 13

1   Put the following in increasing order of size (volume):
A nucleus B DNA thread C protoplasm D chromosome E gene   _____

2   Choose from **A–E** in question **1** the item which:

(*a*) determines synthesis of an enzyme   ____

(*b*) is visible under a light microscope only at cell division   ____

(*c*) becomes divided into two after the nucleus has divided   ____

(*d*) is diploid after fertilisation   ____

3   Link (*a*)–(*g*) with the appropriate items from **A–J** by filling in the blanks:
A phenotype B dominant C homozygous D environment E co-dominant
F genotype G heterozygous H recessive J alleles

(*a*) determine characteristics   ____ ____

(*b*) the appearance of an organism   ____

(*c*) gene that expresses itself as a characteristic   ____

(*d*) gene that only expresses itself if there are two of them   ____

(*e*) two identical genes at a locus   ____

(*f*) name given to two alternative genes at a locus   ____

(*g*) two alternative genes at a locus which both express themselves   ____ ____

4   The number of chromosomes in a gorilla's cheek cell is 48. The number in a gorilla's ovum is:
A 24 B 48 C 96 D 23   ____

5   Choose the type of cell division that reduces the chromosome number by half:
A mitosis B meiosis C growth cell divisions D binary fission   ____

6   Choose from the following those that do *not* apply to meiosis:
A products are haploid B there are four products from each original cell
C there are two products from each original cell D products are not identical
E ensures that a species does not double its diploid number F occurs at growing points

    ____ ____

7   A certain mollusc can be either striped or unstriped. If an organism of genotype **Bb** is crossed with a homozygous dominant having a striped shell:

(*i*) the expected ratio of genotypes in the offspring is
A all **BB** B ½**Bb**:½**BB** C all **bb** D all **Bb**   ____

(*ii*) the expected ratio of phenotypes is
A all striped B all unstriped C ½ striped and ½ unstriped D all faintly striped   ____

8   Pure lines of red flowers crossed with white ones give only pink offspring.

(*i*) What will be the ratio of red, white and pink flowers if the following crosses are made:

(*a*) white × pink: _____

(*b*) red × pink: _____

(*c*) pink × pink: _____

(*ii*) Show your reasoning for answer (*i*) (*a*)–(*c*) by drawing Punnett squares for each cross: (*a*)   (*b*)   (c)

9   Eye colour is determined by a dominant/recessive relationship in a certain mammal. The following results were obtained from crosses made. Fill in the *genotypes* of the organisms indicated by letters (*a*)–(*c*), using B = brown, b = blue:

Blue-eyed × Blue-eyed

(*a*) Brown × Blue   Blue   (*b*) Blue   Blue   Blue × (*c*) Brown

(*a*) . . . .   (*b*) . . . .   (*c*) . . . .

Brown Brown Brown Brown   Brown Blue Brown Blue Blue

10   Two male animals, **A** and **B**, both with brown fur, were crossed (at different times) with a grey-furred female, **C**. Whereas mating **A** with **C** gave offspring that were all brown, the offspring of **B** with **C** were 31 brown and 29 grey. State the genotype of each of the animals:

A: ___   **B:** ___   **C:** ___

11   Statements **A–G** below refer to activity within the nucleus of a cell. Insert, in the table, those activities going on at the three stages of mitosis and meiosis indicated:

	mitosis	*meiosis* (first division)
(*a*) interphase		
(*b*) metaphase		
(*c*) anaphase		

A gene number is being duplicated **B** gene number is being halved
C gene number is remaining the same **D** genes are making enzymes
E centromeres divide **F** centromeres do not divide
G pairs of homologous chromosomes line up on the equator of the cell
H individual chromosomes line up on the equator of the cell

12   Plant A with 2n = 16 is grafted onto another plant, B, with 12 chromosomes as the diploid number. State the number of chromosomes in:

(*a*) the pollen of plant A   ___   (*c*) the zygotes formed in plant A   ___
(*b*) the vegetative growth of plant B ___   (*d*) the petals of plant A   ___

Test yourself on chapter 14

1   The theory of evolution by natural selection was originated by:
   A Malthus **B** Lamarck **C** Mendel **D** Darwin   ___   ___   ___

2   Arrange the following statements concerning evolution in a logical order:
   A In any population of organisms there is a variety of individuals
   B Populations remain reasonably constant in numbers
   C All organisms could, theoretically, show an exponential rise in numbers
   D Those varieties best adapted to the environment survive
   E There must be a 'struggle for existence' which keeps populations down

___ ___ ___ ___ ___

3 The forces of natural selection acting on an insect population might include:
A pollination **B** frosts **C** spiders **D** insecticide-resistance **E** scarcity of food
F other insects with similar food requirements   ___ ___ ___ ___

4 Which of the following could not be an adaptation?
A inherited features **B** a wing for flying **C** mutations **D** ability to reason out a solution
E haemoglobin for carrying oxygen **F** sun-tanning of the European skin   ___

5 The following are possible causes of variation in organisms. Select those that are unlikely
to affect their evolution:
A cutting human hair different ways **B** sexual reproduction in mice
C using different levels of fertiliser on crops **D** mutant cells being used in reproduction
E fat (under-exercised) and sleek (exercised) horses.   ___ ___ ___

6 Complete the following sentences:

Irradiation of cells by _____ may cause _____ in them.

These are changes in the _____ of the nuclei of cells and often kill them.

However, sometimes such _____ cells survive.

Only if these cells are _____ or _____ can
the changes in them be passed to future generations.

Only helpful changes of this type have any chance of becoming widespread in a population, thus affecting _____ of the species.

7 The diagram below shows a 'family tree' of organisms evolving. Each letter, e.g. **C** or **D**
represents a species:

By reference to the diagram select those
species which:

(*a*) have become extinct   ___ ___
(*b*) are common ancestors to more
than one species   ___
(*c*) show great variety   ___

8 The types of organism **C¹**, **C²**, **C³**, **C⁴** shown in question 7 could become new species if
breeding between them was prevented. Assuming that these organisms are water beetles
introduced by man to the various lakes in North and South America, list, with a sentence
of explanation, three reasons which might prevent the beetles from interbreeding from
lake to lake:

(*a*) _____

(*b*) _____

(*c*) _____

9 Select an appropriate example from **A–E** below for each of (*a*)–(*e*):

A leg of insect and of cow **B** Shetland pony **C** black (melanic) variety of peppered moth
D eye of monkey and of whale **E** *Archaeopteryx*

(*a*) analogous   ___   (*d*) mutant   ___
(*b*) homologous   ___   (*e*) products of man's selective breeding   ___
(*c*) link-animal   ___

10 Select from the following the item that could *not* be regarded as evidence for Darwin's theory of evolution:
A fossils B selective breeding C acquired characteristics in a lifetime
D similarity of embryos of different species ____

11 Which of the following statements about fossils are incorrect?
A are found in igneous rocks B are found in sedimentary rocks
C are found in amber D none found in rocks older than 600 million years
E usually have mineralised hard parts F have preserved soft parts ____ ____ ____

12 Which of the statements below do not describe the pentadactyl limb accurately?
A is present in all terrestrial animals B is present in almost all vertebrates
C is present in all mammals
D consists of a five-fingered hand, wrist bones and three long bones
E consists of a five-fingered hand, wrist bones and two long bones
F present only in pterodactyls ____ ____ ____

13 Arrange the following groups in order of increasing age (i.e. starting with the most recently evolved):
A fish B dinosaurs C algae D man E birds ____ ____ ____ ____ ____

Test yourself on chapter 15

1 From the environmental factors A–H select those that are:

(a) abiotic ____ ____ ____ ____   (b) biotic ____ ____ ____ ____

A sunlight B parasites C symbionts D wind E snow F competitors G mineral salts
H predators

2 From the biotic factors in question 1 select:

(i) those biotic factors that:
(a) do harm to other organisms ____ ____ ____
(b) do good to other organisms ____

(ii) those abiotic factors that:
(a) influence plant nutrition ____ ____ ____
(b) might harm a tree if it were not deciduous ____ ____

3 Link definitions (a)–(e) below with terms A–E:
(a) place where an organism lives ____
(b) influence of one organism on another ____
(c) a number of species interacting in a locality ____
(d) nutritional interrelationships of organisms ____
(e) interaction of forest organisms both with each other and with their abiotic environment

A community B ecosystem C food web D biotic factor E habitat ____

4 Explain the difference between the following pairs of terms by stating what the first term lacks to make the second:

(a) food chain and food cycle _____
(b) food chain and food web _____
(c) community and ecosystem _____

5 Look at Fig. 15.4 (p. 124) again.

(i) Write down two food chains of four members, each of which includes a different parasite. (Do *not* repeat the food chain in Fig. 15.3):

(a) _____
(b) _____

(*ii*) Write down:

   (*a*) two competitors *of* the rabbits   _____   _____

   (*b*) two competitors *for* the voles   _____   _____

(*iii*) Assuming that the food web is complete, as drawn, what definite *immediate* changes would there be to the number of each kind of organism if:

   (*a*) sow-thistles and dandelions died _____

      _____

   (*b*) all rabbits died of myxomatosis:

      more _____

      fewer _____

      no _____

6 Study Fig. 15.1 (p. 122) again. From it write down:

   (*a*) one food chain with three members in it _____

   (*b*) one food chain with five members in it _____

      _____

   (*c*) two decomposer organisms   _____   _____

   (*d*) a filter-feeder   _____

   (*e*) the organism most likely to be harmed, through the food chain, by DDT in the aquarium   _____

   (*f*) two ways in which bacteria might benefit from the fish over a period of time   _____   _____

   (*g*) two ways in which *Elodea* might benefit from the bacteria   _____   _____

   (*h*) two ways in which the abiotic part of this ecosystem might benefit *named* organisms (other than through nutrition)

      _____

      _____

7 The biosphere does *not* include:

A whole mountains **B** deepest ocean depths **C** air at 8000 metres **D** soil   ____

8 Write down an influence from outer space that:

   (*a*) might change future generations of organisms genetically_____

   (*b*) affects the nutrition of the world _____

   (*c*) affects distribution of organisms on shores_____

   (*d*) causes synthesis of vitamin D in skin _____

   (*e*) adds to the earth's mass _____

9 Sandy soil does not:

A contain a lot of air **B** hold water well **C** have many earthworms **D** warm quickly

                                                                      ____

10 The following constituents of soil are organic:

A water **B** humus **C** rock particles **D** earthworms **E** decay bacteria **F** air

                                                                __ __ __

11 Humus improves soil and crop growth by:

A discouraging earthworms **B** helping to drain sandy soil **C** helping to aerate clay soil **D** providing mineral salts on decaying **E** neutralising acidity **F** liberating CO_2 as it decays

                                                                __ __ __

12 **A–D** are types of bacterium that cause changes in the nitrogen chemistry of soil. Match each with the changes they cause (*a*)–(*d*).

   (*a*) nitrates to nitrogen   ____   (*c*) ammonia to nitrite and nitrate   ____

   (*b*) nitrogen to nitrates   ____   (*d*) protein to ammonia   ____

   A nitrifying **B** nitrogen fixing **C** putrefying (decay) **D** denitrifying

13　Select from the types of bacterium in question **12** those which:

　(a) are harmful to a farmer's interests　　　　　　　　____
　(b) may be present in legume roots　　　　　　　　　　____
　(c) make meat go bad　　　　　　　　　　　　　　　　____
　(d) are present particularly in *fresh* manure heaps　　____
　(e) are active in un-drained soil　　　　　　　　　　　____

14　Name the raw materials that the following organisms need to make their proteins:

　(a) animals　　　　　_____
　(b) green plants　　　_____
　(c) nitrogen fixing bacteria _____

15　Certain activities in the world cause an increase of CO_2 in the air, others a decrease.

　(i) Name the activities that are principally:

　　(a) human, increasing CO_2　　　　　_____
　　(b) bacterial and fungal, increasing CO_2　_____
　　(c) holophytic, reducing CO_2　　　　_____

　(ii) Name two organelles in cells whose activities affect the levels of CO_2 in the air, and state their effects:

　　(a) _____ _____
　　(b) _____ _____

　(iii) Select the average level of CO_2 in the air:
　　A 0.3% B 3.0% C 0.03% D 0.003%　　　　　　____

16　Select those of the following activities of earthworms which are helpful to crop growth:
　A tunnelling B eating humus C dying and decaying D secreting lime
　E being eaten by birds F pulling leaves into tunnels　　____ ____ ____ ____

17　Complete the following sentence:
　A cultivated soil or '_____' has a range of sizes of rock particles ranging from
　0.2 mm (called _____) to _____ mm (called clay).
　This allows it to contain a good supply of _____ , _____ , and _____ all
　of which encourage plant growth. In addition it includes _____ which makes
　it darker in colour and encourages a variety of _____ to feed on it, helping it to
　decay.

Test yourself on chapter 16

　1　Liming the soil is *not* designed to:
　　A kill pests B help to drain clay C neutralise soil acidity
　　D give heavy soils a good 'crumb structure'　　　　____

　2　Rotation of crops is practised principally to:
　　A eliminate pests B replace lost nitrogen compounds C give cattle different pastures
　　D enrich soil with fertilisers　　　　　　　　　　____

　3　Artificial fertilisers do *not* have the disadvantage of:
　　A leaching away into streams easily when it is rainy B benefiting plant slowly
　　C expensiveness D not improving soil structure　　____

　4　The present human population is about 4000 million. By the year 2000 it is expected, on present trends, to reach:
　　A 7000 million B 8000 million C 4000 million D 6000 million　　____

5   Give *one* example of a pollutant, and its effects, arising from each of the following:

	pollutant	*effect*
(*a*) petrol motor car	_____	_____
(*b*) jet aircraft	_____	_____
(*c*) farmer	_____	_____
(*d*) atomic power plant	_____	_____

6   There were no agricultural pests before man became agricultural. This was because the organisms that are now pests:
A kept hidden   B had less plentiful food supplies
C were controlled by natural insecticides
D were controlled by numerous parasitic wasps   ____

7   One species of animal that humans have not yet managed to make extinct is:
A the dodo   B Tasmanian wolf   C the tiger   D the moa   ____

8   Group the following resources in the world into the categories:
(*a*) renewable   ___ ___ ___   (*b*) non-renewable   ___ ___ ___

A soil   B copper ores   C ebony trees   D coal   E blue whales   F ivory

9   Most of the world's population is already undernourished. This is because:
A there is not enough food produced   B people will not eat single-cell protein
C there is enough food, but it is not distributed well enough   D fertilisers are expensive

____

10 From A–F select two diseases that cannot be cured:
A malaria   B goitre   C diabetes   D mongolism   E mumps or influenza
F tuberculosis (TB)   ____ ____

11 Select from the diseases named in question 10 those that are caused by:

(*a*) hormone deficiency	____	(*d*) a virus	____
(*b*) dietary deficiency	____	(*e*) a bacterium	____
(*c*) faulty chromosome number	____	(*f*) a protozoan	____

12 House flies in the Middle East too easily transfer dysentery (disease) bacteria and protozoa from faeces to food by visiting both. Assuming that an abundance of flies and exposed faeces is usual in such places, how could you prevent yourself from getting dysentry if you went to live there? State three methods you would use, each different in principle:

(*a*) _____
(*b*) _____
(*c*) _____

13 Immunity to a disease *cannot* be achieved by:
A catching the disease and recovering   B inoculation with a mild strain of the pathogen
C injection with antibodies to the disease obtained from a rabbit
D taking a preventive drug   ____

14 Passive immunity is:
A long lasting and offers immediate protection
B short lasting but offers immediate protection
C long lasting but offers protection only after some time   D vaccination   ____

15 Link the man to the invention he is associated with:
A aseptic surgery B vaccination C polio vaccine D rabies vaccine E brewing
F antiseptic surgery G anti-malarial drugs H penicillin

(*a*) Pasteur	____	(*c*) Jenner	____
(*b*) Lister	____	(*d*) Fleming	____

Test yourself on chapter 17

In addition to questions requiring straight **recall** of facts about organisms, this section has questions which will give you practice in **comparison** and **contrast** of organisms. This type of question is common in examinations.

1   Select from the following statements **A–F** those that apply to:

(*a*) viruses   ___   ___   ___   (*b*) bacteria   ___   ___   ___

A the smallest cellular organisms **B** invisible under the best light microscopes
C made of nucleic acid and protein only **D** all are parasitic
E many are saprophytic **F** reproduce by binary fission

2   (*a*)–(*d*) below are features of both bacteria and algae such as *Spirogyra*. State in the spaces provided how these features differ in the two groups:

		Bacteria	*Algae*
(*a*)	cell wall		
(*b*)	position of the chromosome material in the cell		
(*c*)	nutrition		
(*d*)	response to direct sunlight		

3   Pair up **A–E** concerning *Spirogyra* with items (*a*)–(*e*):
   A made in pyrenoids **B** spiral and green **C** by-product from nutrition
   D stores mineral salts and water **E** covered by mucilage

(*a*) oxygen   ___   (*d*) chloroplasts   ___
(*b*) starch   ___   (*e*) vacuole   ___
(*c*) cell walls   ___

4   *Spirogyra* differs from *Amoeba* in a number of respects, indicated (*a*)–(*f*) below. Say what the differences are:

		Spirogyra	*Amoeba*
(*a*)	phylum		
(*b*)	three major structural features of the cell		
(*c*)	means of osmo-regulation		
(*d*)	main gas absorbed from solution by day		
(*e*)	reproduction methods		
(*f*)	structures for locomotion		

5   Compare and contrast the following organisms as far as features **A–G** are concerned by placing the appropriate letters against the organism's name:
   A reproduce by binary fission **B** reproduce by spores **C** reproduce by conjugation
   D germinate from zygospores **E** use enzymes to digest food **F** digest food externally
   G have no cell walls

(*a*) Bacteria   ___   ___   ___   ___
(*b*) *Spirogyra*   ___   ___
(*c*) *Mucor*   ___   ___   ___   ___
(*d*) *Amoeba*   ___   ___   ___

6   Name and give the phylum of the organisms which have the following effects on health:

		Name	Phylum
(a)	cause malaria	_____	_____
(b)	transmit malaria	_____	_____
(c)	cause influenza	_____	
(d)	cause athlete's foot	_____	_____
(e)	provide man with a rich source of B vitamins	_____	_____
(f)	provide penicillin	_____	_____
(g)	cause tetanus		_____
(h)	transmit veneral disease	_____	_____

7   Complete the following passage which refs to *Hydra:*

Hydra is a simple _____ which lives in _____. It catches prey such as

_____ with special _____ cells on its _____, which paralyse the prey. The

food is digested by_____ secreted into the_____ and waste material is egested

(eliminated) via the_____. Green species of *Hydra* also gain food and_____ from

algae living in symbiosis within its _____ cells. Well-fed *Hydra* usually reproduce asexual-

ly by_____. The young are copies of the parent with _____ layers of cells and a

nervous system called a_____ without nerves or a _____

8   Both mosses and ferns show 'alternation of generations' in their life cycles. Link struc-
    tures (a)–(f) concerning this with the appropriate descriptions A–H:

    A reproduces sexually B reproduces asexually C needs water to reach the ovum
    D needs wind for dispersal E grows from the zygote F grows into the gametophyte
    G produces sperm H contains the ovum

    (a) sporophyte   ___ ___   (d) spore   ___ ___
    (b) gametophyte   ___ ___ ___   (e) sperm   ___
    (c) antheridium   ___   (f) archegonium ___

9   Name the structures in a bony fish that fulfil the following functions:

    (a) move the tail from side to side _____
    (b) can act as hydroplanes   _____
    (c) provides buoyancy   _____
    (d) prevent roll   _____
    (e) sense obstacles   _____/_____
    (f) sieve out matter that might
        damage gills   _____
    (g) protects gills externally   _____

10 Name the structures in a bird that assist flight by:

    (a) streamlining the body   _____
    (b) providing a large surface area for 'lift' _____
    (c) providing the power for wing-flapping   _____
    (d) providing the muscles with enough oxygen (two organs)_____

11 (*a*) Fill in the blanks in the diagram below which shows an *aerofoil* in section.

(i) —————

(ii) —————

Forward motion

(iii) —————

(*b*) What is missing from the diagram if flight of the aerofoil is to be achieved?

_____

12 Contrast the methods of gaseous exchange, locomotion, feeding and 'hearing' in a fish (such as the minnow or stickleback) with those of an adult frog by naming the structures involved in each case below:

	fish	*frog*
(*a*) gaseous exchange		
(*b*) locomotion		
(*c*) feeding		
(*d*) hearing		

13 In a developing bird's egg name the structures within the shell that:

(*a*) enable gaseous exchange _____

(*b*) supply water to the embryo _____

(*c*) provide a food store for the embryo _____

(*d*) allow the embryo to float in 'water' _____

14 Name the stage, after the egg, in the life cycle of insects such as flies, butterflies and bees at which:

(*a*) ecdysis occurs _____

(*b*) sexual maturity is attained _____

(*c*) feeding for growth occurs _____

(*d*) wings appear _____

(*e*) a period of immobility (other than hibernation) occurs _____

15 Name the stage, after the egg, in the life cycle of insects such as the locust or cockroach at which:

(*a*) ecdysis occurs _____

(*b*) sexual maturity is attained _____

(*c*) feeding for growth occurs _____

(*d*) wings appear _____

(*e*) a period of immobility (other than hibernation) occurs _____

16 Apply descriptions **A–G** to the three types of honey-bee (*a*)–(*c*):
A female **B** male **C** fertile **D** infertile **E** longest lived **F** lacking sting **G** smallest

(*a*) drone ___ ___ ___   (*b*) worker ___ ___ ___   (*c*) queen ___ ___ ___

17 Contrast the characteristics of insects with those of mammals by filling in the blanks below:

	insect	*mammal*
(*a*) position of skeleton in body		
(*b*) main material of skeleton		
(*c*) temperature control		
(*d*) number of walking limbs		
(*e*) where gaseous exchange occurs		
(*f*) source of developing embryo's food		

18   Compare any two parasites that you have studied by filling in the blanks below:

name		
(a) primary host (A)		
(b) secondary host (B)		
(c) means of transmission: (i) from A to B		
(ii) from B to A		
(d) means of reproduction: (i) in/on primary host		
(ii) in/on secondary host		
(e) food and means of feeding from primary host		
(f) example of a non-parasitic member of the same group (phylum)		
(g) food and means of feeding of (f)		

19   A–F below are stages in the reproduction and early development of the frog. Arrange them in the sequence in which they occur in the frog's life cycle:
    A fertilisation occurs   **B** albumen swells   **C** eggs are laid
    D male grips female under armpits   **E** sperm is shed into water
    F zygote develops into a ball of cells   ___ ___ ___ ___ ___ ___

20   (*i*) A–D below are descriptions of the method of feeding at four stages in the life cycle of the frog after it has hatched from the egg. Name the structures that would be used at each stage to obtain oxygen:
    A scavenging on dead animals   _____
    B *not* feeding   _____
    C catching live animals on tongue   _____
    D feeding on water plants   _____

   (*ii*) Arrange letters A–D in the sequence in which the stages of the frog's life cycle described above occur: ___ ___ ___ ___

21   (*i*) A–F below concern stages in the reproduction of an earthworm. Fill in the blanks alongside each to indicate the structures involved:
    A eggs appear from inside the body at _____
    B eggs develop into worms in _____
    C two worms copulate head to tail, _____ surfaces together
    D the other worm's sperm fertilises the eggs inside _____
    E sperm is transferred to the other worm along _____
    F the cocoon is secreted by _____

   (*ii*) Arrage stages A–F above in the sequence in which they occur:

                                        ___ ___ ___ ___ ___ ___

Answers to test-yourself sections

Below you will find answers to all the test-yourself questions. Each answer is keyed back into the relevant topic(s) in the text. After each answer there is a reference in brackets to the section(s) in the book, (e.g. § 2.2 means see Section 2.2 Organelles).

Chapter 2

1 B (§ 2.1)
2 C (§ 2.1)
3 C (§ 2.1)
4 A (§ 2.1)
5 C (§ 2.2)
6 D (§ 2.2)
7 C (§ 2.2)
8 B (§ 2.3)
9 (*a*) e.g. xylem vessel/e.g. neuron or muscle, (*b*) xylem vessel/red blood cell, (*c*) any cell without chloroplasts/red blood cell (§ 2.5, 5.5, 5.8, 9.2, 10.7)
10 (*a*) **CAFBED**, (*b*) (*i*) **D**, (*ii*) **AD**, (*iii*) **B**, (*iv*) **C**, (*v*) **F**, (*vi*) **E** (§ 2.5)

Chapter 3

1 A (§ 3.1)
2 D (Fig. 3.2, § 17.5)
3 B (§ 3.1)
4 C (Fig 3.2)
5 (*i*) (*a*) **C**, (*b*) **F**, (*c*) **A**, (*d*) **H**, (*e*) **AEG**, (*f*) **D**, (*g*) **B**; (*ii*) invertebrate (§ 3.1)
6 (*a*) **BJ**, (*b*) **F**, (*c*) **AC**, (*d*) **ACF**, (*e*) **DH**, (*f*) **FG**, (*g*) **D**, (*h*) **BEJ**, (*j*) **B** (Figs 3.2, 3.3)

Chapter 4

1 (*i*) (*a*) **B** (**CDEF**), (*b*) **A**, (*c*) **D**, (*d*) **BEF**, (*e*) **BC**; (*ii*) omnivorous (§ 4.2)
2 (*a*) **ABE**, (*b*) **AB**, (*c*) **E**, (*d*) **C**, (*e*) **BC**, (*f*) vitamins (§ 4.4, 4.5)
3 (*a*) **C**, (*b*) **E**, (*c*) **B**, (*d*) **AE**, (*e*) **EB**, (*f*) **D**, (*g*) **A**, (*h*) **C** (§ 4.4, 4.5)
4 (*a*) **ABCEF**, (*b*) **CE**, (*c*) **A**, (*d*) **D**, (*e*) **F**, (*f*) **BE** (§ 4.4, 4.5, 4.13)
5 (*i*) (*a*) **C**, (*b*) **AE**, (*c*) **F**, (*d*) **B**, (*e*) **D**, (*f*) **EF**, (*g*) **G**; (*ii*) **E** (§ 4.2, 4.5)
6 (*a*) **BE**, (*b*) **ABDEH**, (*c*) **A**, (*d*) **C**, (*e*) **F**, (*f*) **A**, (*g*) **G** (§ 4.11, 4.12, 4.14)
7 (*a*) **FGACEBD**, (*b*) **F**, (*c*) **EC**, (*d*) **FG**, (*e*) **AC**, (*f*) **EB**, (*g*) **EC**, (*h*) **BD**, (*j*) **C**, (*k*) **A** (Fig. 4.14)
8 (*a*) **FHGE**, (*b*) **BDC**, (*c*) **E**, (*d*) **H**, (*e*) **A**, (*f*) **C**, (*g*) carbohydrate (starch) (§ 4.14, Fig. 4.13)
9 (*a*) **ABDE**, (*b*) **C**, (*c*) **E**, (*d*) **ACDG**, (*e*) **CG**, (*f*) **B**, (*g*) **F**, (*h*) **D** (§ 4.6, 4.7, 4.10)
10 (*i*) (*a*) **B**, (*b*) **C**, (*c*) **A**, (*d*) **D**; (*ii*) **EF**; (*iii*) **E**; (*iv*) **F** (§ 4.6)
11 (*i*) (*a*) **C**, (*b*) **H**, (*c*) **F**; (*ii*) **GEBDEG**; (*iii*) **BDH**; (*iv*) **C**; (*v*) **A** (§ 4.8, Fig. 4.5)
12 B (§ 4.12)
13 C (§ 4.4)
14 A (§ 4.20)
15 D (§ 4.20)
16 C (§ 4.4)
17 A (§ 4.4)
18 B (§ 4.4)
19 B (Fig. 4.1)

Chapter 5

1 (*a*) **B**, (*b*) **D**, (*c*) **A**, (*d*) **E**, (*e*) **C**, (*f*) **A**, (*g*) **D** (§ 5.1)
2 (*i*) (*a*) active transport, (*b*) osmosis, (*c*) diffusion; (*ii*) (*a*) osmosis, (*b*) diffusion, (*c*) active transport (§ 5.2)
3 (*a*) **C**, (*b*) **B**, (*c*) **C**, (*d*) **A** and **B**, (*e*) **B**, (*f*) **C**, (*g*) **A** or **B** (§ 5.2)
4 (*i*) (*a*) **F**, (*b*) **A**, (*c*) **E**, (*d*) **C**, (*e*) **B**, (*f*) **D**; (*ii*) (*a*) **AD**, (*b*) **BF**, (*c*) **CE**, (*d*) **AB**, (*e*) **AC** (§ 5.3)
5 A (§ 5.4)
6 B (§ 5.4)

7 (*a*) **BEH**, (*b*) **AFJ**, (*c*) **GKM**, (*d*) **CDL** (Fig. 4.5)

8 **B** (§ 5.2)

9 (*a*) **F**, (*b*) **F**, (*c*) **T**, (*d*) **T** (§ 5.2)

10 **B** (§ 5.7)

11 (*i*) (*a*) water, (*b*) protein, (*c*) haemoglobin; (*ii*) (*a*) erythrocytes (red), (*b*) phagocytes (§ 5.8, Table 5.4)

12 (*a*) CO_2, (*b*) O_2, (*c*) urea, (*d*) glucose (§ 5.8)

13 **ABE** (§ 5.11)

14 (*a*) **CF**, (*b*) **AB**, (*c*) **DEG** (§ 5.9, Table 5.5)

15 **E** (§ 5.8)

16 (*a*) **BEH(G)**, (*b*) **AD**, (*c*) **AGEC**, (*d*) **FH** (§ 7.1, 7.2, 7.4)

17 **ECHADFB** (Fig. 5.12)

18 **CGBHDE** (Fig. 5.12)

19 (*a*) **D**, (*b*) **E**, (*c*) **C**, (*d*) **B**, (*e*) **F** (Fig. 5.12, § 5.10)

20 (*a*) 5 000 000, (*b*) 10 000, (*c*) 70, (*d*) 4, (*e*) 0, (*f*) 37 (Table 5.4, § 5.9)

Chapter 6

1 (*a*) **B**, (*b*) **C**, (*c*) **E**, (*d*) **A**, (*e*) **D** (§ 6.1)

2 (*a*) **E**, (*b*) **A**, (*c*) **E**, (*d*) **B(C)**, (*e*) **E**, (*f*) **B(C)**, (*g*) **E**, (*h*) **E** (§ 6.1, 6.2, 6.4, 6.6)

3 **D** (§ 6.3)

4 **BDFHJ** (§ 6.6)

5 **CDFGBAE** (§ 6.6)

6 (*a*) **T**, (*b*) **T**, (*c*) **F**, (*d*) **T**, (*e*) **F**, (*f*) **T** (§ 6.6)

7 (*i*) **D** ; (*ii*) **A** 4%, **B** 21%, **C** 79%; (*iii*) **A** he would be suffocated, **B** he would be burnt by the cigarette bursting into flames (§ 6.6)

8 (*a*) **T**, (*b*) **F**, (*c*) **T**, (*d*) **F**, (*e*) **F** (§ 6.2)

9 **E** (§ 6.2)

10 (*a*) **C**, (*b*) **D**, (*c*) **E**, (*d*) **BH**, (*e*) **AF** (§ 6.4)

11 (*a*) **CDEF**, (*b*) **BCGH**, (*c*) **A–H** (§ 6.4)

12 (*a*) **ACDE**, (*b*) **AC**, (*c*) **F** (§ 6.7)

Chapter 7

1 (*a*) **ACDF**, (*b*) **BCEF**, (*c*) **ACDE** (§ 7.1, 5.6)

2 **BD** (§ 7.1)

3 (*a*) liver, (*b*) bladder, (*c*) kidneys (§ 7.2)

4 (*a*) **DCBGFHA**, (*b*) **LJK** (§ 7.2)

5 (*a*) **C**, (*b*) **A**, (*c*) **B**, (*d*) **E**, (*e*) **F**, (*f*) **D** or **F** (§ 7.2)

6 **ABCFG** (§ 7.2)

7 **A** (§ 7.2)

8 **D** (§ 7.2)

9 (*a*) **D**, (*b*) **I**, (*c*) **I**, (*d*) **D**, (*e*) **I** (§ 7.2)

10 (*i*) **A** transpiration/O_2, **B** perspiration/heat or urea, **C** breathing/CO_2, **D** urination/urea, **E** osmoregulation/urea or CO_2 (not their main route); (*ii*) (*a*) **DE**, (*b*) **AB**; (*iii*) (*a*) **BE**, (*b*) **AC** (§ 7.1)

11 **A** (§ 7.4)

12 (*a*) **B**, (*b*) **A**, (*c*) **C** (§ 7.4)

13 (*a*) **DE**, (*b*) **AF**, (*c*) **BC**, (*d*) **DG** (§ 7.5)

14 **C** (§ 7.4)

15 **E** (§ 7.6)

Chapter 8

1 (*a*) **DL**, (*b*) **FC**, (*c*) **AM**, (*d*) **EG**, (*e*) **KN**, (*f*) **BH**, (*g*) **J** (§ 8.3)

2 **B** (§ 8.3)

3 **A** (§ 8.3)

4 (*a*) **B**, (*b*) **C**, (*c*) **D**, (*d*) **AB** (§ 8.3)

5 (*a*) long sight/short/convex (converging) lenses, (*b*) old sight/lens has lost its elasticity (collapsibility), (*c*) short sight/long/concave (diverging) lenses (§ 8.3, Fig. 8.3)

6 (*a*) F, (*b*) ACDE, (*c*) AD, (*d*) B, (*e*) G (§ 8.5)

7 GHJ, FDB, AEBC (§ 8.5)

8 ADEFH (§ 8.5)

Chapter 9

1 (*a*) root and shoot tips/inner ear (semi-circular canals), (*b*) hormonal/nervous, (*c*) slow/rapid, (*d*) geotropism (growth)/righting reflex action (muscular action) (§ 9.1, 9.7, 9.12)

2 (*a*) BCEG, (*b*) F (§ 9.1, 9.11)

3 (*a*) A, (*b*) D, (*c*) E, (*d*) B, (*e*) C (§ 9.2)

4 (*i*) ADBE; (*ii*) muscle *or* gland cells (Fig. 9.5)

5 (*a*) F, (*b*) C, (*c*) A, (*d*) E, (*e*) B, (*f*) C (§ 9.7)

6 (*a*) E, (*b*) B, (*c*) A, (*d*) C, (*e*) D (§ 9.2, 9.5)

7 *badc* (§ 9.2)

8 B (§ 9.5)

9 C (§ 9.5)

10 (*a*) adrenalin/insulin, (*b*) adrenal/islet tissue of pancreas, (*c*) nerves/hormone (from pituitary), (*d*) liver/liver (§ 9.8)

11 B (§ 7.6)

12 (*a*) growth hormone/pituitary, (*b*) sugar diabetes/islet tissue of pancreas, (*c*) ADH (antidiuretic hormone)/pituitary, (*d*) cretinism/thyroxin, (*e*) iodine/diet (§ 9.8, 9.10)

13 (*a*) ACFGH, (*b*) ADE (§ 9.8, Fig. 4.15)

Chapter 10

1 (*i*) D; (*ii*) (*a*) AC, (*b*) B (§ 10.1)

2 B (§ 10.7)

3 (*a*) C, (*b*) DE (§ 10.10)

4 (*a*) wax cuticle, (*b*) protein + chitin, (*c*) chitin (§ 10.6)

5 (*a*) ligament, (*b*) tendon, (*c*) synovial membrane, (*d*) cartilage (§ 10.7, 10.8)

6 BCDF (§ 10.4, 10.8)

7 ABC (§ 10.5)

8 (*i*) A centrum/weight-bearing, B neural canal/protects nerve cord, C neural spine (dorsal process)/tendon and ligament attachment, D zygapophyses/prevent dislocation; (*ii*) (*a*) A, (*b*) A (§ 10.9)

9 (*a*) lumbar, (*b*) sacral, (*c*) axis, (*d*) caudal (coccyx in man), (*e*) thoracic (§ 10.9)

10 A forearm (front), B any movable joint, C upper arm, D lower leg, E fingers or toes, F upper leg, G wrist, H shoulder (Figs. 10.6, 10.10, 10.11)

11 (*a*) A and C, D and F; (*b*) C and H; (*c*) G; (*d*) none (§ 10.8)

Chapter 11

1 (*a*) ACF, (*b*) ACDEF (§ 11.1)

2 branched, large, CO_2, sunlight, water, mineral salts, compact, moving (§ 11.1)

3 (*a*) ACG, (*b*) BDEFG (§ 11.2, 11.3)

4 (*a*) GH, (*b*) AE, (*c*) CF, (*d*) BD (§ 11.6)

5 (*i*) (*a*)–(*c*); (*ii*) (*a*)–(*d*) (§ 11.6, Fig. 12.9)

6 endosperm, enzymes, cotyledon(s), water, warmth, oxygen (§ 11.6)

7 ABEFH (§ 11.6)

8 (*a*) AFH, (*b*) DG (§ 11.6)

9 AD (§ 11.5, 10.3)

Chapter 12

1 BF (§ 12.6, 12.11, 17.23)

2 B (§ 12.1)

3 CE (§ 12.1, 12.7)

4 (*a*) BCF, (*b*) ADE (§ 12.1, 12.2)

5 BE (§ 12.1)

6 (*a*) CG, (*b*) AD, (*c*) AF, (*d*) ADE, (*e*) B (§ 12.2, 12.7, 17.3)

7 (*a*) scale leaves, (*b*) lenticels, (*c*) bark (cork), (*d*) saddle (inflorescence) scar, (*e*) girdle scar (§ 12.3)

8 (*a*) D, (*b*) A, (*c*) C (§ 12.4)

9 (*a*) petals, (*b*) nectary, (*c*) style, (*d*) sepals, (*e*) ovules, (*f*) ovary (carpels) (§ 12.7, 12.8)

10 D (§ 12.9)

11 (*a*) D, (*b*) C, (*c*) A, (*d*) B (§ 12.11, 12.12)

12 (*a*) large surface area, e.g. 'feathery'/exposed, (*b*) small/smooth/very plentiful, (*c*) small/unattractive, e.g. green, unscented, or missing (§ 12.8)

13 (*a*) C, (*b*) B, (*c*) A (§ 12.14)

14 (*a*) anther/testis, (*b*) stigma/vagina, (*c*) ovary (carpel)/uterus, (*d*) endosperm/placenta, (*e*) fruit/uterus (§ 12.7, 12.11, 12.14)

15 (*a*) amniotic fluid and mother's tissues, (*b*) placenta (villi), (*c*) umbilical cord, (*d*) placenta (villi, haemoglobin in embryo's erythrocytes), (*e*) head (of baby), (*f*) placenta (§ 12.14, 12.15)

Chapter 13

1 EBDAC (§ 13.1)

2 (*a*) E, (*b*) D, (*c*) C, (*d*) A (§ 13.1)

3 (*a*) DF, (*b*) A, (*c*) B, (*d*) H, (*e*) C, (*f*) J, (*g*) EG (§ 13.2, 13.3)

4 A (§ 13.12)

5 B (§ 13.14)

6 CF (§ 13.14)

7 (*i*) B; (*ii*) A (§ 13.5)

8 (*a*) $\frac{1}{2}$ pink : $\frac{1}{2}$ white, (*b*) $\frac{1}{2}$ red : $\frac{1}{2}$ pink, (*c*) 1 red : 2 pink : 1 white (§ 13.4, 13.6)

9 (*a*) BB, (*b*) bb, (*c*) Bb (§ 13.4)

10 A:BB, B:Bb, C:bb (§ 13.4)

11 (*a*) AD/AD, (*b*) EH/FG, (*c*) C/B (§ 13.12, 13.13)

12 (*a*) 8, (*b*) 12, (*c*) 16, (*d*) 16 (§ 13.14)

Chapter 14

1 D (§ 14.1, 14.2)

2 CBEAD (§ 14.3)

3 BCEF (§ 14.3)

4 C (§ 14.3)

5 ACE (§ 14.3)

6 ultra violet, gamma or X-rays; mutations; DNA (genes); mutant; sperm; ova (or equivalents, i.e. male or female gametes); evolution (§ 13.11)

7 (*a*) AE, (*b*) E, (*c*) C (§ 14.3 no.8, 14.4 no.1)

8 Any three of *space* (separating the lakes); *time* (different times at which the populations breed – especially on either side of the equator); *genetics* (they accumulate mutations that prevent successful fertilisation; or they may become physically very different so that their genitalia do not fit thus preventing copulation between large and small individuals) (§ 14.3)

9 (*a*) A, (*b*) D, (*c*) E, (*d*) C, (*e*) B (§ 14.4)

10 C (§ 14.4)

11 ADF (§ 14.4)

12 AEF (§ 14.4)

13 DEBAC (§ 14.4)

Chapter 15

1 (*a*) ADEG, (*b*) BCFH (§ 15.1)

2 (*i*) (*a*) BFH, (*b*) C; (*ii*) (*a*) AEG, (*b*) DE (§ 15.3)

3 (*a*) E, (*b*) D, (*c*) A, (*d*) C, (*e*) B (§ 15.1)

4 (*a*) decomposers, (*b*) other related food chains, (*c*) abiotic factors in the environment. (§ 15.2)

5 (*i*) (*a*) e.g. wheat → vole → fox → *tick*; (*b*) dandelion → rabbit → fox → *flea* (hound is *not* a parasite); (*ii*) (*a*) vole, leaf-miner insect, (*b*) owl, fox; (*iii*) (*a*) leaf-miners die, rabbits eat grass only, (*b*) more leaf-miners, grass, dandelions, sow-thistles; fewer voles; no stoats (Fig. 15.4)

6 (*a*) e.g. diatoms → *Daphnia* → fish, (*b*) diatoms → protozoa → *Daphnia* → *Hydra* → fish,
(*c*) bacteria, *Asellus*, (*d*) *Daphnia*, (*e*) fish, (*f*) excreta, dead body, (*g*) CO_2, mineral salts, (*h*) e.g.
gravel anchors *Elodea* roots; water gives organisms support, keeps them coo (Fig. 15.1)

7 A (Fig. 15.1)

8 (*a*) ultra violet light (mutation), (*b*) sunlight (photosynthesis), (*c*) sun and moon's gravity (tides),
(*d*) ultra violet light, (*e*) meteorites (§ 15.1)

9 B (§ 15.5)

10 BDE (§ 15.5)

11 CDF (§ 15.5)

12 (*a*) D, (*b*) B, (*c*) A, (*d*) C (§ 15.6)

13 (*a*) D, (*b*) B, (*c*) C, (*d*) C, (*e*) D (§ 15.6)

14 (*a*) amino acids, (*b*) nitrates and sugars, (*c*) nitrogen and organic matter, e.g. sugars (§ 15.6)

15 (*i*) (*a*) combustion, (*b*) decay (bacterial respiration), (*c*) photosynthesis;
(*ii*) (*a*) chloroplast/photosynthesis turns CO_2 into carbohydrates, (*b*) mitochondrion/respiration
turns carbohydrates into CO_2; (*iii*) C (§ 15.7, 4.6, 2.2)

16 ACDF (§ 15.8)

17 'loam', sand, 0.0002, air (oxygen), water, mineral salts, humus, decomposers *or* earthworms *or*
bacteria (i.e. organisms) (§ 15.5)

Chapter 16

1 A (§ 16.2)

2 B (§ 16.3)

3 B (§ 16.2)

4 D (§ 16.5)

5 (*a*) CO/carboxyhaemoglobin, or Pb/effect on nervous system, (*b*) noise/irritation or possible
deafness if no protection, (*c*) artificial fertilisers/eutrophication, or insecticides/predators, (*d*)
radioactive elements/mutations, or heated water effluent/upset aquatic ecosystem (§ 16.6)

6 B (§ 16.4)

7 C (§ 16.7)

8 (*a*) CEF, (*b*) ABD (§ 16.7)

9 C (§ 16.7)

10 DE (§ 16.10)

11 (*a*) C, (*b*) B, (*c*) D, (*d*) E, (*e*) F, (*f*) A (§ 16.10)

12 (*a*) food covers, e.g. muslin, (*b*) insecticides in home, (*c*) preventive drug (prophylaxis) (§ 16.10)

13 D (§ 16.12, Table 16.3)

14 B (§ 16.11, Table 16.3)

15 (*a*) D, (*b*) F, (*c*) B, (*d*) H (§ 16.12)

Chapter 17

1 (*a*) BCD, (*b*) AEF (§ 17.1, 17.2)

2 (*a*) nitrogenous/cellulose, (*b*) in cytoplasm, free/inside a nuclear membrane, (*c*) saprophytic or
parasitic/holophytic, (*d*) killed by ultra violet light/photosynthesises (§ 17.2, 17.3)

3 (*a*) C, (*b*) A, (*c*) E, (*d*) B, (*e*) D (§ 17.3)

4 (*a*) Algae/protozoa, (*b*) cell wall, large vacuole, green chloroplast/no cell wall, contractile vacuole,
no chloroplast, (*c*) cell wall resists water entry once cell is turgid/contractile vacuole ejects water,
(*d*) CO_2/O_2, (*e*) (asexual growth) and sexual/asexual (binary fission) only, (*f*) none (does not
move) / pseudopodia (§ 17.3, 17.4, 2.1)

5 (*a*) ACEF, (*b*) CD, (*c*) BCDEF, (*d*) AEG (§ 17.2, 17.3, 17.4, 17.5)

6 (*a*) *Plasmodium*/Protozoa, (*b*) e.g. *Aedes* (mosquito)/Arthropoda, (*c*) virus, (*d*) *Tinea*/Fungi,
(*e*) *Saccharomyces* (yeast)/Fungi, (*f*) *Penicillium* (green mould)/Fungi, (*g*) bacteria, (*h*) *Homo*
(man)/Vertebrata (Chordata) (§ 17.1, 17.4, 17.5, 3.2, 3.3)

7 animal, fresh water, e.g. *Daphnia* (water-flea), sting, tentacles, enzymes, enteron (gut), mouth,
oxygen, endoderm, budding, two, nerve net, brain (§ 17.6, 9.4)

8 (*a*) BE, (*b*) AGH, (*c*) G, (*d*) DF, (*e*) C, (*f*) H (§ 17.8)

9 (*a*) muscle blocks, (*b*) pectoral fins, (*c*) swim-bladder, (*d*) (dorsal) fins, (*e*) eyes/lateral line, (*f*) gill-rakers, (*g*) operculum (§ 17.20)

10 (*a*) contour feathers, (*b*) flight feathers, (*c*) large pectoral muscles, (*d*) through-system lungs, large heart (§ 17.23)

11 (*a*) (*i*) lift; (*ii*) drag; (*iii*) mass, (*b*) air movement over aerofoil, left to right (§ 17.23, Fig.17.26)

12 (*a*) gills/lungs, skin, buccal cavity, (*b*) tail, pectoral fins/4 legs, (*c*) jaws/sticky tongue, (*d*) lateral line organ/ear (§ 17.20, 17.22)

13 (*a*) allantois, (*b*) albumen, (*c*) yolk, (*d*) amnion (§ 17.23)

14 (*a*) larva, (*b*) adult, (*c*) larva, (*d*) adult, (*e*) pupa (§ 17.14)

15 (*a*) nymph, (*b*) adult, (*c*) nymph, (*d*) nymph, (*e*) none (no pupa stage) (§ 17.15)

16 (*a*) **BCF**, (*b*) **ADG**, (*c*) **ACE** (§ 17.18)

17 (*a*) outside (exoskeleton)/inside (endoskeleton), (*b*) chitin/bone, (*c*) none (ectothermic)/constant (endothermic), (*d*) 6/4, (*e*) tracheoles/alveoli, (*f*) yolk (in egg)/placenta (within mother) (§ 6.4, 6.6, 7.4, 10.3, Fig. 3.3)

18 Examples: pork tapeworm/dodder. Answers would then be: (*a*) man/clover, gorse etc, (*b*) pig/none, (*c*) (*i*) 'eggs' (embryophores) eaten in pasture by pig/none; (*ii*) 'bladder-worms' (cysticerci) eaten in raw measly pork by man/none, (*d*) (*i*) asexually: budding off proglottids, sexually: within proglottid/sexually: by many flowers; (*ii*) none/none, (*e*) host's digested food absorbed through skin/food absorbed from host's vascular bundles via haustoria, (*f*) *Planaria* (pond flatworm)/any flowering plant, (*g*) uses mouth and gut to scavenge solid food/photosynthesis (leaves) (§ 17.11, 17.13)

19 **DCEABF** (**C** and **E** actually occur at the *same* time) (§ 17.22)

20 (*i*) **A** skin, internal gills, lungs, **B** skin, external gills, **C** skin, lungs, buccal cavity, **D** skin, internal gills; (*ii*) **BDAC** (§ 17.22)

21 (*i*) **A** female pore (segment 14), **B** cocoon, **C** ventral (underside), **D** cocoon, **E** seminal grooves, **F** clitellum; (*ii*) **CEFADB** (§ 17.7)

Part IV
Hints for candidates taking biology examinations

SHOWING THE EXAMINER THAT YOU KNOW THE FACTS – EXAMINATION TECHNIQUE

Students should not be entered for an exam that is beyond their ability. Success in exams for which you have been entered (which assumes that you *do* have the ability) lies in good 'exam technique'. Your teacher will usually advise you on the type of exam you will sit by showing you past question papers. But certain principles of exam technique apply to all methods of examination:

1   **Come fully equipped** with pen, pencil, rubber, ruler and coloured pens or pencils.

2   **Read the exam instructions carefully** – do not leave out compulsory questions.

3   **Plan your time for answering** according to the marks allocated.

4   **Do the maximum number of questions.** If you are asked to do five questions at 20 marks each and you only do four, you can only score a maximum of 80. The first 50% of marks in each question are usually the easiest to gain; thereafter they become harder. Thus it is more likely that you will gain your best result by doing 5 questions reasonably well rather than by doing four questions – as you might think – very well. Five answers averaging a mark of 12 out of 20 = 60%. To gain the same 60% on four questions you must average 15 out of 20.

5   **Choose the right questions to do.** Often you can spot which ones will give you best marks from the mark allocation shown in brackets on the question paper. Add up what you think you would get from the sections you would attempt.

6   **Understand what the question asks.** Never twist the examiner's words into a meaning he did not intend. Perhaps half of those who fail exams do so because they answer a completely different question from that written on the exam paper. If someone asks you how to mend a bicycle puncture and you reply with an excellent description of how to raise the saddle, you have not answered their question, nor have you given them any help! In an exam, mis-information of this kind earns you no marks. And you fail. Perhaps you knew the correct answer all along. But you failed to show the examiner that you knew. What a reward for all your hours of work. What a waste!

7   **Plan essay answers before writing.** Organise key words into a logical order or pattern (see below).

8   **Only use large labelled diagrams** in your answers if they *save* words and make your answer clearer.

9   **Set out your work neatly.** An examiner is human. If your written answers are neatly set out he is much more likely to give you the benefit of the doubt where your answers are not entirely clear.

10   **Keep a cool head.** You can only do this by getting plenty of sleep and some exercise over the exam period. You will reason better if you do *not* stay up all night revising.

TACKLING VARIOUS TYPES OF QUESTION

Multiple choice questions

These are sometimes called fixed response or objective questions. At first sight these questions seem to be comparatively easy because answering them is simply a matter of choosing one correct answer from the possible answers given. However, the questions are designed to test how well you know specific topics and students do not always obtain as high a mark as they expected. But providing you know or can work out each answer (see below), the multiple choice questions in an examination should not be troublesome. (You will have had plenty of practice in answering these types of question if you have worked your way through most of the test-yourself questions in Part III of this book.)

If four choices of answer are offered, usually two are very obviously wrong. You now have a 50% chance of being right even if you don't know the answer. Don't leave the odds at 25% by a blind guess.

Suppose the question asks you to *recall* a name – for example the topmost bone in your vertebral column (backbone). The answer choices are: (*a*) radius, (*b*) humerus, (*c*) atlas, (*d*) axis. If you don't know the answer, but do at least remember that (*a*) and (*b*) are bones in the arm, you are left with a guess between (*c*) and (*d*). You *are* likely to know the answer, however, if you use one of the memory aids suggested in Section 1.4.

Suppose, however, the question requires you to *reason* from facts you should know. If the question is 'Which gas(es) are produced by a green plant's leaves in the dark?' and the answer choices are: (*a*) CO_2, (*b*) N_2, (*c*) CO_2 and O_2, (*d*) O_2. From these (*b*) can be eliminated because nitrogen gas is neither used nor produced by green plants on their own. Leaves readily suggest photosynthesis, a by-product of which is oxygen. But *light* is needed for photosynthesis and the question states that the leaves are in the *dark*. So (*c*) and (*d*) must be wrong because both include oxygen. That leaves (*a*) as the answer. There are also other types of 'choice' questions which are more testing.

Essay questions

Most essay questions today are 'structured' into sections which require paragraph answers. The principles for writing essays or paragraphs are the same. The examiner is looking for a number of facts that you should be remembering as key words – just how many is often suggested by the mark allocation. On rough paper write down the key words and join these by lines into a pattern-diagram where necessary. Number the key words according to the order in which you are going to use the facts in your answer. In this way your facts will be presented logically; and nothing will be left out. If examples make your answer clearer, use them.

Take the following example of a structured question:

"(*a*) Why are enzymes frequently referred to as 'biological catalysts'?   (4)

(*b*) What are the effects of changing (*i*) temperature, (*ii*) pH upon the rate   (7)
of action of any **named** enzyme?"

(there followed a third section to complete the question.)   (*Oxford*)

The way to go about planning your answers is illustrated below:

Notice that this student used the key words from the question to build up this pattern-diagram

From this pattern-diagram, done in a minute or two, might come a written answer like:

(*a*)   Catalysts are substances which in small amounts can greatly increase the rate of certain chemical reactions.   Catalysts remain uncharged at the end of the reaction. Enzymes, unlike catalysts used in chemical works, are proteins. They control the rate of reactions in living things e.g. in respiration and digestion.

(i) Pepsin digests proteins in the stomach where conditions are acid. It will not do so if conditions are alkaline.

(ii) Pepsin works best at body temperature. If it is boiled it is destroyed and stops working. If it is cooled by ice it will also stop working but it is not destroyed.

'State' and 'explain' essays: 'state' or 'list' means 'put down as simple facts' – nothing else. 'Name' is a similar instruction: no explanations are required.
'Explain' requires not only the facts or principles but also the reasons behind them. When you are thinking out the answer to an 'explain' question, ask yourself 'which?', 'what?', 'where?', 'why?' and 'when ?' about the subject. These questions will help you to avoid leaving out information that you know. You *must,* however, only give the information that is asked for – for example 'which ?' and 'when?' may be irrelevant (unnecessary) in a particular question. Try these:

"State three features commonly shown by animals at their respiratory surfaces."

The answer could be: 'Large surface area; wet surface; often associated with a blood system' – to give the bare essentials. No *reasons* are required; and only three lines were allocated for the answer.

"(*a*) *Name two* enzymes which are produced in the mammalian pancreas and which are used in the digestion of food in the alimentary canal.

(i) ....
(ii) ....
(*b*) Select *one* of these enzymes, *name* the substrate which it digests and the product or products formed.
Name of enzyme ....
(i) Substrate ....
(ii) Product or products ....

(*A.E.B.* 1976)

When reading through questions you have decided to answer, **underline vital words**.

Note that the examiners have been particularly helpful here by putting in italics vital words that *you* would have underlined. However, as you read through it would be worth underlining 'pancreas', to emphasise where the enzymes come from. The remaining words that you would have underlined are already emphasised for you after the numerals (i) and (ii).
The answers may be found in Section 4.15.

'Compare' and 'contrast' essays: 'contrast' means pick out the *differences* between. If you are asked to do this you must use such words as 'Whereas ...' and 'however ...'. It is not sufficient to give two *separate* accounts of the two organisms or processes to be contrasted.
   'Compare' means pick out *differences* (contrasts) *and similarities.* Thus your answer will include not only 'whereas ...' and 'however ...' statements but also 'both ...'.

In planning such answers it is vital to write down on rough paper, in three columns, the features to be compared or contrasted and alongside, the comparison you have made mentally.

Feature, or characteristic	Organism, or process A	Organism, or process B
1 ... 2 ... etc.	Differences (i.e. *contrasts*)	
1 ... 2 ... etc.	Similarities	

} *Comparison*

You will have seen ample examples of constructions of this sort if you have tried the test-yourself questions for Chapter 17. Try these:

"Contrast the actions of nerves and hormones in co-ordination in a mammal.   [10]"

(*O. and C.*)

The answers may be found in Section 9.9

Distinguish carefully between the two terms in *each* of the following pairs:
(*a*) respiration: breathing,
(*b*) excretion: secretion,
(*c*) canine tooth: molar tooth,
(*d*) clay soil: sandy soil,
(*e*) stigma: anther.

Answers may be found in Section 6.1; Sections 7.1 and 9.8, Section 4.14, Section 15.5, and Section 12.7 respectively.

"Compare and contrast the external features of a bird, a fish and an amphibian, showing how each is adapted to its own particular way of life."

(*S.U.J.B.*)

The words to underline here are, apart from 'compare and contrast', 'external' and 'adapted'. The question does *not* concern itself with the fact that all three animals have vertebrae (which are *internal*), for example. It *is* concerned with *why* birds have beaks; and *why* frogs (amphibians) have wide gapes to their mouths. Adaptations (see Section 14.3) are answers to biological problems; and beaks and wide gapes are indeed solutions to these animals' feeding needs. Points of similarity include two eyes and two nostrils. Finally, in any such *general* comparison, recall the mnemonic BERLIN GOD SEES (see Sections 1.4 and 2.1). The first nine of these letters do remind you, after all, of *functions;* and adaptations are very much concerned with function. With this lead, try constructing your 'compare and contrast' table using the features that B,E,R,L,I,N in BERLIN GOD remind you of.

Graphs, Diagrams and Experiments

Graphs: If you are asked to put information on a graph, it is vital that on both axes you state the relevant *units*, e.g. 'g' or 'cm³/h' or 'numbers of live insects'. Usually the title of the graph is implied by the question – but sometimes it is important that *you* should provide it. All plots must be precise and ringed. You will avoid wrong plots by using a ruler to lead your eye to the precise spot.

Diagrams:

1 *Draw in pencil* – in case you need to use an eraser.
2 *Draw large* – for clarity and easy labelling, then put down your pencil.
3 *Label* in ink or biro neatly and add a *title*.
4 *Rule your labelling lines* in biro, avoiding crosses. Biro does not smudge against the ruler.

Nor can the straight labelling lines be confused with being part of the detail of the drawing (which is in pencil).

If you follow this drill *in sequence* you will save time. And time is often marks!

Experiments

Experiments must be written up in a logical order under subheadings. The account usually includes a diagram which *saves* words. Do not duplicate the information in a diagram by also giving a *written* account of what it shows. Only write what the diagram does *not* say.

The following is an outline of the structure of such an account:

Aim: 'To discover . . .' or 'To investigate . . .'. If you start off with 'Experiment to prove . . .', it makes a mockery of what scientific investigation is all about. This start indicates to examiners that the 'experiments' you did were actually *demonstrations* of something you knew already – and some examiners may not give you much credit in consequence.

Materials and Method: 'The materials were set up as shown in the diagram' could be the opening sentence. There follows a fully labelled diagram. Only supplementary information is now needed, e.g. 'The plant used in the experiment had first been de-starched by keeping it in the dark for 48 hours' or, 'The length of the root was measured again after 24 hours'.

Note the use of the impersonal 'was measured' which is preferable to the personal 'I measured'. A list of the materials used is unnecessary. Do not forget to emphasise which was the *test* and which the *control* part of the experiment.

Results: a plain statement of what happened in both test *and* control – no discussion. The discussion can be left to a separate subheading, if it is necessary.

Conclusion: the *answer* to the 'aim'. This is a plain statement, not an essay. Thus the aim might have been to find out if light is necessary for photosynthesis, and the experiment's conclusion is likely to have been 'Light is necessary for photosynthesis'.

Too often candidates run out of their allocated time by giving rambling accounts which both score poorly and leave insufficient time for the remaining questions (so costing marks *both* ways). Try this:

"Describe, in detail, how it could be shown conclusively that light is necessary for the synthesis of carbohydrates in green plants"
(There followed a more theoretical part to the question)

(S.U.J.B.)

Here the 'aim' is supplied. As the question uses the words 'could be shown', the remaining subheadings 'Materials and method' and 'Results' must both be used; the conclusion is implied by the wording. Many other questions of this type simply ask for the method. For the answer, see Section 4.6.

Relevance

Sadly, a large number of reasonably knowledgeable candidates do not do themselves justice by writing irrelevant answers. Sheer length of an answer will not gain any marks. It is the key facts and principles that the examiner is looking for, *whatever* the length of the answer. So do not 'pad out' your answers.

The length of answer required is often suggested either by the marks awarded to it in the mark scheme (often stated alongside the question), or by the space allocated to it on an answer sheet. If your answer is about to be either much shorter or much longer than these two indicators suggest, think again. Re-read the question – and your underlining of the important words in it.

A composite question to end with:
'What is excretion? and why is it necessary in living organisms?' Give the origins of the excretory compounds in (*a*) a flowering plant and (*b*) a mammal. Describe how the kidney functions as an excretory organ in a mammal.   (2,2,6,4,11)

Analysis of the question:
Definition: 2 marks (see Section 2.1)

Reason for excretion: 2 marks. Chemical processes in the body (metabolism) are inefficient or produce by-products, e.g. not all the amino acids absorbed by a mammal can be used, so some are excreted as urea (see Section 4.20).

Excretory compounds (and origin) see Section 7.1.
Mammal: 6 marks – H_2O, CO_2 (respiration); urea (excess protein); bile pigments (worn out red blood cells) would suffice.
Note: waste heat (from respiration) is *not* an excretory *compound*.

Flowering plant: 4 marks – O_2 (photosynthesis); CO_2 and H_2O (respiration) would suffice. Wastes (tannins) in fallen bark or leaves could gain credit.

Kidney function: 11 marks. Blood, containing wastes, enters the kidney in the renal artery and leaves 'purified' in the renal vein.

Draw a labelled diagram of a nephron (see Section 7.2) with explanation of the functions of its parts.

Urine, carrying wastes, drips into the pelvis of the kidney.

Note: a diagram of the whole urinary system is *not* required; nor does the question ask for details of the kidney's osmoregulatory function; nor does it ask about malfunction of the kidney.

Note: the skeleton answers provided above are only for the guidance of candidates. They do not necessarily represent what the Examining Boards themselves would require as adequate answers. The author himself is, however, an experienced examiner.